D1487131

ANIMAL TISSUE TECHNIQUES

A Series of Biology Books

EDITORS

George W. Beadle (1946–1961), Ralph Emerson, Douglas M. Whitaker

Laboratory Studies in Biology:
Observations and their Implications
*Chester A. Lawson, Ralph W. Lewis,
Mary Alice Burmester, Garrett Hardin*

Experiments in General Biology
Graham DuShane, David Regnery

General Genetics
Adrian M. Srb, Ray D. Owen

Principles of Human Genetics
(Second Edition)
Curt Stern

An Introduction to Bacterial Physiology
(Second Edition)
Evelyn L. Oginsky, Wayne W. Umbreit

Principles of Plant Physiology
James Bonner, Arthur W. Galston

Plants in Action: A Laboratory
Manual of Plant Physiology
Leonard Machlis, John G. Torrey

Comparative Morphology of Vascular Plants
Adriance S. Foster, Ernest M. Gifford, Jr.

Taxonomy of Flowering Plants
C. L. Porter

Biology: Its Principles and Implications
Garrett Hardin

Growth, Development, and Pattern
N. J. Berrill

Genetics and Evolution: Selected Papers of
A. H. Sturtevant
E. B. Lewis, Editor

Animal Tissue Techniques
Gretchen L. Humason

ANIMAL TISSUE TECHNIQUES

Gretchen L. Humason

LOS ALAMOS SCIENTIFIC LABORATORIES

SAN FRANCISCO
AND LONDON

W. H. FREEMAN AND COMPANY

WITHDRAWN
IOWA STATE UNIVERSITY
LIBRARY

© Copyright 1962 by W. H. Freeman and Company

The publisher reserves all rights to reproduce this book in whole or in part, with the exception of the right to use short quotations for review of the book.

Printed in the United States of America

Library of Congress Catalog Card Number: 61–17383

QH231
H88a

Preface

In the area of histological studies the requirements for a useful laboratory handbook and textbook are both diverse and exceedingly complex. The needs of beginning students in premedical courses, of medical technicians in training, of zoology majors, and of other students are similar but not identical. The needs of research assistants and of experienced tissue technicians at work in the field resemble, but are not identical with, the needs of the students. The author has tried to keep these diversities in mind while pursuing her two major goals: (1) to familiarize the student with basic—standard—procedures and introduce him to specialized technics, and (2) to furnish the working technician with a prop during the first job and an occasional reference point in later work, until consulting specialized references and journals has become a habit.

Basic procedures are applicable to both normal and pathological tissues in zoological and medical fields. Because most histological reactions follow a logical and specific sequence, a simplified discussion of principles has been written for many of the technics. Then perhaps an understanding of each step can prevent mistakes during first trials of a method. There are an infinite number of problems and blunders which can plague a tissue technician. Suggestions concerning such stumbling blocks and some of their remedies may forewarn the novice and be of assistance to others.

This book is not intended to form a complete "reference"; the experienced worker knows of numerous such tomes as well as journals that specialize in biological subjects. However, special methods of wide usage and exceptional merit are included, particularly those

569347

v

methods that are not overly complicated or unpredictable. It is hoped that the technician will watch the literature for modifications and improvements of "standard" technics; in this way his work can be kept up to date and perhaps simplified. Methods for fixation are fairly well established, and only occasional variations appear from time to time. The section on fixation presented here is as modern as the author can make it, and it includes a brief description of the chemicals employed. The perfecting of old staining technics, as well as the development of new ones, continue to appear in the literature; an attempt has been made to incorporate the latest procedures and modifications in this book. The discussion of fixation and its solutions and of dyes and their action is given for the benefit of those who cannot, or will not, seek out the source material.

Certain important fields are not covered in this book either because they are not widely used methods or because they are considered too highly specialized. A few of these fields are: *vital staining*—the selective dyeing of certain isolated cells while alive; *tissue transplantation*—transferring a tissue from its normal location to a different one, where it can be observed more easily; *tissue culture* methods—growing cells in artificial habitats; *tracer technics*—using radioactive isotopes which can be traced in the body; and *microincineration*—the study of minerals in the tissue. However, three fields of increasing popularity and importance are introduced—*autoradiography, histochemical methods,* and *electron microscopy.* The coverage on these three subjects is held to a minimum, but appended references and bibliography can help a technician find more extensive source material.

A logical arrangement of special staining methods is hard to come by, so the author has followed her own inclinations. Some sections are organized by related tissues, others by related methods. The latter was considered desirable for such processes as silver impregnation, metachromasia, and methods using Schiff's reagent. It has been impossible to draw a hard and fast line, but it is hoped that cross-referencing and indexing will provide the answers. The author has had personal experience with most of the methods, and has also tried to include modifications which might appeal to other adventurous technicians.

The book is divided into four parts: *I.* General procedures and considerations which every tissue technician should know and understand. This part will be of particular value in a beginners' course; *II.* Special staining methods for most tissues. The idea here is that an instructor can choose a few favorites for teaching purposes to round out a course, while the professional technician can find most of the special methods required on the job; *III*. Special procedures, special in the sense that they are not common to every lab, but are important to many. Discussion is far from complete for many of them, but references are appended. *IV*. Laboratory aids, general information handy to have in any lab. The list of references includes those occurring in the text and others whose titles may lead an occasional technician to otherwise undiscovered source material.

Acknowledgments

An invaluable personal satisfaction has been derived by the author from her association with students, no matter what their caliber. Students force a teacher to develop tolerance and patience, qualities essential in this temperamental profession. Students also are a blessing, because there is no surer way to master a subject than to teach it. One student in particular should receive credit for her encouragement and her prodding toward this book—Miss Marlies Natzler of the University of California at Los Angeles.

Acknowledgment is due the artist, Marvin Linke, for his quick understanding of the subjects he was asked to illustrate.

Gratitude is extended to the Zoology Department of the University of California at Los Angeles for the lessons the author learned while a student, a departmental technician, and a lecturer, and to Dr. C. C. Lushbaugh of Los Alamos for guidance in pathology.

August 1961   Gretchen L. Humason

Standard References in Histology

Every technician should have at least a nodding acquaintance with the following text and reference books.

BAKER, J. R., *Principles of Biological Microtechnique,* Methuen and Company, London, 1958.

CONN, H. J., *Biological Stains,* Biotech Publications, Geneva, N.Y., 1953.

———, DARROW, MARY, and EMMEL, VICTOR, *Staining Procedures,* The Williams and Wilkins Company, Baltimore, 1960.

COWDRY, E. V., *Laboratory Technique in Biology and Medicine,* The Williams and Wilkins Company, Baltimore, 1952.

CULLING, C. F. A., *Handbook of Histopathological Technique,* Butterworth and Company, London, 1957.

DAVENPORT, H. A., *Histological and Histochemical Techniques,* W. B. Saunders and Company, Philadelphia, 1960.

GLICK, DAVID, *Techniques of Histo- and Cytochemistry,* Interscience Publishers, N.Y., 1949.

GOMORI, GEORGE, *Microscopic Histochemistry,* University of Chicago Press, 1952.

GRIDLEY, MARY FRANCES, *Manual of Histologic and Special Staining Technics,* Armed Forces Institute of Pathology, Washington D.C., 1957.

GURR, EDWARD, *A Practical Manual of Medical and Biological Staining Techniques,* Interscience Publishers, N.Y., 1956.

———, *Methods of Analytical Histology and Histochemistry,* Leonard Hill, Ltd., London, 1958.

———, *Encyclopaedia of Microscopic Stains,* Edward Gurr, London, 1960.

KRAJIAN, ARAM A., and GRADWOHL, R. B. H., *Histopathological Technic,* C. V. Mosby Company, St. Louis, 1952.

LILLIE, R. D., *Histopathologic Technic and Practical Histochemistry,* Blakiston Company, 1954.

McMANUS, J. F. A. and MOWRY, ROBERT W., *Staining Methods: Histologic and Histochemical,* Paul B. Hoeber, 1960.

MALLORY, FRANK B., *Pathological Technique,* W. B. Saunders Company, 1944.

PEARSE, A. G. E., *Histochemistry, Theoretical and Applied,* Little Brown and Company, Boston, 1960.

ROMEIS, B., *Mikrosckopische Technick.,* Leibniz Verlag, München, 1948.

Contents

PART II. SPECIFIC STAINING METHODS

PART III. HISTOCHEMISTRY AND MISCELLANEOUS SPECIAL PROCEDURES

BASIC
PROCEDURES

Chapter **1**

Fixation

When a tissue is removed from a living condition, several changes are initiated in its cells. Bacteria begin to multiply and destroy them. Also **autolysis** (self-digestion), a lysis or dissolution of the cells by contained enzymes, sets in. The enzymes appear to reverse their action; instead of synthesizing amino acids into cell proteins, they begin to split proteins into amino acids. These amino acids diffuse out of the cells, and as a result proteins no longer are coagulable by chemical reagents. The above changes lead to so-called post-mortem conditions. For purposes of laboratory examination it is necessary to treat the tissue to prevent these post-mortem effects; it is also necessary to convert the cell parts into materials that will remain insoluble during subsequent treatment, and to protect the cells from distortion and shrinkage when subjected to fluids such as alcohols and hot paraffin. Further important objectives of tissue preparation are to improve the staining potential of tissue parts and to change their refractive indices toward improved visibility. The procedure used to meet the above requirements is called *fixation* and the fluids are called *fixatives* or *fixing solutions*. Fixing solutions should meet the following principal objectives:

1. Penetrate rapidly to prevent post-mortem changes.
2. Coagulate cell contents into insoluble substances.
3. Protect tissue against shrinkage and distortion during dehydration, embedding and sectioning.
4. Allow cell parts to become selectively and clearly visible by means of dyes and improved refractive indices.

3

In some cases the fixative may have a mordanting (combining insolubly) effect on the tissue, thereby bringing the two together in a staining action and assisting in the attachment of dyes and proteins to each other.

Tissues must be placed in fixatives as soon as possible after death. If, however, delay is unavoidable, they should be placed in a refrigerator, thus reducing autolysis and putrefaction to a minimum until the fixative can be applied.

A single chemical seldom possesses all of the requisite qualities of a good fixative; a fixing solution therefore is rarely composed of only one chemical. A familiar exception is formalin. Other reliable fixatives contain one or more chemicals to coagulate the proteins of the cells, and one or more chemicals to render the proteins insoluble without actually coagulating them. Coagulant fixatives change the spongework of proteins into meshes through which paraffin can easily pass, thus forming a tissue of proper consistency for sectioning. In addition, the protein linkages are strengthened by coagulants against breaking down during later procedures. Used alone, however, coagulants have disadvantages in that they may form too coarse a network for the best cytological detail. Also, coagulation tends to induce the formation of artificial structures (**artifacts**). Noncoagulant fixatives produce fewer artifacts but if used alone have the disadvantage of giving the tissue a poor consistency for embedding. It therefore follows that the ideal fixing fluid is a combination of one or more protein coagulants and one or more noncoagulants. The most efficient solutions are of this nature, and combine if possible all types of action. This excludes those designed for the fixation of some specific cell component, such as chromosomes, glycogen, mitochondria.

Because they contain ingredients which act upon each other, many mixtures are most efficient when made up fresh. However, the individual parts usually can be made up as stock solutions and mixed together immediately before use. Among the frequently used chemicals are formaldehyde, ethyl alcohol, acetic acid, picric acid, potassium dichromate, mercuric chloride, chromic acid and osmium tetroxide. Since every chemical possesses its own set of advantages and disadvantages, each solution component should, whenever possible, compensate for a defect in some other component. For example, in the case of the widely used fixative, *Bouin's solution:* 1. Formaldehyde fixes the cytoplasm but in such a manner that it retards paraffin penetration. It fixes chromatin poorly and makes cytoplasm basiphilic. 2. Picric acid coagulates cytoplasm so that it admits paraffin, leaves the tissue soft, fixes chromatin and makes the cytoplasm acidophilic, but it shrinks and makes chromatin acidophilic. 3. Acetic acid compensates for both the latter defects.

No hard and fast rule exists concerning the choice of a fixative; generally selection is determined by the type of investigation. If there is any question as to future plans for a tissue, formalin is a safe choice; it permits secondary or post-fixation. Some suggestions can be included. If over-all anatomy of the tissue is satisfactory, the routine fixatives can be used: *formalin, Susa, Zenker, Helly,* or *Bouin.* Special fixatives for cell inclusions are *Carnoy, Flemming, Champy, Helly, Schaudinn, Regaud,* and others. For histochemistry the researcher is limited to *formalin, acetone,* or ethyl alcohol.

Most fixing solutions are named after the person originating them; Zenker and Bouin are examples. If the same man originated more than one combination of chemicals, additional means of designating them have been used. Flemming's *weak* and *strong* solutions, Allen's *B3, B15* series, etc. *Susa* fluid was named by Heidenhain after the first two letters of two words: *s*ublimate and *sä*ure.

Chemicals Commonly Used in Fixing Solutions

Acetic Acid, CH₃COOH

Acetic acid is called glacial acetic acid because it is solid at temperatures below 17°C. It can be considered one of the oldest fixatives on record—in the 18th century vinegar (4–10% acetic acid content) was used to preserve *Hydra.* In modern technics it is rarely used alone but is a frequent component of fixing solutions. Its efficient fixing action on the nucleus and its rapid penetration make it an important part of good fixatives. It fixes the nucleoproteins, but not the proteins of the cytoplasm. Acetic acid does not harden the tissue; actually it prevents some of the hardening that may without it be induced by subsequent alcoholic treatment. In some technics, however, acetic acid must be avoided because it dissolves out certain cell inclusions, such as Golgi and mitochondria. Some lipids are miscible with acetic acid, or actually soluble in it. It neither fixes nor destroys carbohydrates.

Acids in general cause swelling in tissues—in collagen in particular—by breaking down some of the cross-linkages between protein molecules and releasing lyophil radicles which associate with water molecules. This swelling in some cases may be a desirable property of acids, counteracting and preventing some of the shrinkage caused by the majority of fixing chemicals. In order to curtail continued swelling after fixation with acetic or trichloracetic acid solutions, transfer the tissues to an alcoholic washing solution in preference to water.

Acetone, CH_3COCH_3

Acetone is used only for tissue enzymes, such as phosphatases and lipases. It is used cold and penetrates slowly. Only small pieces of tissue will be fixed in this chemical.

Chromium Trioxide (chromic acid), CrO_3

Crystalline chromium trioxide forms chromic acid when added to water, usually a 0.5% solution. It is a valuable fixative, but rarely used alone. It penetrates slowly, hardens moderately, causes some shrinkage, forms vacuoles in the cytoplasm and often leaves the nuclei in abnormal shapes. It is a fine coagulant of nucleoproteins and increases the stainability of the nuclei. It oxidizes polysaccharides and converts them into aldehydes—an action forming the basis of Bauer's histochemical test for glycogen and other polysaccharides. Better fixation, however, is obtained with acetic acid, which will fix water-soluble polysaccharides; later these can be post-treated with chormic acid. Fat can be made insoluble in lipid solvents by partial oxidation with chromic acid, but the action can go too far. Potassium dichromate, which reacts in a similar fashion, is safer and is therefore more commonly used.

Excess chromic acid must be washed out, because later it can be reduced (undesirably, for our purpose) to green chromic oxide, Cr_2O_2. Formalin and alcohol are reducing agents and must not be mixed with chromic acid until immediately before use.

Ethyl Alcohol (ethanol), C_2H_5OH

Ethyl alcohol hardens tissue but causes serious shrinkage. It is a strong cytoplasmic coagulant, but does not fix chromatin. Nucleic acid is transformed into a soluble precipitate and is lost in subsequent solutions and during staining. Alcohol cannot be a fixative for lipids because it does not make them insoluble in lipid solvents. It does not fix carbohydrates, but neither does it extract mucins, glycogen, iron and calcium. Alcohol seldom is used alone; occasionally it is used alone for fixation of enzymes.

Formaldehyde, HCHO

Formaldehyde is a gas sold as a solution in water (approximately 40% in content), in which form it is known as *formalin*. The use of the term *formol* is incorrect, since a terminal *-ol* designates an alcohol or phenol. Unless the author of a technic specifies that the dilution of his formalin is in terms of actual formaldehyde content, dilutions are to be made from the commercial product; i.e., a 10% solution would be 10 volumes of formalin (40% formaldehyde saturated aqueous solution) to 90 volumes of water.

Formaldehyde on standing over long periods of time may either polymerize to form paraformaldehyde, or oxidize into formic acid. A white precipitate in a stock solution indicates polymerization; the solution has been weakened. *Cares (1945)* suggests: shake the solution to suspend the sediment. Pour into Mason jars and seal them tightly. Autoclave at 15 lbs. for thirty minutes. Cool. This should produce a clear solution. Dilute solutions (such as 10%) tend to oxidize more readily than do stock solutions (40%). Marble chips may be left in the bottom of diluted stock jars to keep the solution neutralized.

Formalin progressively hardens tissue, but is a mild coagulant of proteins; in fact it is so weak that it might be considered a noncoagulant. It neutralizes basic groups and increases the acidity of proteins. In consequence, formalin-fixed proteins will stain well in basic dyes, but less well in acidic dyes. Formalin has a moderate speed of penetration but its action is slow and somewhat incomplete unless tissues are left in it for some time. It reacts most efficiently at pH 7.5–8. Although formalin preserves the cells adequately it may not protect them completely, because it requires a long time to harden the tissue. Shrinkage, therefore, can take place if dehydration, clearing and infiltration are initiated before the hardening action is complete. Since these processes are not employed in the freezing technic, formalin is a satisfactory fixative for this method.

Formalin is a good fixative for lipids; it does not dissolve lipoids or fats. It does not fix soluble carbohydrates and it does dissolve glycogen and urea.

The so-called formalin pigment may appear in tissues rich in blood. This pigment is formed when hematein of the hemoglobin has escaped from red blood corpuscles before or during death and reacts with the formalin. It may be prevented by a short period of fixation in formalin followed by a prolonged soaking in 5% mercuric chloride. Once formed, however, the pigment can be removed in a solution of 1% potassium hydroxide in 80% alcohol or picric acid dissolved in alcohol (*Baker, 1958*). (See also page 244.)

Mercuric Chloride (corrosive sublimate), $HgCl_2$

Mercuric chloride usually is applied as a saturated aqueous solution (approximately 7%) and is acidic in action, owing to the release of H^+ and Cl^- ions in a water solution. It is a coagulant of proteins, both cytoplasmic and nucleic. It penetrates reasonably well, but not as rapidly as acetic acid. It shrinks less than the other protein coagulants, hardens moderately, and distorts the cells less than other fixatives. It is excellent for mucin.

One disadvantage of mercuric chloride is that it deposits in the tissue a precipitate of uncertain chemical composition. This precipitate is crystalline, perhaps being mercurous chloride (needle shaped) and metallic mercury (amorphous, irregular lumps). It may be removed by iodine, the following reaction probably taking place: $2HgCl + I_2 = HgCl_2 + HgI_2$. Any metallic mercury also will be converted into mercuric iodide. The latter is soluble in alcohol, but the brown color of iodine may remain in the tissue. This can be removed by prolonged soaking in 70% alcohol, or more quickly by treatment with 5% sodium thiosulfate, aqueous. A further disadvantage is that mercuric chloride crystals inhibit adequate freezing, making it difficult to prepare good frozen sections.

Most stains react brilliantly on tissue fixed in mercuric chloride. Chromatin will stain strongly with basic stains and lakes; cytoplasmic structures will react equally well with acidic or basic stains.

Osmium Tetroxide, OsO_4

In solution, usually 1% aqueous, osmium tetroxide takes up a molecle of water and becomes H_2OsO_5, erroneously called osmic acid. In solution ionization is so minute that the pH is almost exactly that of the distilled water used in making the solution. The substance is chemically neutral, is not an acid and cannot be isolated. (Osmic acid would be H_2OsO_4.) *Baker (1958)* suggests that its name might be hydrogen per-persomate. The solution penetrates poorly and leaves tissue soft, later becoming so friable in paraffin that tissues section badly. Osmic acid preserves the cytoplasm and nuclei, but while it increases the stainability of chromatin in basic dyes it reduces the stainability of the cytoplasm. Fats and other lipids reduce osmium tetroxide, or combine with it to form a dark compound. Thus fat sites become black and insoluble in absolute alcohol, cedar oil and paraffin; but they remain soluble in xylene, toluene and benzene, and if left too long in xylene or toluene (more than 5 minutes) they become colorless. Osmic acid is not a fixative for carbohydrates.

When action is complete excess osmic must be washed out of the tissue or it may be reduced during treatment in alcohol, forming an insoluble precipitate. Since osmium tetroxide is also easily reduced by light and heat, it must be kept stored in a cool and dark place.

Picric Acid, $C_6H_2(NO_2)_3OH$

Picric acid is usually used in a saturated aqueous solution, 0.9–1.2%. It is an excellent protein coagulant, forming protein picrates having a strong affinity for acid dyes. However, it penetrates slowly, causes extreme shrinkage, and offers no protection against subsequent shrinkage. (There is no tendency to swell in this case, because of acidity.) The shrinkage has been found to be close to 50% of the original tissue volume by the time it has undergone paraffin infiltration. It does not dissolve lipids, does not fix carbohydrates, but is recommended as a fixative for glycogen. It is a desirable constituent of many fixing fluids because it does not harden, but it cannot be used alone because of the unfavorable shrinkage it produces. Acetic acid frequently accompanies it to counteract this poor quality.

Potassium Dichromate, $K_2Cr_2O_7$

This substance, often incorrectly called potassium bichromate (which would be potassium hydrogen chromate), is a noncoagulant of proteins, making them more basic in action, but it dissolves nucleoproteins. Chromosomes, therefore, are poorly shown, if at all. Potassium dichromate leaves tissues soft and in poor condition for paraffin sectioning. One valuable use, however, is the fixation of mitochondria (as with Champy fluid); the lipid components are made capable of resisting solution in lipid solvents. After fixation, tissues may be soaked in potassium dichromate to insure that lipids are well preserved.

Potassium dichromate can be mixed with mercuric chloride, picric acid and osmic acid, but it reacts with formalin and must not be mixed with it until immediately before use. If acetic acid is added, mitochondria are lost, but chromosomes are shown better than when the chromate is used alone. It usually is necessary to wash out the dichromate with water in order to prevent the formation of an insoluble precipitate of Cr_2O_3; this will form if the tissue is carried directly to alcohol.

Trichloracetic Acid, CCl_3COOH

This acid never is used alone and is similar to acetic acid in action. It swells tissues and has a slight decalcifying property. As was noted under acetic acid, washing should be done in alcoholic solutions.

"Indifferent Salts"

Baker (1958) applied this term to a group of chemicals (sodium sulfate, sodium chloride, and others) the action of which is not clearly understood. Zenker's and Helly's solutions often have sodium sulfate added. Sometimes sodium chloride is added to formalin or mercuric chloride fixatives, particularly when marine forms are to be fixed.

References: Baker (1945, 1958).

Maceration (a prefixation process)

There are occasions when tissues are extremely dense and cannot be manipulated while in fresh condition. It may be desirable to separate the individual fibers of a muscle or nerve, and this is simplified by maceration. The fluids used are not fixing solutions, so maceration usually must be followed by some form of fixation. The following are various suggestions for macerating fluids. (*Hale, 1958*)

1. *30% alcohol,* 24 hours or longer (3–4 days).
2. *formalin,* 1 part in 10% salt (NaCl) solution, 100 parts: 24 hours or longer.
3. *10% sodium chloride:* 24 hours or longer.
4. *chromic acid,* 0.2% aqueous: 24 hours.
5. *nitric acid,* 20% aqueous: 24 hours.
6. *boric acid,* saturated solution in saline (sea water for marine forms), plus 2 drops *Lugol's iodine solution* (page 410), each 25 ml.: 2–3 days.
7. *potassium hydroxide,* 33% aqueous. Good for isolation of smooth and striated muscle. After 1–1½ hours, tease apart with needles.

8. *Maceration by enzymes,* good for connective tissue, reticulum. (*Galigher, 1934*)

Place frozen sections in:

pancreatin siccum	5.0 gm.
sodium bicarbonate	10.0 gm.
distilled water	100.0 ml.

wash thoroughly and stain.

Fixing the Tissue

First consideration in the choice of fixative should lie in the purpose to be served in preparing the tissue for future use. Is a routine all-purpose fixative adequate or must some special part of a cell be preserved. For example: an aqueous fixing fluid will dissolve out glycogen, and an alcoholic one can remove lipids. Thought should be given to the rate of penetration of the fluid and the density of the tissue to be fixed. Obviously an extremely dense tissue might not fix well in a fixative which penetrates slowly and poorly. With fixatives of poor penetration, the size of the pieces must be trimmed to a minimum. In all cases, pieces never should be any larger than is absolutely necessary; the smaller the bulk, the more perfect the fixation.

The hardening effect of fixatives should be considered. An excessively hardening fixative might lead to difficulties with liver and muscle. Maybe some other fixative could be used with less hardening effect. If there is any doubt concerning future needs for a tissue, place it in formalin; this can be followed by post-fixation treatments.

Use a large volume of fixing fluid—at least ten times the bulk of the tissue if possible. Remove the tissues from the animal and place them in the fixative as rapidly as is feasible, thereby reducing post-mortem changes to a minimum. In most cases, do not attempt to fix the entire organ; it will be too large to allow rapid and complete penetration of the fixative. This is particularly true of an organ covered by a tough membrane. An ideal piece would be 1 to 2 cm. in size; or place a larger piece in the fixative for 15 to 30 minutes, then trim it to smaller size and return it to the fixative. This sometimes is necessary when tissue is very soft or easily crushed. Trim the piece with a new razor blade or sharp scalpel. This will cause less damage than the squeezing action of scissors. Do not crush or tear the tissue while removing it; such material is worthless. Never allow tissue to become dry before placing it in the solution. Keep it moist with normal saline and wash off accumulated blood with normal saline. Blood retards the penetration of a fixative. Gently shake the solution and contained tissues several times to make certain that the fluid can reach all surfaces and that pieces are not sticking to the bottom or sides of the container. A chunk of glass wool may be laid in the bottle to aid in keeping the tissue free of the bottom.

Thin pieces of tissue that show muscular contraction or that may turn inside out (tissues of the gastrointestinal tract are particularly likely to do this) may be placed on thick filter paper, outside wall against the paper, and dropped in the fixative. Tiny, easily lost specimens, biopsies, bone marrow, etc., may be wrapped in lens paper or coffee filter paper (page 228).

The length of time required for complete fixation depends on the rate of penetration and action of the fixative. Most coagulant fixatives produce complete fixation as fast as they can penetrate the tissue. But some fixatives, such as formalin, exhibit progressive improvement in fixing action after the tissue has become completely penetrated. Prolonged action in this case improves the condition of the tissue and rarely is harmful. Occasionally some type of post-fixation treatment as noted on page 23 is advisable.

Washing the Tissue

After fixation is accomplished, the excess of many fixatives must be washed out of the tissue to prevent interference with subsequent processes. Often washing is done with running water; sometimes the tissue may be carried directly to 50% alcohol or higher. Some technicians maintain, for instance, that Bouin's tissue washed in water may lose some of the soluble picrates and that this tissue should be transferred from the fixative directly to 50% alcohol. When a freezing step is planned, formalin-fixed tissue may be washed a brief moment in water, but in rush problems it can be taken from the fixing solution directly to the freezing microtome. The presence of alcohol will prevent freezing action and its use must be avoided, or it must be thoroughly washed out before attempting to freeze the tissue.

When tissue has been fixed with a mercuric chloride solution additional treatment is necessary. After washing in 50% alcohol, transfer the tissue to 70% alcohol containing enough iodine-alcohol (saturated solution of iodine in 70% alcohol) to give the solution a deep brown color. Leave the tissue in this solution from 5 to 8 hours, but not longer. If during this time the solution loses color, add some more iodine-alcohol. The iodine removes some, but probably not all, of the excess mercuric chloride precipitate left in the tissue. Later, when staining the sections, iodine-alcohol or Lugol's solution (page 410) must be included in the staining series. This should eliminate remaining crystals which otherwise will persist as dark clumps and needles in the finished slides.

After washing, the tissue may be stored for several weeks or months in 70% alcohol, but it is always safer to dehydrate and embed as soon as possible. Storage in alcohol for long periods of time (a year or longer) tends to reduce the stainability of tissues. This is also true after long immersion in chromate and decalcifying solutions, or if traces of acid or iodine are present.

Do not use corked bottles for fixing or for alcoholic solutions; extractives from corks can be injurious to tissues.

Fixing Solutions and their Uses

Routine Fixatives and Fixing Procedures for General Microanatomy

BOUIN'S FIXATIVE: 24 hours or longer—several weeks causes no damage.

picric acid, saturated aqueous	75.0 ml.
formalin	25.0 ml.
glacial acetic acid	5.0 ml.

Because of acetic acid content do not use for cytoplasmic inclusions. Large vacuoles often form in tissues. Wash in 50% alcohol. The yellow color must disappear before staining sections. It usually is removed in the alcohol series, but if not, treat slides in 70% alcohol plus a few drops of saturated lithium carbonate until the color is extracted.

BOUIN-DUBOSCQ (*Alcoholic Bouin's*) FIXATIVE (*Pantin, 1946*): 1–3 days.

80% ethyl alcohol	150.0 ml.
formalin	60.0 ml.
glacial acetic acid	15.0 ml.
picric acid crystals	1.0 gm.

Prepare just before using. This is better than Bouin's for objects difficult to penetrate. Go directly to 95% alcohol.

BUFFERED FORMALIN: may remain indefinitely, progressive action.

10% formalin .... 1000.0 ml.
sodium acid phosphate, $NaH_2PO_4 \cdot H_2O$ .... 4.0 gm.
anhydrous disodium phosphate, Na_2HPO_4 .... 6.5 gm.

Wash in water.

FORMALIN (*Baker, 1944*): may remain indefinitely, progressive action.

calcium chloride .... 1.0 gm.
cadmium chloride .... 1.0 gm.
formalin .... 10.0 ml.
distilled water .... 100.0 ml.

Wash in water.

FORMALIN (*Baker, 1958*): may remain indefinitely, progressive action.

formalin .... 10.0 ml.
calcium chloride (anhydrous) 10% aqueous solution (10 gm./100 ml. water) .... 10.0 ml.
distilled water .... 80.0 ml.

Wash in water.

HELLY'S FIXATIVE (ZENKER FORMOL): 6–24 hours. If the tissue seems to harden excessively, follow a maximum of 18 hours in fixative with a 12–24 hour chromating in 3% potassium dichromate.

potassium dichromate .... 2.5 gm.
mercuric chloride .... 4.0–5.0 gm.
sodium sulfate .... 1.0 gm.

(may be omitted, see *indifferent salts,* page 10)

distilled water .... 100.0 ml.
formalin (add just before using) .... 5.0 ml.

Formalin reduces dichromate and should not be left in stock solutions. The above stock, without formalin, can be used for Zenker's fixative, page 16. Excellent for bone marrow and blood-forming organs, also intercalated discs. Wash in running water overnight, post-treat for mercuric chloride. *Maximow modification:* add 10% of formalin instead of 5%, and sometimes 10% of osmic acid. The latter should be fixed in the dark.

HOLLANDE BOUIN'S FIXATIVE (*Romeis, 1948*): 8 hours–3 days.

copper acetate	2.5 gm.
picric acid crystals	4.0 gm.
formalin	10.0 ml.
distilled water	100.0 ml.
glacial acetic acid	1.5 ml.

Dissolve copper acetate in water without heat; add picric acid slowly with stirring. When dissolved, filter, and add formalin and acetic acid. Keeps indefinitely. *Hartz (1947)* recommends this for fixation of calcified areas as in lymph nodes or fat necrosis. It is a good general fixative. Wash for several hours in 2 or 3 changes of distilled water.

ORTH'S FIXATIVE (*Gatenby, 1950 and Galigher, 1934*): 12 hours at room temperature, 3 hours at 37°C.

formalin	10.0 ml.
potassium dichromate	2.5 gm.
sodium sulfate	1.0 gm.
distilled water	100.0 ml.

Mix fresh. A good routine fixative, also for glycogen and fat. Wash in running water overnight.

Lillie's (1954B) variation:

2.5% potassium dichromate	100.0 ml.
formalin	10.0 ml.

STIEVE'S FIXATIVE (*Romeis, 1948*): 24 hours.

mercuric chloride, saturated aqueous	76.0 ml.
formalin	20.0 ml.
glacial acetic acid	4.0 ml.

Similar in effect to Susa's below, but simpler to prepare. Penetrates rapidly, good for large pieces. Time not critical. Go directly to 70% alcohol. Post-treat for mercuric chloride.

SUSA'S FIXATIVE (*Romeis, 1948*): 24 hours.

mercuric chloride saturated in 0.6% NaCl	50.0 ml.
trichloracetic acid	2.0 gm.
glacial acetic acid	4.0 ml.
formalin	20.0 ml.
distilled water	30.0 ml.

Good substitute for Zenker's if dichromate is not required. Hardens less. Rapid penetration. Go directly to 70% alcohol. Post-treat for mercuric chloride.

ZENKER'S FIXATIVE: 4–24 hours. If tissue seems to harden excessively, follow a maximum of 18 hours in Zenker's with a 12–24 hour chromating in 3% potassium dichromate.

potassium dichromate	2.5 gm.
mercuric chloride	4.0–5.0 gm.
sodium sulfate	1.0 gm.

(may be omitted, see *indifferent salts,* page 10)

distilled water	100.0 ml.
glacial acetic acid	5.0 ml.

Excellent general fixative, fairly rapid penetration. Wash in running water overnight. Post-treat for mercuric chloride. Zenker's may serve for Helly's (page 14) if acetic acid is not added to the stock solution.

Fixatives for Cell Inclusions and Special Technics

ALTMANN'S FIXATIVE (*Gatenby, 1950*): 12 hours.

5% potassium dichromate	10.0 ml.
2% osmic acid	10.0 ml.

Good for fat and mitochondria.
Wash in running water overnight.

AMMERMAN'S FIXATIVE (*1950*): 2 hours.

chromium potassium sulfate (chrome alum)	3.0 gm.
formalin	30.0 ml.
glacial acetic acid	2.0 ml.
distilled water	238.0 ml.

Good for yolk-rich material and insect larvae. Do not fix longer than 2 hours, or swelling occurs. Does not harden and gives good cytological detail. Wash in 70% alcohol or water.

CARNOY FIXATIVE (*Gatenby, 1950*): 3–6 hours.

Formula A:

glacial acetic acid	20.0 ml.
absolute ethyl alcohol	60.0 ml.

Formula B:

glacial acetic acid	10.x
absolute ethyl alcohol	60.0
chloroform	30.0 n

Chloroform is said to make action more rapid. Important fix
glycogen and Nissl substance, but dissolves most other cyto
elements. Wash 2–3 hours in absolute alcohol to remove chlor
particularly if embedding in nitrocellulose.

CARNOY-LEBRUN FIXATIVE (*Lillie, 1954B*): 3–6 hours

absolute ethyl alcohol	15.0 ml.
glacial acetic acid	15.0 ml.
chloroform	15.0 ml.
mercuric chloride crystals	4.0 gm.

Lee of *The Mecrotomist's Vade Mecum* fame considers this a very fine
fixative. It does not keep; mix fresh. Penetrates rapidly. Wash well in
alcohol to remove chloroform.

CHAMPY FIXATIVE (*Gatenby, 1950*): 12 hours.

potassum dichromate, 3% aqueous (3 gm./100 ml. water)	7.0 ml.
chromic acid, 1% aqueous (1 gm./100 ml. water)	7.0 ml.
osmic acid, 2% aqueous (2 gm./100 ml. water)	4.0 ml.

Prepare immediately before use. Good for cytological detail, mitochondria, lipids, etc. Penetrates poorly; use only small pieces of tissue. Wash in running water overnight.

DAFANO FIXATIVE (*Romeis, 1948*): 12–24 hours.

cobalt nitrate	1.0 gm.
formalin	15.0 ml.
distilled water	100.0 ml.

Wash in water. Good for Golgi apparatus.

FLEMMING'S FIXATIVES: 12–24 hours.

A. Strong solution

chromic acid, 1% aqueous (1 gm./100 ml. water)	15.0 ml.
osmic acid, 2% aqueous (2 gm./100 ml. water)	4.0 ml.
glacial acetic acid	1.0 ml.

Good for invertebrate material. Does not give a good histological picture; cytoplasm is badly shrunken. Wash in 50% alcohol. Post-treat for mercuric chloride. Good for beginners, easy to work with.

JOHNSON'S FIXATIVE (*Gatenby, 1950*): 12 hours.

potassium dichromate, 2.5% aqueous (2.5 gm./ 100 ml. water)	70.0 ml.
osmic acid, 2% aqueous (2 gm./100 ml. water)	10.0 ml.
platinum chloride, 1% aqueous (1 gm./100 ml. water)	15.0 ml.
glacial acetic acid	5.0 ml.

Contracts spongy protoplasm less than Flemming's. Wash in water.

Hermann's modification: 12–16 hours.

platinum chloride, 1% aqueous (1 gm./100 ml. water)	15.0 ml.
glacial acetic acid	1.0 ml.
osmic acid, 2% aqueous (2 gm./100 ml. water)	2.0–4.0 ml.

Better protoplasm than with chromic mixtures. Good nuclear staining, but not of plasma. Some shrinkage of chromatin. Without acetic it is good for mitochondria.

KOLMER'S FIXATIVE: 24 hours.

potassium dichromate, 5% aqueous (5 gm./100 ml. water)	20.0 ml.
10% formalin	20.0 ml.
glacial acetic acid	5.0 ml
trichloracetic acid, 50% aqueous (50 gm./100 ml. water)	5.0 ml.
uranyl acetate, 10% aqueous (10 gm./100 ml. water)	5.0 ml.

Good for entire eye (*Wall, 1938*) or nerve tissue, due to presence of uranium salts. Wash in running water.

LAVDOWSKY FLUID (*Swigart et al., 1960*): 12–24 hours.

distilled water	80.0 ml.
95% ethyl alcohol	10.0 ml.
chromic acid, 2% aqueous (2 gm./100 ml. water)	10.0 ml.
glacial acetic acid	0.5 ml.

Good for glycogen. Transfer to 80% alcohol.

NAVASHIN'S FIXATIVE (*Randolph, 1935*): 24 hours.

Solution A:

chromic acid	1.0 gm.
glacial acetic acid	10.0 ml.
distilled water	90.0 ml.

Solution B:

formalin	40.0 ml.
distilled water	60.0 ml.

Mix equal parts of *A* and *B* just before using. At end of six hours change to a new solution for another 18 hours. Useful for preserving cellular detail in plant materials; as good as Flemming's on root tips, and less erratic. Transfer to 75% alcohol.

PERENYI'S FIXATIVE (*Galigher, 1934*): 12–24 hours.

chromic acid, 1% aqueous (1 gm./100 ml. water)	15.0 ml.
nitric acid, 10% aqueous (10 ml./ 90 ml. water)	40.0 ml.
95% ethyl alcohol	30.0 ml.
distilled water	15.0 ml.

Good for eyes. Always when fixing the entire eye make a small hole near the ciliary body so the fluids of both chambers can exchange with the fixing fluid. For the best fixing results, inject a little of the fixative into the chambers. Decalcifies small deposits of calcium; good fixative for calcified arteries and glands. Trichromes stain poorly; hematoxylin is satisfactory. Wash in 50% or 70% alcohol.

REGAUD (*Kopsch*) FIXATIVE (*Romeis, 1948*): 4–24 hours.

potassium dichromate, 3% aqueous (3 gm./100 ml. water)	40.0 ml.
formalin	10.0 ml.

Mix immediately before use. Recommended for mitochondria and cytoplasmic granules. Tends to harden. Follow fixation by chromating several days in 3% potassium dichromate. Renew solution once every 24 hours. Wash in running water overnight.

ROSSMAN'S FIXATIVE (*Lillie, 1954B*): 12–24 hours.

absolute alcohol, saturated with picric acid ...	90.0 ml.
formalin	10.0 ml.

Good for glycogen. Wash in 95% alcohol.

SANFELICE FIXATIVE (*Baker, 1958*): 4–6 hours.

    chromic acid, 1% aqueous (1 gm./100 ml. water)   80.0 ml.

    formalin ....   40.0 ml.

    glacial acetic acid ....   5.0 ml.

Mix immediately before use. Good for chromosomes and mitotic spindles. Fix small pieces. Produces less final shrinkage than others of this type. Wash in running water. 6–12 hours.

SCHAUDINN'S FIXATIVE (*Kessel, 1925*): 10–20 minutes for smears, 40°C.

    mercuric chloride, saturated aqueous ....   66.0 ml.

    95% ethyl alcohol ....   33.0 ml.

    glacial acetic acid ....   5.0–10.0 ml.

Recommended for protozoan fixation, smears on slides, or in bulk. Not for tissue; produces excessive shrinkage. Transfer directly to 50% or 70% alcohol. Post-treat for mercuric chloride.

SINHA'S FIXATIVE: 4–6 days.

    picric acid, saturated in 90% alcohol ....   75.0 ml.

    formalin ....   25.0 ml.

    nitric acid, concentrated ....   8.0 ml.

Sinha (1953) adds that 5% mercuric chloride may be included; possibly this means 5 grams per 100.0 ml. of above solution. Recommended for insects; softens hard parts, but with no damage to internal structure. Transfer directly to 95% alcohol.

SMITH'S FIXATIVE (*Galigher, 1934*): 24 hours.

    potassium dichromate ....   5.0 gm.

    formalin ....   10.0 ml.

    distilled water ....   87.5 ml.

    glacial acetic acid ....   2.5 ml.

Mix immediately before use. Good for yolk-rich material (*Laufer, 1949*). Wash in running water overnight.

The pH of some fixatives changes after mixing and again after tissue is added. This may be a factor worth considering under certain conditions—when effect on stainability or silver impregnation is important, for instance (*Freeman et al., 1955*).

Fixation by Perfusion

Perfusion (forceful flooding of tissue) is of advantage only for a tissue that requires rapid fixation but is not readily accessible for rapid removal. A prime example is the central nervous system. Many organs are not adequately fixed by this method because the perfusion fluid may be carried away from rather than to the cells.

Special equipment necessary for perfusion includes (1) a glass cannula which fits the specific aorta to be used; (2) rubber tubing to connect the cannula to the (3) perfusion bottle.

When the animal is dead or under deep anesthesia, cut the large vessels in the neck and drain out as much blood as possible. Expose the pericardium by cutting the costal cartilages and elevating the sternum. Cut the pericardium and reflect it back to expose the large arteries. Free part of the aorta from the surrounding tissue and place a moistened ligature behind it. Make a small slit directed posteriorly in the wall of the aorta and insert the moistened cannula. Bring the two ends of the thread together and tie the cannula firmly in place. Cut open the right atrium to permit escape of blood and other fluids.

Precede fixation with a small amount of saline (50–100 ml.). Fill just the rubber tubing leading from the perfusion bottle to the cannula. (Separate the saline from the fixative with a clamp near the attachment of the rubber tubing to the bottle.) Fill the perfusion bottle with fixative (500–1000 ml. depending on size of animal). The fluid should be warmed to body temperature. The saline precedes the fixative to wash out residue blood before it becomes fixed to the vessel walls. If a formalin-dichromate fixative is being used substitute 2.5% potassium dichromate for normal saline.

When ready to start perfusion, with bottle at table level open clamp on rubber tubing. Gradually raise the bottle to increase pressure of fluid. Continue to raise the bottle gradually until at a height of 4 to 5 feet enough pressure is exerted to force out most of the blood. After 5 minutes, open the abdomen and examine the organ to be perfused. If the surface vessels are still filled with blood and the organ has not begun to take on the color of the perfusing solution, it is possible that the perfusion has failed. But sometimes stubborn cases may require 10 to 30 minutes to perfuse. When blood color is absent, perfusion is complete.

Observe these suggestions: (1) the cannula used should be as large as possible to permit as rapid a flow as possible. This aids in washing out blood ahead of the fixative. (2) If the head alone is to be fixed, clamp off the thoracic duct, and if the brain and spinal cord are to be fixed, clamp off intestinal vessels. The fixative is then directed toward brain and spinal cord. (3) When the perfusion bottle is being filled, allow some of the fluid to flow through the rubber tubing and cannula to release air bubbles. This can also be done with the saline. Air bubbles will block the perfusion. (4) Do not allow the injection pressure to exceed the blood pressure; artifacts will result.

If only a small piece of an organ is to be fixed, a modified and easier perfusion may be undertaken. Inject the organ with a hypodermic syringe of fixative. This usually will be found adequate. Immediately after injection, cut out a small piece of tissue close to the injection and immerse in the same type of fixative.

Lillie (1954B) lists two disadvantages of perfusion: the blood content of the vessels is lost and perfusion cannot be used if post-mortem clotting is present. But he does favor perfusion as the outstanding method for brain fixation, saying that immersion of the whole brain without perfusion "can only be condemned." If whole brain perfusion is not possible he suggests the following as the preferred method of fixation for topographic study.

1. Cut a single transverse section anterior to oculomotor roots and interior margin of anterior colliculi, separating the cerebrum from midbrain and hindbrain.
2. Make a series of transverse sections through the brain stem and cerebellum (5–10 mm. intervals) leaving part of meninges uncut to keep slices in position.
3. Separate two cerebral hemispheres by a sagittal section. On sagittal surface identify points through which sections can be cut to agree with standard frontal sections. Make cuts perpendicular to sagittal surface. Cut rest of brain at 10 mm. intervals.
4. Fix in a large quantity of solution.

References: Bensley and Bensley (1938); Cowdry (1952); and Lillie (1954B). *See also* Koenig *et al.* (1945) and Eayrs (1950).

Post-fixation Treatments

Chromatization

2.5–3% aqueous potassium dichromate (2.5–3 gm./100 ml. water): overnight for small gross specimens (1–2cm.), 2–3 days for larger ones; 1–2 hours for sections on slides before staining (may be left overnight).

Wash thoroughly in running water, overnight for large gross tissues; 15–30 minutes for slides.

Improves preservation and staining, particularly of mitochondria.

Deformalization

The removal of bound formalin frequently is necessary in silver impregnation methods, such as Ramón y Cajal, del Río-Hortega methods, and the Feulgen technique.

Lhotka and Ferreira's (1950) Method

1. Wash tissue blocks in distilled water: 15 minutes.
2. Transfer through 2 changes of chloral hydrate, 20% aqueous (20 gm./100 ml. water): 24 hours each.
3. Wash in distilled water: 15 minutes.
4. Proceed to any method. With silver stains, time of impregnation needs to be lengthened: Ramón y Cajal to 2 weeks; del Río-Hortega to 24 hours.

Krajian and Gradwohl's (1952) Method, on Slides

1. Place in ammonia water (40 drops ammonia in 100.0 ml. water): 1 hour.
2. Wash, running water: 1 hour.
3. Fix in special fixative if necessary: 1 hour.
4. Wash, running water: 1 hour.
5. Proceed to stain.

Removal of Mercuric Chloride Crystals

Iodine method: see page 12.

Gonzalez method (1959A). Gonzalez suggests the following if necessary to avoid mordant action of iodine. After fixation, wash for a short time, or immerse directly in cellosole (ethylene-glycol-monoethyl-ether, *Carbide and Carbon Chemical Co.*): 24–48 hours, 3 changes. Follow with toluene: 1–2 hours; infiltrate and embed.

Decalcification

Calcium deposits may be so heavily concentrated that they interfere with future sectioning and result in torn sections and nicks on the knife edge. If deposits are sparse, overnight soaking in water will soften them sufficiently for sectioning. This is undertaken when the tissue is blocked and ready for sectioning (page 55). Heavy deposits may be removed by any of several methods. Opinions are varied as to preferred method, but do not leave tissues in any of the fluids longer than necessary. If any doubt arises concerning completion of decalcification, check for calcium by the following method.

To 5 ml. of the solution containing the tissue, add 1 ml. of 5% sodium or ammonium oxalate. Allow to stand 5 minutes. If a precipitate forms, decalcification is not complete. A clear solution indicates it is complete. Sticking needles in the tissue to check hardness is sloppy technic which can damage the cells.

Acid Reagents

After using an acid for decalcification, transfer directly to 70% alcohol to prevent swelling in the tissue and impaired staining reactions: 3–4 hours or overnight.

a. formic acid	5.0–25.0 ml.
formalin	5.0 ml.
distilled water to make	100.0 ml.

With 5 ml. formic acid content, 2–5 days. If increased to 25 ml. less time is required, but with some loss of cellular detail.

b. formic acid, 50% aqueous (50 ml./50 ml. water)	50.0 ml.
sodium citrate, 15% aqueous (15 gm./100 ml. water)	50.0 ml.
c. formalin	10.0 ml.
nitric acid, concentrated	5.0 ml.
distilled water	85.0 ml.

If acidity is a problem for staining, treat with 2% aqueous lithium carbonate solution, or 5% sodium sulfate: 6–12 hours, then into 70% alcohol.

d. Citrate-citric acid buffer, pH 4.5 (controlled hydrogen ion concentration) (*Culling, 1957*) citric acid monohydrate, 7% aqueous (7 gm./100 ml. water)	5.0 ml.
ammonium citrate, anhydrous, 7.45% aqueous (7.45 gm./100 ml. water)	95.0 ml.
zinc sulfate, 1% aqueous (1 gm./100 ml. water)	0.2 ml.
chloroform	few drops

Calcium ions are insoluble at *p*H 4.5, so buffer solutions may be used. Slower than other methods, but no perceptible tissue damage.

   e. Kristensen's (1948) fluid is highly recommended.
      8N formic acid (see page 408) .... 50.0 ml.
      1N sodium formate .... 50.0 ml.

(*p*H 2.2) 24 hours. Wash in running water: 24 hours.

Pros and Cons in Use of Acid Reagents

Schajowicz and Cabrini (1955) observe that strong acids, such as nitric acid, do alter histochemical behavior of bone and cartilage, and must be used with care. Formic acid and citrate do not have this disadvantage if used for only a few days.

   Case (1953) added 1% phloroglucinol to formic acid for improved cell detail and preservation, and for staining qualities. *Culling (1957)* disagrees and maintains that staining is poor after phloroglucinol.

   Morris and Benton (1956) found 1–2M hydrochloric acid the most rapid decalcifier (approximately 3 hours). He found that this produced adequate staining reactions if slides were mordanted in 5% aqueous ammonium chloride for 30 minutes before staining.

Ion-exchange-resin Method of Decalcification

Dotti et al. (1951) theorized that replacing sodium citrate (formic acid-citrate mixture) by a cation exchange resin might result in speedier decalcification. The liberated calcium could be removed more rapidly from the solution—requiring about half the time necessary for formic acid-citrate decalcification. They recommend 40% of resin in formic acid. If speed is not essential, they recommend 10% of resin. The resin is *Win 3000*, ammonium salt of sulfonated resin (*Winthrop Stearns Inc., N.Y.*).

Electrolysis Method of Decalcification

The principle of electrolysis is based on the theory that there is an attraction of Ca ion to a negative electrode. The bone is suspended by a platinum wire, becoming the anode, and a second platinum wire forms the cathode. Then by electrolysis the calcium ions are freed from the bone.[1] *Case (1953)* considered the electrolysis method to be inferior to the use of either nitric or formic acid. *Clayden (1952)* and *Lillie et al. (1951)* demonstrated that an increase in temperature accomplished the same thing. Probably the rise in temperature was the principal reason for speed of decalcification. *Culling (1957)* agreed that heat speeds up decalcification but causes severe swelling and is not to be recommended. *Lucas (1952)* found no evidence that the passage of a current by itself accelerated decalcification. Experiments by *Lillie et al. (1951)* indicate that in respect to temperature there is another story. Decalcification at room temperature or even cooler produces the best results for staining. The present author finds nothing to be recommended about the electrolysis method.

Chelating Agents for Decalcification

These agents during decalcification offer the advantage of maintaining good fixation and sharp staining. They are organic compounds that have the power of binding certain metals, such as calcium and iron. *Versene* (Dow Chemical Company) or *Sequestrene* (Geigey Chemical Company), the disodium salt of ethylene diamine tetracetic acid (EDTA), is the most commonly used agent. The method does have two disadvantages; the tissue tends to harden and decalcification is slow.

Hilleman and Lee (1953)

200 ml. of a 5.5% solution of either Versene or Sequestrene in 10% formalin, for pieces $40 \times 10 \times 10$ mm. It may require up to 3 weeks. Renew the solution at the end of each week. Transfer directly to 70% alcohol.

Vacek and Plackova (1959)

0.5M solution of EDTA at pH 8.2–8.5 yields better results in silver methods than does decalcification with acids.

Schajowicz and Cabrini (1955)

Versene is here considered the better of the two solutions. The solution should be adjusted to a pH 7.0 with NaOH and HCl. Hematoxylin and eosin stains as usual, but glycogen is lost, and alkaline phosphatase has to be reactivated after chelating agents.

[1] Bone Decalcifier, Portable, Chicago Apparatus Co. Catalog #28–712.

Decalcification Combined with Other Processes

FIXATION-DECALCIFICATION

1. *Lillie (1954B)* recommends 1–2 days:

   picric acid, 1–2% aqueous (1–2 gm./100 ml.
       water) . . . .   85.0 ml.
   formalin . . . .   10.0 ml.
   formic acid, 90–95% aqueous (90–95 ml./10–5
       ml. water) . . . .   5.0 ml.

   Extract some of the yellow: 2–3 days in 70–80% alcohol.

2. *Lillie (1954B)* also recommends:

   Add 5% of 90% formic acid to Zenker's fixative.

3. *McNamara et al. (1940)*:

   mercuric chloride . . . .   10.0 gm.
   distilled water . . . .   300.0 ml.
   Dissolve with heat. Cool.
   trichloracetic acid . . . .   30.0 gm.
   distilled water . . . .   100.0 ml.
   Dissolve and then add:
   nitric acid, concentrated . . . .   5.0 ml.
   95% ethyl alcohol . . . .   50.0 ml.
   formalin . . . .   40.0 ml.

   Mix the two solutions. Change daily until bone is soft. If more than 7 days are required, nuclear staining is impaired. Running water: 24 hours; dehydrate and embed.

4. *Perenyi's fluid,* also a fixative, page 000.

   Good for small deposits. Little hardening effect. Excellent cytological detail. Good for calcified arteries, and glands, thyroid. 12–24 hours. Wash in 50–70% alcohol.

5. *Schmidt (1956)* uses the following for 24–48 hours, pH 7–9.

   plus 1 gm. sodium acetate) . . . .   100.0 ml.
   disodium versenate . . . .   10.0 gm.

   No washing necessary. Dehydrate and embed as usual.

DECALCIFICATION-DEHYDRATION

Jenkin's fluid (Culling, 1957):

absolute ethyl alcohol	73.0 ml.
distilled water	10.0 ml.
chloroform	10.0 ml.
glacial acetic acid	3.0 ml.
hydrochloric acid, concentrated	4.0 ml.

The swelling action of the acid is counteracted by the inclusion of alcohol. Large amounts of solution should be used, 40–50 times bulk of tissue. After decalcification, transfer to absolute alcohol for several changes, then clear and embed.

The major portion of this book will be devoted to sectioning methods for preparing tissue for staining, because of complexity and quantity of such methods. Brief mention, however, should be given to other means of examining tissues.

Exceedingly thin membranes can be examined directly by mounting in glycerol or other aqueous media. Considerable detail can be observed with reduced light or under the phase microscope. Sometimes a bit of stain can be added to sharpen or differentiate certain elements. More permanent preparations can be secured with fixation as discussed in the preceding pages.

"Touch" preparations are made by pressing the cut surface of fresh tissue against a dry slide. Cells adhere to the surface and can be examined unstained, or the slide may be immediately immersed in a fixative and then stained.

Occasionally, free-hand sections of relatively tough tissue are cut for examination.

Smears are one of the commonest devices for simple slide preparation: blood and bone marrow (page 219), Papanicolaou (page 357), fecal (page 386), and chromosomes (squash preparations, a modification of smears, page 367).

"Cell blocks"—concentrated clusters of individual cells or grouped cells—are described in detail on page 38.

Chapter 2

Dehydration

Preparation for Embedding

Tissues fixed in aqueous solutions will maintain a high water content, a condition that can be a hindrance to later processing. Except in special cases (freezing method, water-soluble waxes, and special cell contents), the tissue must be **dehydrated** (water removed) before certain steps in this processing can be successful.

Tissues, during fixing and washing, lack an ideal consistency for sectioning—cutting thin slices of a few microns in thickness. They may be soft, or may contain a lumen or hollow spaces and are easily deformed by sectioning. If the cells were pierced by a knife, their fluid content could be released and this would allow the cells to collapse. To preclude these problems, the fluids in the tissue are replaced by a medium which hardens to a firm, easily sectioned material. The cells are filled intracellularly and enclosed extracellularly with the medium and are thereby protected during physical handling. The most universally used media for this purpose are paraffin and nitrocellulose or some variation thereof. Other media, less frequently used, are gelatin and water-soluble waxes.

Various conditions determine the choice of medium. Paraffin is suitable for most histological and embryological purposes when thin sections (1–15 μ) are required. Thin sections also can be prepared with nitrocellulose. Serial sections, however, are made more easily with the former than with the latter; also paraffin preparation requires a far shorter time. Impregnating with nitrocellulose has distinct advantages when it is desirable to avoid heat and when a tissue becomes hard too readily, or is too large for the paraffin technic. In nitrocellulose, shrinkage is reduced to a minimum, whereas in paraffin it can amount to as much as 8–20% of the original size. Gelatin can be used for extremely friable tissue in the freezing technic, and water soluble waxes are used when alcohols, hydrocarbons and the like must be avoided.

Before embedding in either paraffin or nitrocellulose, all water must be removed from the tissue. This *dehydration* usually is achieved in a series of gradually increasing percentages of alcohol in water. Gradual changing through 30, 50, 70, 80, 95% and absolute alcohol is said to reduce some of the shrinkage occurring in the tissue. In cases where time does not permit such a series, the 30% and 80% steps, and even the 50% change, may be eliminated without great damage to the tissue. The time required for each step depends on the size of the object—½ to 2 hours, maybe 3 hours in extreme cases. A second change of absolute alcohol should be included to insure complete removal of water. But tissue should remain in absolute alcohol only long enough to remove all traces of water; a total of 2–3 hours should be ample, even for large pieces. Too long an exposure to 95% and absolute alcohol tends to harden the material, making it difficult to section.

There are other agents which are just as successful dehydrants as *ethyl alcohol (ethanol)*. The ideal dehydrating fluid would be one that can mix in all proportions with water, ethyl alcohol, xylene and paraffin. Two such solutions are *dioxane* (page 39) and *tertiary butyl alcohol (butanol)*. Absolute butyl alcohol is miscible with paraffin, and after infiltration with warm (50°C) butyl-alcohol-paraffin mixture, infiltration with pure paraffin can follow. If *isobutyl alcohol* is used, there may be some difficulty with impregnation, probably due to the limited miscibility of this alcohol with paraffin and water. In both cases—tertiary and isobutyl alcohol—there is more shrinkage than with other alcohols. *Isopropyl* (99%) *alcohol (isopropanol)* is an excellent substitute for ethyl alcohol, and is sufficiently water free for use as absolute alcohol. Actually isopropyl alcohol has less shrinkage and hardening effect than ethyl alcohol; it is cheaper and free of internal revenue restrictions. One disadvantage must be remembered, isopropyl alcohol cannot be used prior to nitrocellulose embedding, since nitrocellulose is practically insoluble in it. Also dyes are not soluble in it, so it cannot be used for staining solutions.

For the preparation of dilutions of ethyl alcohol, it is customary to use 95% alcohol and dilute it with distilled water in the following manner: if a 70% solution is required, measure 70 parts of 95% alcohol and add 25 parts of distilled water to make 95 parts of 70% dilution. In other words, into a 100 ml. graduated cylinder pour 95% alcohol to the 70 ml. mark, and then add distilled water up to the 95 ml. mark.

Absolute alcohol is not accurately 100%, but may contain as much as 1 or 2% water. If the water content is no higher than this, the absolute alcohol is considered 100% for practical purposes in microtechnic. If it is necessary to make certain that the water content is no more than 2%, add a few ml. of the alcohol to a few ml. of toluene or xylene. If a turbidity persists, there is more than 2% water present. But if a clear mixture remains, the alcohol is satisfactory as an absolute grade.

Dilutions of isopropyl alcohol (99%) can be handled as a 100% solution; that is, for 70% use 30 ml. water to 70 ml. of alcohol, etc.

If distilled water is not provided in the laboratory building, a Barnstead Still [1] can provide a sufficient amount of water for an average microtechnic laboratory. The stills are available in sizes of $\frac{1}{2}$ up to 10 gallons of water produced per hour. A special model will produce 30 gallons per hour.

Special Treatment for Small, Colorless Tissues

Often a tissue is small and lacking in color, and seems to disappear into the opaqueness of the paraffin. An easy answer to this problem is to add some eosin to the last change of 95% alcohol; the tissue can then be seen more readily and oriented with greater facility. This, however, cannot be done if isopropyl alcohol is being used, since stains are not soluble in it. The eosin will not interfere with future staining; it is lost in the hydration series following deparaffinization.

[1] Barnstead Still and Sterlizer Company, 49 Lanesville Terrace, Boston 13, Massachusetts.

Chapter 3

Clearing, Infiltrating, and Embedding for the Paraffin Method

Clearing

In most technics that require dehydration and infiltration, an intermediary step is necessary to hurdle the transition between the two. Because the alcohol used for dehydration will not dissolve or mix with paraffin (exception, tertiary butyl alcohol as noted previously) some fluid miscible with both alcohol and paraffin must be used before infiltration can take place.

The hydrocarbons *benzene, toluene* and *xylene* are reagents commonly used for this purpose, but if the tissue contains considerable cartilage, or is fibrous or muscular, thus tending to harden readily, sometimes it is wise to avoid these solutions. Xylene, formerly one of the most widely used reagents, is the worst offender of the three in this connection, and in most cases of clearing for infiltration it should be abandoned in favor of one of the other two. Benzene presents fewer hardening problems than either of the others, but because of its low boiling point (80°C) sometimes is difficult for beginners to use. If a student is too slow while making his transfers from benzene into paraffin, the benzene may evaporate out of the tissue and leave air pockets. These will not infiltrate with paraffin. Of the three reagents toluene probably is the safest to use; it does not harden as excessively as xylene, and it has a higher boiling point (111°C) than benzene, thus eliminating some of the hazards of evaporation. (Boiling point of xylene, 142°C.) In conclusion, benzene produces less shrinkage than either toluene or xylene.

If tissue hardening does present a serious problem, then one of the clearing oils can be used. *Cedarwood oil* is well known and is relatively safe for the beginner, but overnight usually is required for complete replacement of the alcohol in the tissue. Also, as is true of all oils, every trace of oil must be removed during infiltration. Sometimes this condition is difficult to judge, since the oil may have a boiling point in the 200s and be slow moving out of the tissue. The action may be improved by mixing oil with an equal amount of toluene. The cedarwood oil method is an expensive one involving the use of a costly oil as well as absolute alcohol. In this case the latter fluid may not be eliminated.

Chloroform is used in many laboratories, but has outstanding disadvantages. It dessicates some tissues, connective tissue in particular, and has a boiling point of 61°C, making it highly volatile. *Aniline* can be used with good results but it too is difficult to remove during infiltration. A mixture of equal parts of *oil of wintergreen* (methyl salicylate) and aniline followed by pure *methyl salicylate,* and then methyl salicylate-paraffin offers quicker and surer results. Methyl salicylate may be used alone; also there are *bergamot, clove, creosote, terpinol* and other oils. *Amyl acetate* and *cellosolve* (ethylene-glycol-monoethyl ether, *Carbide and Carbon Co.*) do not harden excessively; the latter, however, is highly volatile.

If at any time during the clearing process the clearer (xylene, toluene or benzene) becomes turbid, water is present and the tissue is not completely dehydrated. The only remedy is to return the tissue to absolute alcohol to eliminate the water, then place it again in a fresh supply of clearer. The solution originally used may contain water. Embedded tissue containing water can shrink as much as 50%, and it offers difficulties in sectioning and mounting sections on slides.

"Clearing" may seem a strange nomenclature for this intermediary step, but it happens to be a special property of the reagents mentioned above. They remove, or *clear,* opacity from dehydrated tissues, making them transparent. Blocks of tissue appear to deepen in color; also they seem almost crystalline, never milky.

Infiltration with Paraffin

Paraffin is considered to be either soft or hard. The melting point of the former lies in either the 50–52°C or 53–55°C ranges; of the latter in the 56–58°C or 60–68°C ranges. The choice of melting point depends upon the thickness at which the tissue is to be sectioned, or upon the type of tissue—hard paraffin for hard tissues and soft paraffin for soft ones. If relatively thick sections are to be cut, use a soft paraffin; otherwise the sections will not adhere to each other in a ribbon. If thinner sections are desired, down to a thickness of 5–7 microns, use a paraffin in the 56–58° grade. For extremely thin sections of less than 5 microns, sometimes the best results can be obtained with a hard paraffin of 60–68° melting point. The sections will retain their shape and size without excessive compression and will ribbon better than if the paraffin is too soft. In addition, room and temperature conditions can influence the choice of paraffin. Often hot weather will force the use of a harder paraffin than might be chosen during cool weather. If it is impractical to stock more than one kind of melting point paraffin, usually a 56–58°C is the safest choice.

Except in the case of friable tissues, the following step may be omitted. After the tissue is well cleared by benzene or other clearer, begin to saturate the solution with fine shavings of paraffin until some of the paraffin remains undissolved. Leave the tissue in the saturated clearer for 4–6 hours, or overnight for large pieces. Then with a warm spatula remove the tissue to melted paraffin already prepared in an oven.

In normal cases which eliminate the preceding step, tissues are transferred directly from clearer to paraffin. Keep the oven temperature only high enough to maintain the paraffin in a melted state, no higher. This lessens the danger of overheated tissue, which can initiate hardness and shrinkage. Paraffin standing in a warm oven in a melted condition for several days or weeks is better for infiltrating and embedding purposes than freshly melted paraffin. After ½–1 hour in the first bath the tissue is removed to a fresh dish of paraffin for a similar length of time. Two changes of paraffin are sufficient for most normal requirements, but for some cases of difficult infiltration, such as horny skin or bone, a third change may be necessary, and the time of infiltration may need to be extended to as much as six hours over-all, even overnight. Such crises fortunately are rare.

The use of a vacuum oven for infiltrating will remove air from some tissues (lung) and eliminate holes in the final paraffin block. (*Weiner, 1957; Luna and Ballou, 1959*)

Embedding with Paraffin

As soon as the tissue is thoroughly infiltrated with paraffin, it is ready to be embedded; the paraffin is allowed to solidify around and within the tissue. The tissue is placed in a small container or paper box already filled with melted paraffin and the whole is cooled rapidly in water. Before transferring the tissue, warm the instruments which manipulate it. This will prevent congealing of paraffin on metal surfaces. Handle the tissue and paraffin as rapidly as possible to prevent the paraffin from solidifying before the tissue is oriented in it. Orientation is important. If the tissue is placed in a known position and carefully marked with a slip of paper in the hardening paraffin (Fig. 9), it remains a simple matter to determine the proper surface for sectioning. If a paper box is used, the orienting mark may be made directly on one of its flaps.

Each technician eventually adopts his or her own pet embedding mold or container. A few suggestions: petri dishes, syracuse watch glasses, shallow stender dishes, test tubes to concentrate solid contents of tissue or body fluids, and a neat little dish for tiny pieces—perhaps a miniature syracuse watch glass (*watch glasses, U.S. Bureau of Plant Industry Model, 20 mm. inside diameter, 8 mm. deep, A. H. Thomas Co., #9850*). Lightly coat the insides of glass dishes with glycerol; then the solidified paraffin block loosens readily. Cast lead L s (*Lipshaw #334, Diamond embedding boxes*) when placed on a small flat metal rectangle can be adjusted to almost any size for embedding, and, being metal, they cool the paraffin more quickly than glass. Also they break loose immediately from the paraffin. *Lipshaw* also has a *Pop-out Embedding Mold.*

Paper boxes may be fashioned according to Figs. 1, 2, 3. Perhaps the one advantage of these is that they and any data recorded on them can be left permanently on blocks which have to be stored. The *Lipshaw Company* offers a disposable mold, called the *Peel-A-Way Disposable Embedding Mold.* These molds are made of lightweight plastic, available in five sizes, and are easily broken at the corners so the sides can be peeled down and the moll pulled away. Perforated tabs to fit can be purchased. Various devices such as refrigerator trays with their dividers can be used for embedding a number of large pieces of tissue. *Lipshaw*

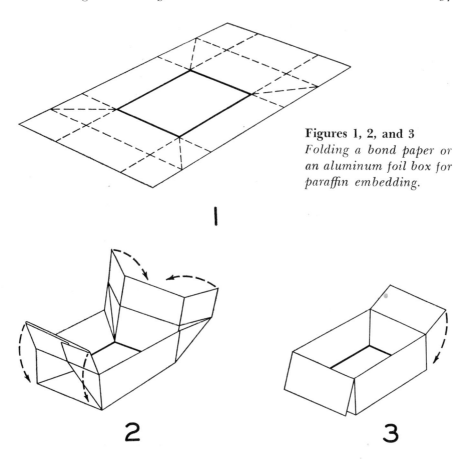

Figures 1, 2, and 3
*Folding a bond paper or
an aluminum foil box for
paraffin embedding.*

offers an embedding combination with 20 or 30 compartments. The literature and catalogs are full of ideas; the above are just a few of them.

When small amounts of paraffin are ready to be solidified, they can be cooled immediately in water, preferably at a temperature of 10–15°C. Make certain that a solidified scum has formed over each potential block before dipping it below the surface of the water. Water colder than 10°C causes the block to contract too strongly and it may finally crack. Furthermore, normal crystals may form in the center, but abnormal ones in the periphery of the block. The perfect block is one in which the paraffin crystals are contiguous with each other and the paraffin appears clear and homogeneous. Paraffin may contain 7–15% air dissolved in it and will appear clear when that air is distributed evenly through its mass. But pockets of air produce milky spots, a condition called "crystallization." Either slow hardening of the block in the air, or too rapid cooling may cause this effect, particularly in the case of large blocks.

Quick hardening of outer surfaces will trap the air. When these problems arise, cool the blocks from the bottom, and with a hot instrument keep the upper surface melted for a short time, thus releasing some of the air. Then blow across the top until a scum forms, and ease the block into water. This treatment also prevents excessive shrinkage in the center of the block and the enclosed tissue. (*Dempster, 1944.*)

If the paraffin does crystallize, difficulty may be encountered during sectioning; the only remedy is to return the block to melted paraffin, allow it remelt and repeat the embedding process. Experienced technicians soon learn how fast to handle the paraffin and reduce crystallization to a minimum.

Thoroughly hardened paraffin blocks can be stored indefinitely without injury to the tissue, but they must be kept in a cool place where they cannot soften or melt.

Embedding Cellular Contents of Body Fluids

"Cell blocks" are clusters of individual cells which have been concentrated and embedded for sectioning. The process for embedding them is as follows:

1. Collect the material in centrifuge tubes and add fixative: 1 hour, or overnight. Agitate occasionally.
2. Concentrate by centrifuging (preferably in small tubes); decant and add water or alcohol depending on requirement of fixative. Loosen material at bottom of tube and stir with small glass rod: 5–10 minutes, or longer.
3. Centrifuge and decant. Add next solution and stir thoroughly. Dehydrate in this manner, and clear: approximately 10–15 minutes for each step depending on size of particles.
4. Add melted paraffin and place tube upright in a glass or beaker in oven. Stir slightly with warm instrument to work paraffin to bottom of tube: 30 minutes. Stir a bit once during this period.
5. Cool test tube.
6. Break tube. Place paraffin block in tiny paper box in a small dish of paraffin in the oven. Leave only long enough for block to begin to soften. Quickly cool paper box.

Clark (1947) suggest an alternate method:

1. Warm tube carefully in water, slightly warmer than paraffin. As soon as paraffin against glass melts, tip tube and allow paraffin block to slide out.

2. Mount block in a small hole dug in a square of paraffin and blend two together with a warm needle or spatula.

Farnsworth (1956) transfers minute pieces with a pipette to a piece of lens paper lying on a blotter. The latter absorbs the fluid, then the lens paper bearing the tissue is laid flat on the surface of melted paraffin. She embeds in depression slides wiped with glycerine.

Arnold (1952) concentrates small organisms in agar and carries through with the usual processes.

[*See also* DelVecchio *et al.* (1959); DeWitt *et al.* (1957); McCormick (1959B); Seal (1956); Taft and Arizaga-Cruz (1960).]

Dehydration and Clearing Combinations

Dioxane Method.

Any procedure which shortens the processing time for embedding has considerable merit and finds favor among technicians. In 1931 an article appeared concerning a reagent, which dehydrated as well as cleared in a minimum of steps. *Graupner and Weissberger (1931)* proposed the use of dioxane (diethyl dioxide), miscible with water, alcohol, hydrocarbons and paraffin. It seemed to eliminate some shrinkage and hardening, and was a relatively inexpensive method because fewer solutions were required. Dioxane itself, however, is far more costly than alcohol.

Some technicians claim that it has other disadvantages. *Conn (1939)* cautioned that dioxane was cumulatively toxic and that it should not be used by any person with liver or kidney trouble. *Navasquez (1935)* reported that dioxane toxicity for animals was relatively low, that there was no accumulative effect, and that a tolerance would develop. Such cases as were noted in man came after a period of heavy exposure to the vapor. It was acute, not a chronic, poisoning. *Fairly et al. (1936)* said there is some evidence that toxic effects are due to oxidation products: oxalic acid and diglycolic acid, which are considered to be nontoxic to man. Perhaps it is well to be cautious; use dioxane only in a well-ventilated room and away from the nose. Avoid unnecessary soaking of hands in it. Keep dioxane containers tightly closed at all times.

Because of its low tolerance to water, carelessness in the use of dioxane can lead to trouble. If the tissue shrinks (it may shrink as much as 40–50%) during infiltration with paraffin, water is present. The author has seen this happen frequently for beginning students. *Stowell (1941)* reported 35% shrinkage with dioxane and further condemned it, saying that some brands already contain at least 10% water and other impurities even before use. Cloudiness appears at 1% water content.

Miller's Schedule for Dioxane (1937)

1. Move directly from fixative into dioxane 3 parts, distilled water 1 part: $\frac{1}{2}$–1 hour.
2. Dioxane: 1 hour.
3. Fresh dioxane: 2 hours.
4. Paraffin 1 part, dioxane 1 part (in paraffin oven): 2–4 hours.
5. Paraffin: overnight.
6. Embed.

Many technicians consider it advisable to place anhydrous calcium chloride in the bottom of the dioxane container during dehydration as an aid in removal of all water, thereby reducing the possibility of carrying water into the paraffin. *Mossman (1937)* observed that dioxane reacts with $CaCl_2$ and makes it swell as though water is present. He suggested that CaO (calcium oxide) is better, but feels that this step is unnecessary.

If a fixative containing potassium dichromate is used, the tissues must be washed thoroughly before using dioxane; otherwise the dichromate will crystallize.

Tetrahydrofuran (THF) for Dehydration

Haust (1958, 1959) recommends THF for dehydration for several reasons. It mixes with water in all proportions, also with paraffin depending upon temperature, becoming increasingly miscible as the temperature rises. It is miscible with nearly all solvents and can be used as a solvent for mounting media. Most dyes are not soluble in THF, but iodine, mercuric chloride, acetic acid and picric acid are soluble in it. THF has a low boiling point (65°C) so it evaporates rapidly and must be kept tightly closed at all times. It has to be regenerated occasionally to remove accumulated peroxides and water.

Haust's Method, Following Fixation

1. THF 1 part, water 1 part: 2 hours.
2. THF, 3 changes: 2 hours each.
3. THF 1 part, paraffin 1 part, 53–54°C: 2 hours.
4. Paraffin: 2 hours.
5. Embed.

Tetrahydrofuran, highest quality, can be obtained from *Eastman Kodak Co.*, and *Fisher Scientific Co.*

The Fisher Company in *The Laboratory, Clinical Edition (28, #C4, 1960)*, suggests that instead of repurifying THF over metallic sodium, a simpler and safer way involves passing the THF through a column of activated alumina.

Timing Schedule for Paraffin Method

Size 10 ± mm.—smaller pieces will require less time, larger pieces more time.

Schedule Using Ethyl Alcohol

1. A general fixative: overnight or 24 hours. (Bouin's, Susa's, Stieve's, Formalin, Zenker's[1])
2. Wash in water, running if possible: 6–8 hours or overnight. *Exceptions:* Bouin's, Susa's and Stieve's fixed tissue can be transferred directly to 50 or 70% alcohol without washing.
3. Transfer to 50% alcohol: 1 hour.
4. Transfer to 70% alcohol: 1 hour.

   (See special iodine treatment for mercuric chloride fixatives, page 12)

5. Transfer to 95% ethyl alcohol: 1 to $1\frac{1}{2}$ hours.
6. Transfer to absolute ethyl alcohol #1: $\frac{1}{2}$ to 1 hour.
7. Transfer to absolute ethyl alcohol #2: $\frac{1}{2}$ to 1 hour.
8. Transfer to toluene #1: $\frac{1}{2}$ to 1 hour.
9. Transfer to toluene #2: $\frac{1}{2}$ to 1 hour.
10. Transfer to melted paraffin #1: $\frac{1}{2}$ to 1 hour.
11. Transfer to melted paraffin #2: $\frac{1}{2}$ to 1 hour.
12. Embed.

Alternate Schedule Using Isopropyl Alcohol
(steps 1 through 4 the same as above)

5. Transfer to isopropyl alcohol #1: $\frac{1}{2}$ to 1 hour.
6. Transfer to isopropyl alcohol #2: $\frac{1}{2}$ to 1 hour.
7. Transfer to toluene #1: $\frac{1}{2}$ to 1 hour.
8. Transfer to toluene #2: $\frac{1}{2}$ to 1 hour.
9. Transfer to melted paraffin #1: $\frac{1}{2}$ to 1 hour.

[1] If tissue fixed in Zenker's tends to harden, do not leave it overnight in the fixative; transfer to 3–5% aqueous potassium dichromate for overnight, then proceed as usual on schedule.

10. Transfer to melted paraffin #2: $\frac{1}{2}$ to hour.
11. Embed.

If the tissue is well hardened by the fixative, it is not necessary to dehydrate the tissue through a number of graduated steps, such as 50, 60, 70, 80, 95% and absolute alcohol. Even the elimination of the 50% step is possible when time presents a problem; also the use of isopropyl alcohol materially shortens the schedule.

In passing tissues from one fluid to another, use the decantation method. This avoids excessive manipulation with forceps and reduces injury to the tissue. After pouring off a solution, drain the tissue bottle briefly against a paper towel or cleansing tissue to pull off as much as possible of the discarded solution. This reduces contamination of the new solution. Since 95% alcohol, absolute alcohol, clearers and melted paraffin all contribute to the hardening of the tissue, avoid leaving it in any of these fluids for longer than the maximum time (preferably leave only for the minimum period), and never overnight. Effective infiltration takes place only when the paraffin is actually melted. Partly melted, "mushy" paraffin penetrates poorly, if at all.

Automatic Tissue Processors

Most large laboratories now handle the foregoing processes by machine; the changes are controlled with a timing device, and the tissues are shifted automatically through a series of beakers or other type of container. The timing device can be set on a schedule to handle the changes during the night in order that the tissues will be ready for embedding when the technician arrives at the laboratory in the morning. Small metal or plastic receptacles with snap-on lids hold the tissues and labels, and are deposited in a basket which clips into the bottom of the lid of the instrument. When the time arrives for removal of the tissues to a new solution, the lid rises and rotates to lower the basket into the next container. The two final beakers are thermostatically controlled paraffin baths. The technician can set the timing device for any interval desired—15 minutes, 30 minutes, 1 or more hours, etc.—over a period of 24 hours. The newest models have a clock which can control the instrument over a week end or several days. (The above description applies to the *Autotechnicon of Technicon Company*.)

There are several tissue processors on the market; in addition to the *Autotechnicon*, there is a *Lipshaw* model, and the *Tissuematon* of the *Fisher Scientific Company*. Complete operational directions are supplied with all models.

Chapter **4**

Microtomes and
Microtome Knives

Microtomes

The first instrument for cutting sections was made by Cummings in 1770. It was a hand model that held the specimen in a cylinder and raised it for sectioning with a screw. In 1835, Pritchard adapted the instrument to a table model by fastening it to a table with a clamp and cutting across the section with a two-handled knife. These instruments were called cutting machines until Chevalier introduced the name *microtome* in 1839. Sliding cutting machines were developed in 1798, rotary microtomes in 1883 and 1886, and the *Spencer Lens Company* manufactured the first clinical microtome in 1901. The large Spencer Rotary with increased precision became available in 1910. (*Richards, 1949.*)

1. The rotary microtome for paraffin sections; the most widely used method.
2. The sliding microtome for nitrocellulose (celloidin) sections; not always the most practical method, slow and expensive, but often unexcelled for hard and large objects such as eyes, bone and cartilage, also in cases when shrinkage must be kept to a minimum.
3. The clinical (freezing) microtome for unembedded tissues; quick, cheap,

and required for some processes when certain cell components must be retained, such as fat and enzymes, also for immediate diagnosis.

4. The ultra-thin sectioning microtome for sections thinner than 1 micron, electron microscopy. Only for special technics and not commonly found in laboratories.

5. The base sledge microtome for exceedingly large tissues (brains) and hard blocks of tissues. Only for special technics and not commonly found in laboratories.

Microtomes should always be kept well oiled to prevent parts from wearing unnecessarily or sticking. Either of the latter faults can cause imperfect sectioning—sections of variable thickness. Obtain advice from an expert concerning the parts to be kept oiled, and consult the booklet accompanying the instrument. The best oil recommended for this purpose is *Pike Oil*, manufactured by *Behr-Manning, Troy, N.Y., a Division of Norton Co., Abrasives.*

Microtome Knives

There are three familiar types of microtome knives:

1. The plane-edge for frozen sections and paraffin ribbons.
2. The biconcave used sometimes for paraffin work.
3. The plane-concave for celloidin, sometimes for paraffin.

Because knives seem to demand hours of attention, they often become the technician's nightmare, and the task of keeping them in optimum condition presents problems.

Theoretically, a perfect cutting edge is the juncture of two plane smooth surfaces meeting at as small an angle as is feasible—ideally 14° as suggested by Dr. Lorimer Rutty (*Krajian and Gradwohl, 1952, page 28*). These cutting surfaces are called the cutting facets. The cutting edge of a very sharp knife, when examined by reflected light under 100 magnifications, appears as a fine discontinuous line. It may vary slightly in width, but it should show only a slight reflection, a narrow, straight bright line. At a higher magnification of about 500 times, the edge will have a finely serrated appearance. The fineness or coarseness of these serrations depends on the degree of success in sharpening the knife. The facets are determined by the "back" which is slipped on the knife during sharpening to raise it just enough to form these facets (Fig. 4). Every knife must have its own back. Never interchange backs. The back must

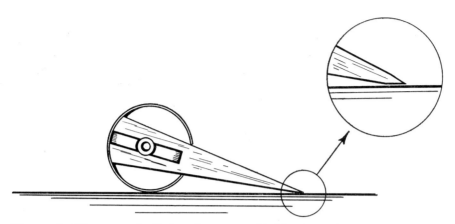

Figure 4. *Microtome knife bevel as controlled by knife back.*

fit tight enough so that it does not move about on the knife. When it shows considerable wear, buy a new one, because as the back wears the cutting facets are widening. Do not ram the knife into the back; hold the knife in one hand and the back in the other and work it on gradually with a rocking motion.

The importance of taking good care of a knife cannot be overemphasized. Clean it after use; some materials like blood and water, when left on the knife edge, corrode it. Clean with xylene on soft cleansing tissue and finally wipe it dry. Do not strike the edge with hard objects (section lifter, dissecting needle); the edge can be damaged or dented.

Sharpening Knives

The glass plate has had the longest and most successful use as a sharpening instrument. In 1857 von Mohl used a thick glass plate; a rotating one was developed by von Apathy in 1913, and a vertical one by Long in 1927. Leather strops were advocated in 1922, and a couple of years later carborundum hones, followed by finer grained hones or stropping on canvas or leather. Many argue against a strop, saying that a knife can be honed sharp enough for good sectioning. If, however, there are fine serrations, gentle stropping frequently can remove them and improve the cutting ability of the knife.

If a glass plate is used, it should be at least $\frac{3}{16}$ of an inch thick, approximately 14 inches long, and an inch or two wider than a microtome knife. Levigated alumina (approxiemately 1%) added to a neutral soap solution is excellent for sharpening; the polishing should be done

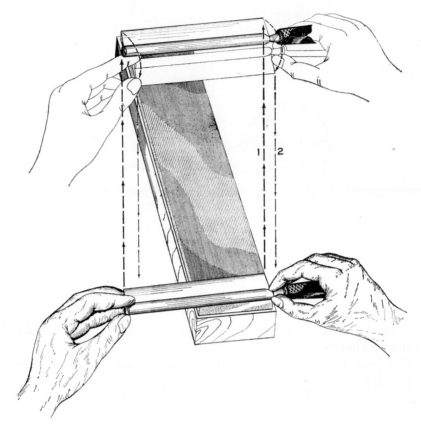

Figure 5. *First set of strokes for microtome knife honing.*

with Diamantine—a small amount. A final stropping will finish off fine serrations (*Uber, 1936*).

Arthur H. Thomas manufactures a knife sharpener, the Fanz model, using a revolving glass disc over which the knife is swept back and forth.

Some pointers on the use and care of hones and strops may be of help to beginners. Never apply oil to hones, only water and neutral soap solution or Lava soap. Never allow the hone to dry while in use; always keep it wet with water, or water plus soap. Two types of hones can be used, a coarse one for fast grinding of the knife edge when the nicks are deep, and a polishing hone to remove serrations and small amounts of metal left by the preliminary honing. A yellow Belgian hone is one of the best.

Two patterns are followed, using the same number of strokes per pattern. In Fig. 5 follow course #1, moving from bottom right to top

Figure 6. *Second set of strokes for microtome knife honing.*

left, roll knife over on its back, and return over same path in opposite direction (course #2) moving from top left to bottom right—3 or 4 times. Move knife toward left into position in Fig. 6 and follow course #3, moving from bottom left to top right, and return from top right to bottom left (course #4)—same number of times as above. Repeat these strokes on hone until deep nicks and scratches are eliminated.

When all nicks and deep serrations have been removed (check under dissecting scope), the knife is ready to be stropped, a final polishing action. Do not use a sagging hammock-like strop unless it can be held tightly flat, otherwise it rounds the knife edge. The best type is mounted on a felt pad on a hardwood block. This allows a bit of cushion, but on a solid surface. With a soft cloth keep the strop surface clean and free of dust. Rubbing the leather with the hand improves the texture. Do not use mineral oil on it. If the leather becomes dry, work in Neetsfoot oil, working over small areas at a time, not the entire strop. Buff with soft towelling at once; do not allow the oil to sit on it and soak in or develop a gummy mess.

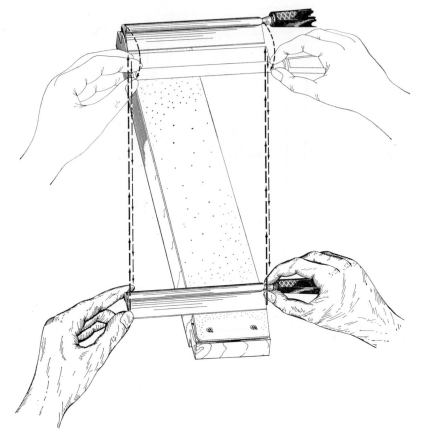

Figure 7. *First set of strokes for microtome knife stropping.*

Lipshaw offers several block strop combinations; the revolving one is especially handy.

First use a honing strop, usually made of pigskin with a fine abrasive embedded in it. Then follow with the finishing strop, a fine-grain horsehide. The two patterns for stropping are similar to those of honing, but with the cutting edge moving away from the strop. (Figs. 7, 8) Repeat these strokes on the honing strop until fine abrasions caused by the hone have been smoothed away, then polish with a few strokes on the finishing strop. Only a dozen strokes on the latter should be necessary if the preliminary honing and stropping have been properly done. While honing and stropping, use both hands, left one on the back and adjacent knife surface, and the right hand on the handle. Press on *lightly,* guid-

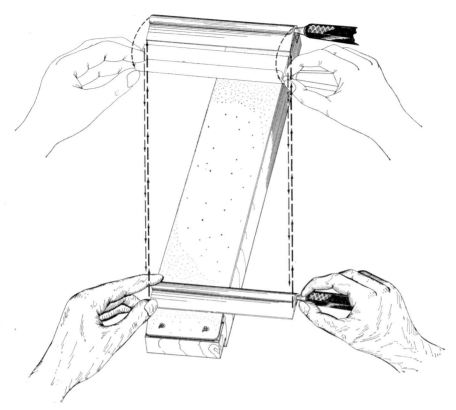

Figure 8. *Second set of strokes for microtome knife stropping.*

ing with both hands and with uniform pressure from both. Always use the same pressure on the forward strokes as on the return ones. Never hurry honing or stropping; use at least one full second for each stroke.

Mechanical knife sharpeners are on the market; almost every scientific supply company has at least one. One of the best, an automatic sharpener, is now in production by the *American Optical Company*. Most technicians develop a fancy for one type in preference to others; the author, therefore, considers it expedient not to offer any recommendation.

If the cost of microtome knives and their maintenance is prohibitive for a class of beginning students, the *Spencer Razor Blade Holder* can be used to advantage. A student can use a razor blade once and throw it away if the edge has become dull, or sharpen it up a bit on an old knife strop.

The life of the sharp edge of a good knife can be prolonged if the technician has another knife for the preliminary trimming of paraffin blocks. After undesirable parts of the tissue block have been trimmed away, the good knife can be substituted for the old one, and the required sections collected.

Chapter **5**

Paraffin Method

Sectioning

The embedded blocks (Fig. 9) are trimmed into squares or rectangles, depending on the shape of the tissue, with two edges parallel (Fig. 10). The two short or side edges need not be parallel, sometimes with advantage as will be indicated later. Wooden blocks or metal object discs, such as are sold by supply houses (*Lipshaw #800*), are covered with a layer of paraffin. (*Suggestion:* Keep a 1-inch brush in a beaker of melted paraffin in the paraffin oven.) Then a heated instrument (spatula or

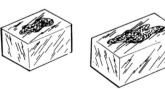

Figure 9. *Untrimmed   paraffin   tissue block.*

Figure 10. *Trimmed   paraffin tissue blocks.*

slide) is held between the paraffin on the object disc and the under surface of the tissue block (Fig. 11). When both surfaces are melted, the instrument is withdrawn and the tissue block pressed firmly into the paraffin on the object disc. After cooling, the block is ready to be sectioned (Fig. 12).

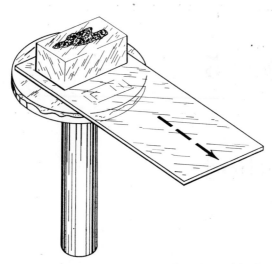

Figure 11. *Mounting paraffin tissue block on an object disc.*

Set the Rotary microtome for section thickness (5 or 6 microns, etc.) . Raise the tissue carrier and place in it the object disc with its mounted tissue block. Tighten the clamp of the tissue carrier onto the stem of the object disc. If using a wooden block, allow it to extend about $\frac{1}{4}$ inch beyond the metal clamps; this will prevent the paraffin block from breaking loose from the wooden block when the clamp is tightened.

Insert the microtome knife and tighten its clamps. The knife must be held in the clamps at a proper angle for optimal sectioning, producing a minimal amount of compression, and allowing the sections to adhere to each other. Many suggestions can be made concerning angle determination, but in most instances the technician finds the answer after a process of trial and error. The cutting facets are small as determined by the back. When placed in the microtome, the knife must be tilted just enough so the cutting facet next to the block and the surface of the block clear each other. If the tilt is not sufficient (Fig. 13), the surface of the block is pressed down with the wedging effect of the facet and no section results. At the next stroke of the knife, this compression increases, and finally a thick section is cut, a composite of the compressed sections. Too great a tilt of the knife makes it scrape through like a chisel, rather than cut through the tissue (Fig. 14).

Turn the feed screw handle (left side of instrument), moving the feed mechanism backward or forward until the face of the tissue block barely touches the cutting edge of the knife. With an old knife start trimming into the block until the desired area is reached. Change to a good knife and readjust tissue carrier if necessary. Never touch the edge of the knife with anything hard. Fragments of paraffin can be flicked off with a camel hair brush, or removed with a finger tip. Scratches appearing in sections often can be remedied by rubbing the knife edge with a finger tip, *upwards*. Also try this motion on the back of the knife; it will remove bits of paraffin which can cause scratches. Cleansing tissue dipped in xylene also is helpful. (Warning: discard the first section after cleaning the knife; it probably is a thick one.) When all sectioning is completed, xylene must be used to clean the knife; leave no corrosive material on its edge.

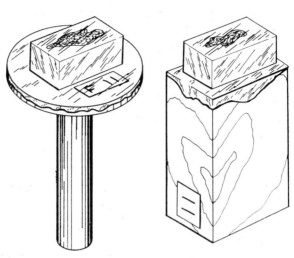

Figure 12. *Tissue blocks mounted on an object disc or wooden block and ready for sectioning.*

Section with an easy rhythm; never rush, or variable thickness of sections is likely to occur. As the sections move down on the knife they form a "ribbon," each section adhering to the one that precedes it as well as the one that follows it. During the cutting of the sections, a bit of heat is generated, enough to soften the paraffin and cause the indi-

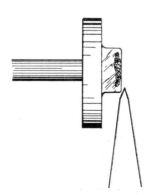

Figure 13. *Insufficient paraffin knife tilt.*

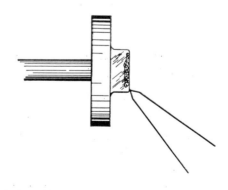

Figure 14. *Excessive paraffin knife tilt.*

vidual sections to stick to each other. As the ribbon forms, hold it away
from the knife with a camel hair brush and ease it forward so that the
sections do not remain on the knife. This is advisable to prevent the
sections from bunching and piling on each other. They can stack high
enough to topple over the edge and get caught between the tissue carrier
and the next stroke of the knife. The parallel edges of the paraffin block
must be cut clean and parallel. If the edges have not been trimmed, but
remain as the original sides formed by the mold, a ribbon will not form.

In dry weather static frequently becomes a problem during sectioning. The sections stick to the knife or to parts of the microtome. They
break apart and stay bunched up instead of lying flat. The friction of
the knife as it crosses the paraffin block forms static electricity on its
surface. An inexpensive little instrument, the *Reco Neutra-Stat*,[1] may
be used to relieve this situation. An alpha radiating static eliminator
strip in a slot on the head of the instrument irradiates the air with
harmless alpha particles. These ionize the air and discharge static
charges from the block surface.

The ribbons formed during sectioning can be mounted directly on
slides, floated on a water bath, or laid in order in a box. The latter is
particularly convenient when the slides cannot be made immediately, or
when numerous sections have to be cut, serial sections for instance.
Hosiery boxes make handy containers, and if painted black inside with
India ink, provide an excellent dark background for the sections. If the
shorter edges of the block were not trimmed parallel, a serrated edge
along the ribbon indicates the exact position of each individual section,
minimizing the danger of cutting through one. The sections can be
stored in boxes until all required slides have been mounted. Valuable
sectioning time is conserved by this means.

*Difficulties Encountered While Sectioning and
Suggested Remedies*[2]

1. *Ribbons are crooked.*
    a. Wedge-shaped sections caused by poor trimming; sides of paraffin
       block are not parallel, or not parallel to edge of knife.
    b. Part of knife edge may be dull; try another part of it.
    c. Uneven hardness of the paraffin; one side may be softer than the
       other, or contain areas of crystallization. Reimbed.

[1] #61–579 Reco Neutra-Stat, Model M, for microtomes. E. Machlett and Son, 220 E. 23rd
Street, New York 10, N.Y., or from Lipshaw Manufacturing Company.
[2] Modified after Richards, 1949.

2. *Sections fail to form ribbons,* usually due to hardness of paraffin.
   a. Use softer paraffin (lower melting point).
   b. Blow on knife to warm it or dip it in warm water.
   c. Cut thinner sections.
   d. Place table lamp near knife and block to warm it.
   e. Resharpen knife.
   f. Lessen tilt of knife, and clean edge.
   g. Dip block in softer paraffin and retrim so a layer of this paraffin surrounds original block.
3. *Sections are wrinkled or compressed.*
   a. Resharpen knife; a dull knife compresses badly.
   b. Paraffin too soft; reimbed in harder paraffin.
   c. Cool block and knife.
   d. Increase tilt of knife.
   e. Clean edge of knife with finger or xylene, remove any paraffin collected there.
   f. Tissue is not completely infiltrated,* or too much crystallization is present.
   g. Soak tissue block in water,† ½–1 hour or overnight if necessary.
4. *Ribbons are split or scratched longitudinally.*
   a. Nick in knife; move to another part of edge or resharpen it.
   b. Knife dirty or gritty along edge.
   c. Dirt or hard particles in tissue or in paraffin, crystals from fixing solution not adequately removed. Filter paraffin, decalcify or desilicify tissue.
   d. Decrease tilt of knife.
   e. Tissue too hard; soak in water.†
5. *Tissue crumbles or falls out of paraffin.*
   a. Poor infiltration;* reimbed.
   b. Not completely dehydrated.
   c. Not completely dealcoholized.
   d. Too long in paraffin bath or too hot while there; soak in water.†
   e. Clearing fluid made tissue too brittle; soak in water.

---

* Most conditions of poor infiltration are due to traces of water or alcohol. This will have to be corrected by first removing such paraffin as is present. Soak the block in toluene for 2 or 3 hours (or more); change twice, then place in absolute alcohol for 1 or more hours. This should remove all traces of water. Clear again in toluene (check against milky appearance); re-infiltrate and embed.

† When soaking in water is recommended, the cut face of the tissue is exposed to tap water for ½–1 hour, or overnight for stubborn cases and when time is of no concern. The author has found this treatment completely satisfactory, but some technicians advocate the addition of glycerol (1 part to 9 parts water) or 60% ethyl alcohol (*Lendrum, 1944*). The fluid works in through the cut tissue surface and softens tough parts. *Exception:* Do not soak nervous system tissue at any time and lymph nodes and fatty tissue only briefly.

6. *Sections cling to block instead of knife.*
    a. Knife too dull or dirty.
    b. Increase tilt of knife.
    c. Paraffin too soft or room too warm. Try harder paraffin or cool block.
    d. Infiltrating paraffin too hot, or too long exposure to solutions which harden; soak in water.†
7. *Tissue makes scratching noise while sectioning.*
    a. Tissue too hard; paraffin too hot or too long exposure to solutions which harden; soak in water.†
    b. Crystals in tissue; fixing reagents not removed sufficiently by washing; calcium or silicon deposits present. (See pages 24 and 372.)
8. *Knife rings as it passes over tissue.*
    a. Knife tilted too much or too little.
    b. Tissue too hard and springs back edge of knife; soak in water.†
    c. Knife blade too thin; try a heavier one.
9. *Sections curl, fly about or stick to things;* this is due to electrification from friction during cutting, especially in weather of low humidity.
    a. Increase humidity in room by boiling water in open pan.
    b. Ground microtome to water pipe.
    c. Postpone sectioning until weather is more humid. Early morning sectioning often is best.
    d. See page 54.
10. *Sections are skipped or vary in thickness.*
    a. Microtome in need of adjustment or new parts.
    b. Tighten all parts, including knife holder and object holder clamp.
    c. Large or tough blocks of tissue may spring the knife; soak in water.†
    d. Knife tilt too great or too little.

Mounting

Slides and Cover Glasses

Most microscopic materials (sections, whole mounts, smears, touch preparations) are mounted on glass slides and are covered with microscopic cover glasses. A noncorrosive quality should be purchased to insure a nonreacting surface. The slides may be obtained in the regular 3×1 inch size or in 3×2 inch for larger tissue sections. The brands labeled "Cleaned, ready for use," save many technician hours devoted to cleaning the uncleaned varieties. In addition, they permit a uniform smear for blood smears and the like.

Cover glasses are manufactured in circles, squares and rectangles, in thickness ranging from #0 to #3. Thickness #0 is used rarely, when an oil immersion objective rides unusually close to the slide. This size is so thin that it fractures easily. Thickness #1 (about 0.15 mm.) usually is adequate for oil immersion work. Thickness #2 (about 0.20 mm.) can be used for whole mounts or when oil immersion is unnecessary. Thickness #3 (about 0.30–0.35 mm.) is occasionally used when a tougher glass is required and for large whole mounts. Circles and squares are purchasable in sizes up to $\frac{7}{8}$ inch in diameter. Circles are designed for mounts when ringing the cover is necessary. Whole mounts in glycerol jelly or any other volatile mountant must be sealed against evaporation. A ringing table can be used to make the supporting ring for the cover glass and then the final seal around the edge of the cover glass. The rectangles come in 22 and 24 mm. widths, and in 30, 40, 50 and 60 mm. lengths. Cover glasses will mount more efficiently if they are cleaned in absolute alcohol and wiped dry. Fewer bubbles cling to the glass when it is pressed into place over the mounting medium.

Mounting Technics

If paraffin sections are to be stained uniformly, the embedding solution is removed, but the sections could lose their unity if they are not affixed to the slides. Also mounting on slides permits handling of many sections simultaneously, as is desirable for serial sections.

Before sections are mounted, a glass marking pencil should be used to make an identifying mark on one end of the slide—a tissue number, student locker number, research project number or a similar identification to prevent confusion with other slides. In addition, this enables the worker to distinguish on which side of the slides the sections are mounted and thus prevent failure during the staining process. Types of permanent glass marking pencils include *diamond points* (a real commercial diamond mounted in a handle) and *steel pencils* with *tungsten-carbide tips* (*Fisher Scientific Company #13-378*). A *vibro-engraver* or vibro-tool can be used for engraved marking on the glass. *Wax china-marking pencils* make only temporary inscriptions which dissolve in the staining solutions. Some inks are reasonably satisfactory; one of the best is *Gold Seal Laboratory Ink* (*#A-1408, Clay-Adams, Inc., N.Y.*). *Stafford (1960)* uses a waterproof pencil (*Venus Unique Blue Waterproof Pencil #1206, American Pencil Co.*) on slides with frosted ends, but this may be removable in xylene or alcohol.

The customary means of affixing sections to slides is attachment with **egg albumen** and water. (**Gelatine** and **blood serum** also can be used, page 414.) Absolutely clean slides are essential to insure adherence of the sections throughout any staining procedure. With one finger smear a thin film of albumen fixative (adhesive, page 412) on the slide, and with a second finger wipe off excess albumen. This should keep the film thin enough. Thick albumen picks up stain, makes a messy looking slide, and can obstruct a clear image of sharp uncluttered tissue elements. If there is a continued tendency to get too much albumen on the slide, try a "floating solution"; dilute a couple of drops of albumen fixative with about 10 ml. of distilled water and float the sections on the solution on the slide (also see *Schleicher, 1951*). *Lillie (1954B)* suggests that since water is used to float the sections on a thin coat of fixative and since the fixative constituents are water soluble, it is doubtful that enough albumen remains on the slide to actually be an adhesive agent. He considers it probable that the albumen acts as a surface tension depressant and aids in closer attraction of sections to slide.

If a water bath is used for spreading the sections, have the temperature of the bath about 5°C below the melting point of the paraffin being used. When removing the sections from the microtome knife or from the box, stretch them as flat as possible as they are placed on the water surface. After they have warmed a bit, they can then be pulled more nearly to their original size with a couple of dissecting needles. With a hot needle or spatula separate the required sections from the rest of the ribbon. Dip an albumenized slide under them and with a needle hold them against the slide while removing it from the bath. Drain off excess water and dry the slide on a warming table or in an oven. Sections collected (glossy side down) in a box can be separated with a spatula or razor and removed to an albumenized slide. Add enough distilled water to spread well beyond the edge of the sections. Place the slide on a slide warmer[3] to correct any compression acquired during sectioning and until the sections are stretched flat. Dense tissues will compress less than the paraffin surrounding them and often will develop folds because the paraffin does not expand sufficiently on the warm plate to permit the tissues to flatten. Pieces with a lumen will invariably demonstrate this fault. One of the simplest ways to correct this difficulty is to break away the paraffin from the outside edge of the tissue. Do this

[3] One of the best is Fisher's Slide Warmer, Catalog #12–594–5.

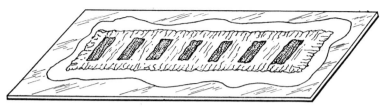

Figure 15. *Compressed or folded paraffin sections.*

when the ribbon is floating on the water on the slide, but not while it is warm, or the paraffin will stick to the dissecting needles. Have the slide cool and split away the paraffin with care so that the tissue is not injured (Figs. 15, 16, and 17). A rather violent method for straightening

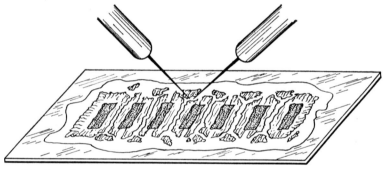

Figure 16. *Breaking paraffin with dissecting needles to permit ribbon expansion without folds.*

stubborn ribbons is the addition of some acetone or alcohol to the water.

Slides that do not take the water smoothly may be dirty slides, but it is more likely that the albumen was omitted. Excessive heat for flattening may cause shrinkage of cell structures and tearing and displacement

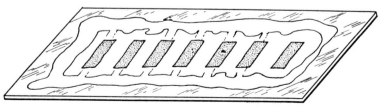

Figure 17. *Expanded and flattened paraffin sections.*

of tissue parts. A safe temperature is approximately 5–10°C lower than the melting point of the paraffin. When the sections are spread smooth, the excess water may be drained off; this is facilitated by touching a piece of cleansing tissue or filter paper to the edge of the slide and around the sections. Permit slides to dry overnight on the warm plate or in an oven of comparable temperature. If they must be stained on the same day as they are mounted, dry them in one of the mechanical hot air dryers (*Technicon or Lipshaw Companies*).

Certain tissues frequently develop cracks through the sections while drying—an aggravation common to spleen, liver, lymph nodes and nervous tissue. To prevent this, as soon as the sections are spread, drain and blot them free of as much water as possible and dry them at a higher temperature (60–65°) or in the mechanical hot-air dryer.

Properly mounted sections will have a smooth, almost clear appearance. If they have a creamy, opaque texture, and when examined from the undersurface reflect light, air is caught between the glass and sections. Such tissues will float off in aqueous solutions. The cause usually lies either in poorly cleaned slides or in drying at too low a temperature or not long enough. If, when mounting, an excess of bubbles appear under the sections, use distilled water which has been boiled for some time to release trapped air. Poorly infiltrated sections and nervous tissue which has been soaked in water usually fail to adhere; these can possibly be saved by the following method.

Because of their tendency to loosen from slides, certain types of tissues may require special treatment. These tissues include brittle sections, tissues containing a large amount of yolk or osmic acid, and sections which will be subjected to strong acids or alkalis during staining (as well as the poorly infiltrated sections and nervous tissue mentioned above). After drying, and when ready to stain, dissolve out the paraffin with toluene or xylene. Place the preparations for 1–2 minutes in absolute *ethyl* alchohol, followed by 1–2 minutes in a dilute solution (about 0.5%) of nitrocellulose in ether-absolute alcohol (50:50). Drain off excess nitrocellulose, but do not allow it to completely dry; wave slide in air a second and place it in 70% or 80% alcohol. Continue with the planned staining method.

Serial Sections

With a few exceptions, the usual paraffin method is used for serial sections, and in most cases, every section is mounted and in correct order. While sectioning, the ribbons are arranged in a cardboard box from left to right and top to bottom (like a printed page). When the sectioning is finished, the sections are removed to slides in the above order. Serially number each slide with a glass marking pencil (do not use a grease pencil and have it wash off in staining solutions). This system affords simple sorting of slides when all processing is complete.

Chapter 6

Freezing Method

The freezing technic for preparing specimens is unsurpassed in two ways: (1) it is rapid—essential for diagnosis in hospitals; and (2) it can be used for the preparation of sections containing such elements as fats enzymes and some radioscopes that would be lost in alcohol, paraffin solvents or by heat. One disadvantage is that some distortion may be caused by the freezing and cutting.

Freezing methods formerly used ether, ethyl chloride or other volatile liquids. Present methods employ compressed carbon dioxide gas blown into a chamber. There the gas expands, cooling the chamber, and freezing the tissue mounted on it. For this procedure most laboratories use the clinical microtome with a freezing attachment. An attachment also can be used on sliding microtomes, but not, efficiently, on rotary models. There are also dry ice holders available, such as the one manufactured by *Fisher Scientific Company*—a *Dry Ice Freezing Chamber*. Dry ice is held inside the chamber and the specimen is frozen simply by pushing the dry ice up against the metal top holding the specimen. *Nickerson (1944)* fitted the object clamp of a rotary microtome with a small metal box holding dry ice. A new freezing system using Freon is on the market—the *Histo-Freeze*—a portable freezing unit, 12×18 inches, with Freon 12 circulating through the unit (manufactured by *Scientific Products, Evanston, Illinois*). Model *67027A* fits *American Optical, 67027B* fits *Bausch and Lomb,* and *67027C* fits the *Sartorius* freezing microtomes. *Lipshaw* has a tissue freeze refrigerating unit, counter or desk height, fitting *American Optical, Bausch and Lomb, Sartorious* or *Reichert* microtomes.

Fixation, Blocking, and Sectioning

Fresh tissues may be used, but it is preferable to fix the material, usually in formalin, which leaves the tissue in a consistency ideal for the freezing technic. Formalin is a water solution and requires no washing. *Hartz (1945)*, however, recommends Bouin's as better than formalin, but says that the tissue must be washed for a short time before freezing. If the fixative contains mercuric chloride, the crystals may be removed immediately after sectioning with an iodine solution, such as Lugol's, which contains no alcohol. If the tissues are extremely friable it may be advantageous to embed them in gelatine (page 66) or immerse them in a thick aqueous gum syrup, such as gum arabic.

When it is necessary to section immediately (example: surgical biopsy), and yet fixation is desirable, boil a small piece for a couple of minutes in 10% formalin. Rinse in water and freeze. *Reiner (1953)* adds tissue to undiluted formalin at room temperature, then heats the solution and tissue to 56–60°C in a water bath for 2 minutes. Agitate the tissue during the heating. Reiner claims inferior results without agitation and also says that placing tissues in preheated formalin is disadvantageous.

Friedland (1951) Method, Using Agar

1. Boil tissue in formalin.
2. Replace formalin with 2% sterile agar (previously heated to its melting point) in water. Boil gently 1 minute.
3. Pour off and freeze tissue immediately.
   The Agar can be kept ready in Pyrex tubes, and melted quickly over an open flame.

Lev and Thomas (1955) Method

This method fixes tissue at 80°C and produces excellent results. The following solution is placed in a baby's bottle-warmer and comes to a boil in 1 minute. Add the tissue and allow it to boil for 1 more minute.

formalin	10.0 ml.
glacial acetic acid	1.0 ml.
95% ethyl alcohol	80.0 ml.

The tissue will have to be washed to remove the alcohol before freezing can be attempted, possibly a disadvantage when speed is imperative.

The pieces to be cut should be no more than 2–4 mm. thick for rapid and uniform freezing. One surface should be flat to provide sufficient contact with the tissue carrier. If, during freezing, there is a tendency for the tissue to break loose from the carrier, cut a piece of filter paper to fit the top of the carrier and place it, wet, under the tissue. This may help to hold the tissue in place while freezing and sectioning.

Consider the shape and type of tissue when it is oriented on the carrier. If one side is narrower than the other, place that side, or any straight side, parallel to the knife. If there is a tough membrane on one side of the tissue, place that side toward the knife, otherwise the membrane can break away from the rest of the block during sectioning. Usually the amount of water carried over with the tissue is sufficient for firm attachment to the carrier. (Use normal saline for fresh tissues.) Avoid too much water and do not allow it to settle around the tissue in a wall of ice that can deflect the knife or tear through the tissue during sectioning. Uneven or torn sections result. If, however, gum is being used, it is necessary to build the gum around the tissue while freezing it. In this case the tissue must be completely encased by the medium.

With a finger, gently press the tissue upon the tissue carrier. Slowly freeze the tissue by turning on CO_2 for a moment or two, and then turn it off. A series of successive jets of gas freezes better and wastes less gas than a continuous stream. When the tissue is frozen fast and the finger can be removed, move the knife over the block so it too is in the path of the cooling gas. This aids in uniform freezing of the tissue by deflecting some of the gas onto the top of it, and at the same time cools the knife.

Good sections depend on the proper temperature in the tissue. Material frozen too hard forms white brittle fragments on the knife; if too soft it forms a mushy mass. In both cases, the sections break up when placed in water. Difficulties may be avoided by slightly over-freezing the block and then as it warms and reaches the correct temperature, a number of sections can be cut in close succession. When these fall on the tissue carrier, allow several to accumulate and pick up the group with one sweep of the finger. Or, as soon as the section is cut, remove it from the knife with a finger tip and place it in a dish of water. Do not allow water to collect on the knife. Keep both knife and fingers dry. Some tissues (adipose for one) tend to stick to the finger and will not shake loose in water. Transfer them to 70 or 80% alcohol.

Occasionally, when there is no time for gelatine embedding, one encounters a tissue difficult to section because it tends to fall apart. *Bush and Hewitt* (*1952*) support the tissue with *Kodak Frozen Section Film.* The film is softened in water, excess moisture sponged off, and the film pressed down on the freshly cut surface of the frozen tissue. The film freezes and adheres to the tissue while a section is cut; this is carefully raised as the knife passes under it. The film with the section is laid face down on a slide. As the section thaws, it will cling to the slide, and a thin layer of moisture develops by capillarity between it and the film. When this has dried, the section can be stained. (Also see use of cellulose tape, page 394.)

Mounting

If the sections are collected in a glass dish, place the dish on a black surface—a table top or a piece of black paper. The sections are more easily manipulated over the black background and the best ones can be selected. Dip one end of an albumenized slide into the water. With a needle or preferably a small round-tipped glass rod, gently bring a section against the slide. Hold the section at one corner; by maneuvering under water creases can be unfolded and the section unrolled as the slide is drawn out of the solution. If the wrinkles refuse to straighten, drop the section on 70% alcohol and then remove it to a slide. Drain off excess water or pull it off with filter paper. Press section in place with filter paper moistened with 50% alcohol. With a pipette add absolute alcohol directly on top of the section; let stand for approximately 30 seconds. Replace with more absolute alcohol (must be ethyl alcohol). Drain thoroughly, and flood slide with 1% nitrocellulose (dissolved in absolute ethyl alcohol-ether, 1:1) for 1 second. Drain off and wave slide in air until almost dry. Immerse in 70 or 80% alcohol, 5-10 minutes or longer (can be left here for several hours or days). *Caution:* use an old solution of alcohol, either one from the staining series, or one which has been mixed for at least a day. A freshly prepared solution forms bubbles between section and slide.

Fresh tissue sections may be removed from normal saline to the slide and thoroughly drained. Add 95% alcohol to remove the water; let stand 30–60 seconds. Drain off and allow the section to almost dry. Place in 95% alcohol for 1–2 minutes and proceed to stain.

A gelatine fixative can be used to affix the sections. Spread fixative on the slides and dry them in an incubator. (They can be stored for some time in a dust-free box.) Float the sections on the gelatine, drain off excess water and place the slides in a covered dish over formalin. This converts the gelatine into an irreversible gel, thereby holding the sections in place. After 30 minutes over the formalin, wash in running water, 10 minutes, and proceed to stain.

Gelatine Embedding

Culling (1957) Method

Some tissues tend to fall apart when sectioned, and it is necessary to embed them in some medium such as gelatine.

1. After fixation, wash.
2. Place in 10% gelatine in 1% phenol aqueous, 37°C: 24 hours.
3. Transfer to 20% gelatine-phenol, 37°C: 12 hours.
4. Embed in 20% gelatin using a mold as for paraffin.
5. Allow to set, preferably in cold. Trim off excess gelatine close to tissue. Leave as little as possible on under surface; the gelatine tends to inhibit freezing. The tissue block should be small with a minimum of gelatine between the tissue and the freezing stage.
6. Before freezing, immerse trimmed block in 10% formalin to harden: 24 hours.
7. Section as usual on the freezing microtome.
8. Float sections on cold water and transfer to albumenized slides. Drain, and warm slightly to coagulate albumen. Place in warm water to remove gelatine and proceed to stain.

Pearse (1953) Method

1. Fix in cold formalin (15%) at 4°C if it is desired to preserve enzymes: 10–16 hours.
2. Wash, running water: 30 minutes.
3. Infiltrate with gelatine, 37°C: 1 hour.

    gelatine .... 15.0 gm.
    glycerol .... 15.0 ml.
    distilled water .... 70.0 ml.
    small crystal of thymol.

4. Cool and harden in formalin (40%), 17–22°C: 1 hour. Wash.
5. Store at 4°C or below until sectioned.

See Albrecht (1956), Thompson (1957)

Staining

Methods for Staining in Quantity

Nitrocellulose-mounted sections are transferred from the 70% alcohol to water and then into any desired stain. After staining they probably will require special care. If after dehydration the sections are placed in absolute ethyl alcohol and show a tendency to fall off, because the nitrocellulose dissolves, follow the 95% alcohol with isopropyl alcohol, 2 changes, and then xylene. Another method is to follow the 95% alcohol with carbol-xylol (page 000), several changes, until the sections look clear. Fogginess or colored droplets on the slides indicate traces of water. If carbol-xylol is used, rinse it off by dipping the slide for 2–3 seconds in xylene. Carbol-xylol must be removed; any of it left in the sections will fade stains in a short time, almost overnight. *Warning:* keep fingers out of carbol-xylol; it contains carbolic acid. Wash it off immediately if any spills on the skin and use Lanolin for skin irritation.

Irregular staining usually is caused by an uneven coat of nitrocellulose; this can be prevented by tilting the slide immediately after the solution is applied. If the nitrocellulose is thicker than 1% uneven staining may result. A colored background indicates a thick coat of nitrocellulose. Sometimes irregular staining is due to loosening of parts of the section.

Rapid Staining Methods

Pinacyanole Method (Proescher, 1933; Humason and Lushbaugh, 1961)

Staining and mounting time, 30–90 seconds

1. Mount frozen section (fresh or fixed) on slide; drain off excess water.
2. Cover section with several drops of stain: 3–5 seconds.
   (pinacyanole, 0.5% in either 70% methyl or ethyl alcohol; keep stock solution in refrigerator.)
3. Float section off into tap or distilled water: 5–10 seconds or until free of excess stain (longer washing will not alter intensity).
4. Remount on clean slide, blot excess water from around section, cover with Aquamount,[1] glycerine or glycerine jelly, and cover glass.

[1] Edward Gurr, London.

An alternate method can be used and is perhaps preferred by some.

1. Place frozen section in a small amount of stain, 5–10 seconds.
2. Transfer with glass rod into tap or distilled water to remove excess stain, 5–10 seconds or longer.
3. Mount on slide, blot off excess water, add mountant and cover glass.

This method is not recommended for paraffin sections, only for fresh or frozen ones; differential staining is lost in the former. In order to preserve cytoplasmic staining, sections cannot be dehydrated; alcohol decolorizes cytoplasmic structures and only the nucleus will retain appreciable amounts of stain. All mounts are temporary and should be sealed if preservation for several days is desirable. (The stain solution can also be used for sex chromatin staining, page 362.)

Results (of Pinacyanole Staining)

chromatin—well-differentiated blue to reddish blue
connective tissue—pink
elastic tissue—dark violet
muscle—violet to purple
plasma cells—red granuloplasm
hemosiderin—orange
hemoglobin, neutrophil and eosinophil granules—unstained
neutral fat—colorless to faint bluish violet
lipoids—bluish violet to purple
amyloid—carmine red

Humphrey's (1936) Method (Perhaps the Fastest)

1. Place section on a slide and wipe off excess water.
2. Add 1 drop of 0.5% brilliant cresyl blue in saline.
3. Cover with cover glass and examine. Never a permanent mount.

Thionin or Toluidine Blue Method

1. Remove section from water to a solution of either 0.5% thionin or toluidine blue O in 20% ethyl alcohol plus a few drops of glacial acetic acid: 30 seconds.
2. Rine in water and float on slide.
3. Drain off excess water, blot around edges of section, add drop of glycerine and cover glass. This is not a permanent slide.

Reiner (1953) Method (Uses Stock Giemsa)

1. Add 1–2 drops stock Giemsa to section on slide: 5–10 seconds.
2. Float section off into dish of acidulated water (3 drops glacial acetic acid to 500 ml. distilled water). Allow to differentiate until dense clouds of color cease to stream off: 10–15 seconds.
3. Transfer to water and remount on clean slide.
4. Remove excess water, mount in glycerine jelly.

Chapter 7

Nitrocellulose Method

This form of embedding is often classified as the celloidin technic and celloidin becomes something of a generic term inclusive of the various cellulose compounds, such as nitrocellulose and soluble gun cotton or collodion. These are solutions of pyroxylin consisting chiefly of cellulose tetranitrate. Obviously a purified nonexplosive form of pyroxylin is necessary and there are several on the market: *Parloidin, Celloidin,* and *Photoxylin.* (An excellent prepared embedding medium can be purchased from the *Randolph Products Co., Carlstadt, N.J.,* "Tissue Embedding Solution #4700"—a solution of 30% low viscosity nitrocellulose in 35% ether and 35% absolute ethyl alcohol. It is a special low viscosity nitrocellulose (LVN) allowing more rapid infiltration with solutions of higher concentration than is possible with many of the other so-called celloidins. This permits formation of harder blocks in a shorter time and thinner sections can be cut than with the latter types of media.

The chief advantages in using the nitrocellulose method are that larger and harder pieces can be cut in nitrocellulose than in paraffin, and the consistency of nitrocellulose allows mixed (hard and soft) tissues to be cut. This quality is useful for organs such as eyes, teeth and bones and their surrounding tissues, and for problems of shrinkage and the formation of artificial spaces. But a slow dehydration and prolonged infiltration is preferred in these cases. Also the method is costly.

Walls (1932) comments that the method offers many advantages:

1. It will handle anything organic.
2. It produces no artifacts; no shrinkage or swelling; delicate connections, intercellular bridges are preserved.
3. There is no compression of the sections during sectioning as with paraffin, no disruption of delicate parts.
4. Sectioning is independent of temperature, humidity, and atmospheric electricity.
5. Tissues are not rendered brittle or hard.
6. Mounting is quicker; there is no need for albumen, heating, or drying.
7. Hollow objects section better.
8. Celloidin supports tissue constantly; tissues cannot be crushed or displaced.
9. Many stains perform better in it.
10. Time tolerations are great; there is no last minute rush to embed, no worry about tissues staying too long in solutions or hot paraffin.

In this method toluene cannot be used as a solvent, but there are many other solvents for nitrocellulose. One of the commonest is a combination of two so-called *latent* solvents (not in themselves efficient solvents, but possessing excellent solvent qualities when mixed with other compounds), diethyl ether and ethyl alcohol. The solution is made up of equal parts of the two, ether and absolute ethyl alcohol.

Dehydration and Infiltration

The tissue is fixed, washed and can be stored in 70% alcohol as usual. The next step is as follows:

1. 95% ethyl alcohol: 4–24 hours, or longer.
2. absolute ethyl alcohol, 2 changes: 4–24 hours or longer in each.
3. ether-alcohol (equal parts of absolute ethyl alcohol and anhydrous ether): 4–24 hours or longer.
4. 10% nitrocellulose (dissolved in absolute ethyl alcohol-ether, 1:1): 2 days or longer, in a screw-cap jar to keep evaporation to a minimum.
5. 33–35% nitrocellulose (in absolute ethyl alcohol-ether): 2 days or longer, in tight jar.

Nitrocellulose solutions should be stored in the dark; light causes the solution to deteriorate. *Ferreira and Combs (1951)* warn that old light-affected solutions cause fading of nervous tissue blocks.

Embedding

Slow Method

Place the tissue in a small glass-covered dish (stender dish), and over it pour 33–35% nitrocellulose until it is $\frac{1}{4}$ to $\frac{1}{2}$ inch above the tissue. Over this pour a thin layer of ether-alcohol (1:1). Cover the dish tightly, and allow to evaporate slowly until a proper consistency. If bubbles appear in the medium, evaporation is proceeding too rapidy. A little Vaseline on the ground-glass edge of the cover will help to seal it more tightly; in dry, warm weather it may be necessary to enclose the evaporation dish in another dish or jar to slow down the removal of solvent. The process should take several days to a week or more, the slower the better. Do not allow the medium to become too hard; it should reach the consistency of hard rubber and should feel dry and not show finger prints. If a tough film forms quickly on the surface of the solution and sticks to the side of the dish, carefully loosen the film from the glass to allow more efficient evaporation.

When the nitrocellulose is properly formed, trim it down to cutting size, and mount it on a fiber or wooden block. (Figs. 18, 19, 20, 21.) Around the block, tightly wrap a band of hard bond paper, then secure the band with string or stick it down with a paper label. (Do not use a rubber band.) The paper must project high enough above the mounting block to enclose the tissue block. Moisten the mounting block and paper with ether-alcohol, then place a small amount of 33–35% nitrocellulose in the container formed by the two. Roughen the underside of the tissue block with a needle, and cover it with a drop or two of ether-alcohol. Press the roughened surface tightly into the nitrocellulose on the paper-wrapped block. After a few minutes in the air, place the block in a closely capped jar with a small amount of chloroform; leave it there 20–30 minutes. Add more chloroform to immerse the entire block, and if possible allow it to "set" in chloroform overnight. There are other and more haphazard ways of mounting nitrocellulose blocks, but the above method is relatively sure.

Romeis (1948) claims that if wooden blocks are used they should be pre-seasoned with nitrocellulose. Cook them in distilled water, then allow them to dry for several days. Extract with equal parts of 70% alcohol and glycerine for a day, and wash the blocks in distilled water until shaking no longer causes a foam. Cover the surface with 8% nitrocellulose, dry, and put the blocks in a glass bottle.

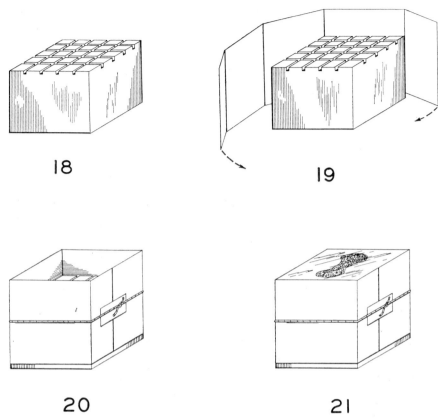

Figures 18, 19, 20, and 21. *Preparation of a fiber block and nitrocellulose tissue block for sectioning.*

Rapid Method

This method will not form as perfect a block as the former one; the nitrocellulose is not always uniform and may section unevenly.

Wrap paper around the fiber block as for the slow method. Fill the cavity with some nitrocellulose from the infiltrating jar and transfer the tissue into the mass of nitrocellulose. Orient the piece of tissue so it can be sectioned along the upper surface. Set the fiber block and nitrocellulose and tissue in a tightly capped jar with a small amount of chloroform. Leave in this situation until the block is firm, but check frequently to see that the chloroform does not evaporate completely. When the nitrocellulose has hardened, add more chloroform to completely immerse the block and tissue until ready to section.

Mounted or unmounted tissue blocks can be stored in chloroform,

70%, 80% or 95% alcohol, but for long storage add a little glycerine
to the alcohol.

Sectioning

Clamp the jaws of the tissue carrier tightly against the lower two-
thirds of the mounting block. If the jaws are clamped against the upper
portion, the resulting compression in the block can loosen the nitrocellulose.

If the knife has a concave surface, clamp that surface uppermost in
the knife holder. The knife holder must be adjusted so the knife is
pushed back on the instrument far enough to clear the tissue before the
tissue is elevated in preparation for the next section. An automatic
lever on a small slide (sliding surface) on the back side of the knife
block can be moved until the correct knife position is determined. If
the knife does not clear the tissue before the latter is elevated, the pressing of the knife can injure the tissue and frequently alters the thickness
of the next section.

The maximum thickness of a section as controlled by the automatic
feed lever may be only 30 or 40 microns on most microtomes. Thicker
sections however can be cut by moving the hand feed counterclockwise
and then releasing it. The hand feed is a large round knob (*American
Optical* sliding microtome) mounted at the base of the tissue carrier
and near the micrometer screw. Each movement of the hand feed will
equal the number of microns indicated by the automatic feed.

Keep the surface of the slide for the knife block well oiled with the
oil provided with the microtome (or *Pike Oil, Norton Co.*). A dry slide
produces a jerky knife movement and rough, irregular sections.

Always maintain a pool of 70% alcohol on the edge of the knife and
the top of the tissue block. Otherwise the sections may shrivel instead of
slicing in a smooth sheet. The following methods are suggested for sectioning.

Method 1. Knife and block are wet with alcohol. Draw the knife
through the block until a section is almost, but not quite, cut to completion, making certain that the cut has cleared the tissue in the block.
If the cut does not clear the tissue, a striation will appear in the tissue
at the point where the knife stopped or hesitated. The section rolls as
it is cut. While the section is still attached at one corner, unroll it
against the knife, and then finish the cut. Squares of paper cut to a
size a little larger than the section are moistened with 70% alcohol.

Hold one of these against the under surface of the knife and slip the section off onto the paper. Invert the section and paper in a dish of 70% alcohol and press them down against the bottom of the dish. The sections can be stacked one on another in this fashion and stored until they are stained. *Caution:* use plain white paper, filter paper or paper towels. Lined paper may stain the nitrocellulose and produce poor staining.

Method 2. An alternate method is to flood the knife with alcohol and moisten a camel hair brush. Hold the brush close to the nitrocellulose block, so the alcohol is held between the block and brush by capillary action. Do not rest the brush too firmly on the block, lest it be cut by the knife. Pull the knife across the block; raise the brush slightly, and it will guide the section onto the knife, smoothly and without rolling. Remove as above. (*Walls, 1932*)

Method 3. Walls (1936) developed a dry method which eliminates the constant soaking with alcohol during sectioning. After the block is hardened, soak it in cedar oil:chloroform (50:50) for 24 hours. Blot the block and allow it to stand in the air for 10–20 minutes. Transfer to cedar oil; this lubricates the block and knife during sectioning. The sections, as removed from the knife, are placed in the same kind of oil, then rinsed in 95% alcohol, 80% alcohol, and transferred to water for staining. This type of oil-soaked block can be sectioned on a rotary microtome as well as a sliding one.

Hot Celloidin Technic

Koneff (1937) Method

This is a more rapid method and can be used when materials are not injured by heat. The procedures are handled in screw-cap jars in a paraffin oven, about 56°C.

1. 70% alcohol, 2 changes: $\frac{1}{2}$ hour each.
2. 80% alcohol, 2 changes: $\frac{1}{2}$ hour each.
3. 95% alcohol, 2 changes: $\frac{1}{2}$ hour each.
4. Absolute alcohol, 2 changes: $\frac{1}{2}$ hour each.
5. Absolute alcohol-ether (equal parts): 1 hour.
6. 10% nitrocellulose: 1 hour.
7. 25–33% nitrocellulose: overnight.
8. Embed as for rapid cold method.

Walls (1932) used bottles with thick lips and corks, and wired on the corks with a wire wound under the lip and over the cork. High pressure builds up in the bottle, and together with the high viscosity of the heated celloidin produces rapid penetration. He maintains that heat is of no concern in this method; in the paraffin method it is the hot paraffin, not the heat itself which, if used too long, produces a brittle block.

Do not hurry the cooling process; leave warm bottles on a wooden table top until they have reached room temperature and they will not break.

Difficulties in Nitrocellulose Sectioning[1]

1. Scratches in sections. Caused by:
    a. nick in knife.
    b. hard material in tissue.
    c. position where knife was stopped while unrolling section.
2. Tissue soft, mushy, crumbles or falls out. Caused by:
    a. imperfect infiltration due either to incomplete dehydration or too short a time in nitrocellulose. Reinfiltrate.
    b. embedding too rapid, as in short method.
3. Sections vary in thickness. Caused by:
    a. worn parts in microtome.
    b. pressing too hard on knife block.
    c. insufficient hardening of nitrocellulose. Too soft and compresses under knife.
    d. tissue block is rising before return stroke of knife has cleared it.
    e. insufficient tilting of knife. Shoulder of facets compresses block instead of cutting it and next section is thick.
    f. embedding too rapid, as in short method.

Staining and Mounting

Sections are stained before mounting in this method. Staining may be handled in syracuse watch glasses or similar flat dish. With forceps or spatula carry the sections through successive watch glasses and follow each change by draining the section against a paper towel or filter paper. In this way, contamination can be held to a minimum. If, however, the solutions do pick up considerable stain, change them as frequently as seems necessary, or even more often. Also, if they have remained un-

[1] Modified after Richards, 1949.

covered for some time it is probable that the alcoholic content has been reduced by evaporation. Never, at any time during the transferring of sections, allow them to become dry. They may be carried directly from the 70% alcohol to the stain if it is an alcoholic one, or first into water, then into stain, if it is aqueous. (Remember to remove undesirable pigments or crystals before staining.)

When ready for dehydration, transfer through 50%, 70% and into 95% alcohol. Then clear the sections by either of the following methods.

Method 1. Transfer sections into carbol-xylol (page 410), 2–3 minutes. Keep carbol-xylol covered at all times to prevent evaporation of xylene. Dip the edge of a slide into the carbol-xylol dish and slip the section in place with a needle or forceps. Drain thoroughly and flush off excess carbol-xylol with toluene or xylene, 2 or 3 times. Add several drops of mountant and cover glass. Press cover firmly in place. Several hours later, after the resin has thickened, press down again. If the cover glass insists on tilting or lifting, place a small weight on it or clamp it with a clothes pin overnight. *Bertram (1958)* describes a weight which will not stick to the mountant and cover glass.

Method 2. Transfer the sections to absolute alcohol containing 5% of chloroform to prevent the alcohol from dissolving the nitrocellulose. Clear with benzene and mount as above, omitting the carbol-xylol.

Do not attempt to dissolve or remove the nitrocellulose from sections; they will become too difficult to manipulate. When using carbol-xylol, keep fingers out of the solution. Wash off any that does get on the fingers and rub lanolin on the skin.

A method for transferring sections to slides, particularly thin sections, is as follows: slip a piece of cigarette paper under a section and spread it smoothly on the paper with a brush or needle. Place the paper plus the section on a slide with the section between the slide and paper. Blot firmly with a piece of filter paper. Peel off the cigarette paper and rinse the section with toluene or xylene. Add mountant and cover glass.

Mounting Before Staining

Sections are affixed to slides for staining in this method.

Method 1

a. Albumenize slide.
b. Press section on with filter paper.

c. Pour clove oil over it: 5–20 minutes.

d. 95% alcohol, 3 changes: 5–10 minutes.

e. Absolute alcohol-ether, 2 changes, to dissolve nitrocellulose.

f. 70% alcohol, etc., to stain.

Method 2 (Lewis, 1945)

a. Rub on slide one drop Haupt's fixative (page 413).

b. Transfer section on cigarette paper to slide.

c. Blot, and firmly press with filter paper.

d. Roll off cigarette paper rapidly; section must not dry.

e. Place immediately in absolute alcohol-ether until nitrocellulose is dissolved: 10–20 minutes.

f. Remove to 70% alcohol, etc., to stain.

Method 3

a. Float sections onto slide and blot firmly with filter paper.

b. Dip slide into 0.5% nitrocellulose for few seconds; drain and wipe back of slide clean.

c. Harden film in chloroform: 5–10 minutes.

d. 95%, 70% alcohol, etc., to stain.

Method 4 (Culling, 1957)

a. Transfer section to 95% alcohol: 1–2 minutes.

b. Float on slide, drain for few minutes, blot lightly to flatten section, but do not dry.

c. Pour ether vapor over sections—only vapor, not liquid. This partially dissolves nitrocellulose and causes it to adhere to slide.

d. Place slide in 80% alcohol: 5 minutes, to harden nitrocellulose.

e. Running water: 10 minutes; stain.

Method 5—Serial Sections

a. Arrange sections on knife from left to right.

b. Lay cigarette paper on sections and saturate with 70% alcohol.

c. With quick sweeping movement, pull paper off knife and carry to slide. Smooth with brush.

d. Place filter paper on top and press flat, until much of alcohol is absorbed.

e. Jerk off paper and cover with clove oil: 3–5 minutes.

f. Submerge in 95% alcohol.

g. 70% alcohol, etc., to stain.

Method 6—Serial Sections (Williams, 1957)

a. Coat clean slides by dipping in warm solution of 1% gelatine. Allow to drain and dry in vertical position.

b. Lay sections on blotting paper moistened with 70% alcohol. Keep covered to prevent drying.

c. Pick up sections, one at a time, dip in 70% alcohol and arrange in order on coated slides.

d. Blot sections with dry filter paper, flattening and pressing them into contact with gelatine.

e. Place in coplin jar containing 2–3 cc. formalin. Do not allow fluid to come in contact with sections, it may cause them to float off slide.

f. Allow slides to remain tightly covered, 2–3 hours, room temperature.

g. 70% alcohol, etc., to stain.

Method 7—Serial Sections (Wetmore, 1932)

a. Place on slide in order cut. Keep slides moist with 95% alcohol.

b. Blot off excess alcohol with filter paper.

c. Paint in spaces between sections with 2–4% nitrocellulose and allow to dry. Thin sections require 2%, thicker ones 4%. Keep as little as possible from getting on sections or margins may curl.

d. Place slides and sections in 95% alcohol plus a little chloroform to harden, approximately 30 minutes.

e. With scalpel or section lifter, remove sheet of sections from slide and store in 95% alcohol until ready to stain.

The author hesitates to recommend any of the above methods over others. Adopt the one that cooperates the most effectively.

Chapter 8

Specialized Embedding Technics

Water-Soluble Wax Embedding and Sectioning

The so-called carbowax compounds and water-soluble polyethylene glycol waxes, a series of **polymers** (compounds composed of the same kind of atoms in the same percentage composition but in different numbers and therefore having different molecular weights), each of which is designated by its average molecular weight. These waxes are used when it is necessary to go directly from fixative or water to the embedding medium; no alcohols or clearing agents are required.

The following compounds are manufactured by the *Carbide and Carbon Chemicals Company: Compound 4000* is hard and dry, in crystalline flakes; *Compound 1540* is not so firm, and will liquefy within a week; *Compound 1000* comes in slippery lumps and liquefies within 24 hours; *Compound 1500* is a blend of equal parts of *polyethylene glycol 300* (a fluid) and *wax 1540*.

Other carbowax compounds are the *polyglycols E9000, E6000, E4000, E2000, and E1000* manufactured by *Dow Chemical Company,* and *HEM (Harleco Embedding Media)* by *Hartman-Leddon Company.*

Wade (1952) finds *4000* too hard for his use and suggests a mixture of 1:9 or 2:8 of *1540* and *4000* depending upon weather, and recommends the latter except in the hottest and most humid climate.

Fixation: any fixative, but after a potassium dichromate fixative wash for 12 hours before embedding.

Infiltration and Embedding: carbowax 1–3 hours, 50–56°C; agitate occasionally.

Prepare the carbowax ahead of time by placing the mixture in a beaker and allowing it to melt in an oven. If it is melted rapidly over a flame, a block formed from it will not cut well. The mixture will keep for an indefinite time in the oven.

Embed by placing the tissue in a second batch of carbowax in a small container or paper box in the refrigerator until it is hard, approximately 30 minutes. Blocks solidified at room temperature will not section as well as those made in the refrigerator. Do not chill blocks in water—it dissolves carbowax. When completely hard, the blocks may be removed from the refrigerator and will turn opaque as they warm to room temperature. This is of no disadvantage, but keep them in polyethylene or cellophane bags or containers if storing them for some time. They must not pick up water, even from the atmosphere.

Sectioning: A cool dry room is recommended. The edges of the block must be parallel in order to obtain ribbons. *Wade* (*1952*) suggests that if the sections do not adhere, if they break up on handling or do not ribbon at all, try exposing the block to air for a day or two. For immediate use, try painting a 25% solution of beeswax in chloroform on the upper and lower surfaces of the block. Make the layer uniform and allow it to become dull dry. Such surfaces should help the sections adhere to each other. Plain water may do as well in some cases.

Hale (*1952*) found that variable and high humidity produces erratic results, because with the absorption of water on the surfaces of the block sectioning becomes impossible. He found that at 24–25°C sections ceased to ribbon at 40% humidity; at 17–18°C humidity had no effect. He, therefore, concluded that, as the temperature drops, greater humidity is permissible. At higher temperatures, a higher percentage of hard wax may be used, but care must be taken that the block does not become too brittle for good sectioning.

Mounting Sections: Water mounting dissolves carbowax, and will result in distorted sections and surface tension problems when trying to affix sections to slides. Various solutions for this problem follow.

Blank and McCarthy (1950) Method

potassium dichromate	0.2 gm.
gelatine	0.2 gm.
distilled water	1000.0 ml.

Boil for 5 minutes. Filter.

Sections while floating on this solution are picked up on a slide and allowed to dry.

Wade (1952) Method

Wade prefers to albumenize slides with a thin coat of Mayer's egg albumen (page 412). Dry overnight or three hours or longer in an oven. Floating ribbons intact and without wrinkles still remains a problem. He suggests that the addition of a wetting agent, *Turgitol 7* (0.005% in distilled water), will reduce surface tension effects. Add 10% of *1540 Carbowax* to reduce shrinkage while sections are drying.

Giovacchini (1958) Method

Giovacchini thinly smears slides with the following solution: Dissolve 15 grams of gelatine in 55.0 ml. distilled water by heating. Add 50.0 ml. glycerine and 0.5 gram phenol. Place sections on slides and place on warming plate at 58–60°C for 15 minutes. Transfer to drying oven, 58°C, for 24 hours. Ready for staining.

Jones et al. (1959) Method

Jones and his coworkers float their sections on:

diethylene glycol	100.0 ml.
formalin	7.0 ml.
carbowax	1.0 ml.
distilled water	400.0 ml.

In this method more spreading results from increasing the proportion of water. If the tissues overexpand, add a small amount of *Zephiram* chloride concentrate (5–10 drops to 500.0 ml. flotation solution); this reduces surface tension and prevents air bubbles from being trapped between tissue and solution surface. Mount on albumenized slides and dry.

Pearse (1953) Method

This method combines features of the above two methods. Pearse smears with Giovacchini's fluid and mounts the sections with the diethylene glycol mixture.

Zugibe et al. (1958) Method

This method cuts off a section from the ribbon with a razor blade. One edge of the section adheres to the blade. Touch the loose section edge against a slide coated with a flotation fluid and draw the rest of the section onto the slide.

Goland et al. (1954) Method

Goland and coworkers follow carbowax infiltration by:

xylene, 61°C: 10 minutes.
paraffin, 61°C: 30 minutes.
embed.

Chill in refrigerator, do not apply ice directly. This overcomes some of the disadvantages of carbowax and produces less shrinkage and distortion than a regular paraffin method. After sectioning, the tissues may be handled as is customary for paraffin sections.

Either albumen or Giovacchini's fluid smeared on slides have been successful methods, but it has been easier to mount sections out of a water bath (of floating solution, Jones *et al.*, 1959) on to gelatine smeared slides than by laying the sections directly on floating solution on slide. Albumen slides mount readily either way. The razor-blade method is tricky, but works.

Double Embedding

Fragile, small and hard objects often crumble when processed in the paraffin method, and some difficulties can be eliminated by substituting a double embedding technic.

1. Fix and wash tissues as usual.
2. Dehydrate in 50%, 70% and 90% ethyl alcohol: 2 hours each.
3. Absolute ethyl alcohol: 2–16 hours.
4. Methyl-benzoate-celloidin solution (see below): 24 hours. Pour off and replace with fresh solution: 48 hours. If tissue is not clear, repeat for 72 hours.
5. Pure benzene, 3 changes: 4 hours, 8 hours, and 12 hours.
6. Mixture of equal parts of paraffin and benzene, in embedding oven: 1 hour.
7. Paraffin, 2 changes: $\frac{1}{2}$ to 6 hours, depending upon thickness and nature of tissue (3 hours for 5 mm. thickness).
8. Embed and proceed as with ordinary paraffin sections.

Methyl-benzoate-celloidin Solution

Add 1 gram air-dried celloidin flakes to 100.0 ml. methyl benzoate. Shake well and allow bottle to stand upright for an hour or longer.

Invert for an hour. Lay bottle on side for an hour, then turn it upright again. Repeat this process until solution is completed, probably the following day.

Mounting Sections and Preparing to Stain

If the sections do not flatten well on slide, but instead want to curl and separate from it, float them on 95% alcohol to soften the celloidin. If there still is a curling problem, soften them with ether vapor, blot with filter paper and soak on 0.5–1.0% celloidin or nitrocellulose. (*Lillie, 1954B.*)

If albumen continues to fail as an adhesive agent, try a fresh solution of Masson's gelatine fixative (page 412) under the sections and warm slides on warming plate. As soon as they have spread, remove the slides and allow them to cool for a few minutes. Drain off excess gelatine solution, blot down sections with filter paper and place in formalin vapor overnight (40–50°C).

When ready to stain, place the slides in chloroform before proceeding to 95% alcohol. The chloroform will remove the paraffin and harden the celloidin simultaneously.

Briggs (1958) Double Embedding Method

1. Fix, wash, and dehydrate through 70%, 95%, and 2 changes of absolute alcohol: 2 hours each.
2. Absolute alcohol-ether (50:50): 12–24 hours.
3. 4% celloidin (or nitrocellulose): 48 hours.
4. Dip tissue in alcohol-ether to remove excess celloidin from surface. Harden in chloroform vapor for few minutes. Drop into chloroform and leave until tissue sinks: 12–24 hours.
5. Infiltrate, 2 changes paraffin: 12–24 hours each.
6. Embed.

Briggs suggests that during staining, add $\frac{1}{3}$ chloroform by volume be added to all hydrating and dehydrating solutions above 70% alcohol to prevent removal of celloidin.

Banhy and Clark (1949) Double Embedding Method

This is similar to the Briggs method with the following modifications:

For step 3:2 changes nitrocellulose, 3% and 6%.
To follow step 4: benzene, overnight.

Dioxane in Double Embedding

1. Fix, decalcify if necessary, and wash.
2. Dioxane: 2 hours.
3. Dioxane-nitrocellulose: 3 days.

dioxane	70.0 ml.
2% nitrocellulose	30.0 ml.

4. Dioxane: 2 hours.
5. Dioxane-paraffin (50:50): 2 hours.
6. Paraffin, 3 changes: 20 minutes, 30 minutes, 1 hour.
7. Embed, and section immediately.

At UCLA, this method was used successfully on hard fish with scales intact. (Also see *Brown, 1948*)

Polyester Embedding

Polyester resins are plastics (**polymers**) formed by the **esterification reaction** (forming a compound from an alcohol and an acid by removal of water) between polyhydric alcohols and polybasic acids. These resins exhibit a wide range of properties and are utilized in a diversity of commercial and scientific endeavors. The alcohols most commonly used are ethylene, propylene, 1,3 and 2,3 butylene and dipropylene glycols. Unsaturated dibasic acids may be maleic anhydride or fumaric acid. Saturated dibasic acids may be phthalic, adipic and azelaic acid, and chlorinated acids or anhydrides.

A polyester as used here is an unsaturated polyester base resin dissolved in a polymerizable monomer, is suitably diluted with the monomer and supplied as a viscous fluid. The **monomer** (smallest unit entering into the formation of high molecular weight polymers) can be styrene, vinyl toluene, diallyl phthalate, methyl methacrylate, triallyl cyanurate or several other vinyl monomers.

To promote polymerization at the time of use a catalyst must be added to modify the velocity of the reaction without becoming a part of the product. The **curing**, as this is called, is sometimes accomplished with elevated temperature and sometimes by the use of an "accelerator" or "promoter" in addition to the catalyst. The speed of cure depends on the amount of catalyst and accelerator used and varies with different resins.

References: Manufacturing Chemists' Association (1957) and Simonds *et al.* (1949).

Kuhn and Lutz (1958) Method

Advantages of the method. Polyester embedding supports hard structures adjacent to soft ones, is faster than the nitrocellulose method and can be sectioned on a rotary microtome. Size of blocks should be 5–16 mm. in diameter and can be sectioned at 5 to 50 microns. The method uses a nonrigid plasticized resin prepared by *Natcol Laboratories (Route 2, Box 575, Redlands, California)*, known as *C.M.E. Tissue Support Resin* (soft, medium and firm), plus a catalyst (#1) and a promoter (#2) also supplied by the company.

PROCEDURE

1. Dehydrate tissue in ethyl or isopropyl alcohol.
2. Remove alcohol in anhydrous ether: 2–4 hours.
3. (*a*) Transfer soft specimens directly to resin with one drop of catalyst (#1) added for each 30 ml. of resin. Keep specimen submerged. Exhaust the ether from the specimen in a vacuum chamber using reduced atmospheric pressure (10–15 in. Hg); 1–4 hours.

   (*b*) For hard or dense tissues prepare 10–20 ml. of a mixture of the resin and styrene monomer (1:1), add one drop of the catalyst (#1). Submerge tissue. Place in vacuum chamber with reduced pressure: 1–4 hours. In stubborn cases, alternate the reduced pressure with positive pressure (20 lb/sq. in.) at 15 to 20 minute intervals. Follow this treatment with undiluted resin as in 3*a*: 1 hour, preferably in vacuum.
4. For embedding, use gelatine capsules #000 and veterinary capsules #10 for larger specimens.
5. Remove tissue from resin and allow excess to drain off.
6. Warm 30 ml. of resin in a beaker set in a water bath at 65°C. Have a stirring rod warming in the resin. Add three drops of catalyst (#1) and four drops of promoter (#2) for a reasonably fast curing solution. If a thinned preparation (as in step 3*b*) was used, add four drops of catalyst, as well as of promoter, to the embedding resin. Stir rapidly until all mixing lines have disappeared.
7. When resin is thoroughly mixed, fill capsules about half full. Place tissue in position and complete filling. If the tissue floats push it back into place until the resin cures enough to prevent floating. If this takes longer than 5 minutes, warm capsules with a lamp, but only until the resin has reached curing stage (obviously begins to thicken).

Allow to harden at room temperature: 12–24 hours. Peel off capsule or dissolve it in warm water. If the resin cures too rapidly or too slowly, the catalyst and promoter may be decreased or increased by one drop of each.

SECTIONING

If the block is made long enough, the block itself can be clamped directly in the tissue carrier. Slow cutting usually produces the best sections. *Ueckert (1960)* recommends the sledge microtome as best for polyester sectioning, but most laboratories do not possess this type of microtome and will have to resort to the use of a rotary type. Sometimes breathing on the surface of the block facilitates sectioning. If the sections curl, the knife is dull or the knife angle is incorrect.

STAINING

Place the sections after cutting in distilled water. Stain them unmounted, because mounted sections trap the stain under the plastic which is never removed.

Kuhn and Lutz recommend safranin and fast green dissolved in alcohol. *Ueckert* has used hematoxylin-eosin, iron hematoxylin-Van Gieson, and silver methods. Follow the staining by floating the sections on absolute alcohol to remove any excess stain. Blot and mount in *Permount* or any similar mountant (page 416). Do not use toluene; it causes the plastic to swell and form wrinkles.

Kuhn and Lutz have used this method for whole decalcified snake heads, chick embryos, leg joints and undecalcified mouse paw and tail; they suggest the possibility of its use for plant material.

Chapter 9

The Microscope

The Compound Microscope

The ordinary laboratory microscope uses **brightfield** illumination with direct light furnished by a substage condenser and mirror. The image of the specimen appears on a bright, well-lit field.

Diagrams designating all the parts of a microscope are provided by the manufacturers and will not be included here; we will, however, give a brief listing of the important parts and pertinent information concerning their use.

The **lenses** of a microscope are the oculars (eyepieces) at the top and the *objectives* at the bottom of the body tube. The objectives magnify the specimen a definite amount, forming an image which is again magnified by the ocular eyepiece. The lenses of a good microscope should not only magnify, but also should improve the visible detail. This is the **resolving power** and is a function of (1) the wave length of the light used, (2) the lowest **refractive index** (refractive index is a measurement of the refraction or bending of light rays as they pass through from one medium to another and at an oblique angle) between the objective and the substage **condenser** (page 90), and (3) the greatest angle between two rays of light entering the front lens of the objective. Blue light increases resolving power over white light, ultraviolet increases it even more, but cannot be seen and results must be photographed.

Oculars are manufactured in a variety of powers of magnification (engraved on them); 5X and 10X are the customary equipment for student and laboratory microscopes—the former for low power over large areas, the latter for general work. Most of these microscopes are equipped with three objectives: 50 to 32 mm. (low power); 16 mm. (middle or intermediate power); and 8 to 4 mm. (high power). All are engraved with their magnifying power. An additional objective will be included on the four-objective nosepiece and can be used interchangeably with the low power (or any other power) on the three-objective nosepiece. As one shifts from low power to higher powers, the magnification increases but the size and depth of the examining field decreases; also, the clearance of the objective above the specimen (working distance) decreases, and more light is required. The working distance is the distance between the front of the objective and the top of the cover glass when the specimen is in focus.

Achromatic objectives (producing an image essentially free of color fringes) are found on most laboratory microscopes. These objectives are corrected chromatically for the light of two wavelengths, the C (red) and F (blue) lines of the spectrum and spherically for the light of one color, usually in the yellow greens. Achromats give a good image in the central portion of the field but not as sharp an image at the edges as can be obtained with *apochromatic objectives.* The latter are essential for critical microscopy and color photography because they are corrected for three colors, including the G (violet) lines of the spectrum, thereby reducing the amount of color fringes. Lenses, if not corrected in this manner, exhibit chromatic aberration, and color fringes will confuse the border of the specimen image. For best results apochromatic objectives should be accompanied by a corrected condenser of a numerical aperture at least equal to that of the objective aperture and compensating ocular eyepieces. A correction collar on the apochromatic objectives can be adjusted to compensate for the thickness of the cover glass on the slide. The collar must be used and can be adjusted with one hand while the fine adjustment is manipulated with the other hand.

The **body tube** supporting the lenses may have a fixed length or it may be equipped with an adjustable drawtube. A scale on the latter is used to determine the length of the tube for the various lenses used in it—usually 160 mm. for American-made objectives. This becomes more critical with higher power objectives than with lower power ones for improving sharpness of detail under a thick cover glass.

At the bottom of the microscope is located a mirror to direct light through the diaphragm and into the condenser. Usually there are two mirrored surfaces: one plane (flat) to direct the light, reflecting a moderate amount of light with parallel rays but no change in form; the other concave to converge the light rays to form a cone, concentrating a large amount of light. The latter replaces a condenser and can be used for lower magnifications, but should not be used when a condenser is present and not for high magnification, when the plane mirror should be used.

Immediately below the microscope stage is the substage **condenser,** whose lenses serve to converge the parallel beam of light from the mirror so a cone of light passes through the aperture of the stage. This cone of light is focused on the specimen under examination and then is extended to fill the back lens of the objective. Without a condenser the back lens of high-power objectives can not be filled with the proper amount of light. By opening or closing the *iris diaphragm* mounted below the condenser, the diameter of the light entering the condenser can be controlled. A two-lens Abbe condenser is found on most laboratory and student microscopes. For critical research microscopy, a corrected condenser with a centering mount should be used. It should be carefully centered to the objective and immersion oil should be used between it and the slide for finest detail of the specimen.

The image seen in the compound microscope is inverted, it is upside down and turned right side to left. The movement of the slide will be reversed. Most images depend for clarity on color in the specimen or color added to it and/or differences in refractive indices in different parts of the specimen and the medium in which it is mounted.

There are innumerable types and sources of light used in laboratories. If a table lamp is used, such as is found in many student laboratories, use a daylight bulb in it. Good, simple types of microscope lamps are equipped with blue ground-glass filters. Place the lamp 10 to 15 inches in front of the mirror and with all of the light directed below the stage of the microscope. The surface of the bulb or of the filter is focused on the specimen by way of the substage condenser. If the lamp is the small substage type of lamp, it may be used either in front of the mirror or, with the mirror removed, is placed under the condenser. A more critical illumination (Köhler method) can be obtained with better kinds of lamps provided with condensing lens and a coil or ribbon filament. **Controlled illumination** is lighting by a cone of rays whose proportions are regulated by a stop at the illuminator and by the iris diaphragm of the condenser. The aperture of the objective is completely used and none of the refracted light should fall on the lens mounting or draw tube.

The Operation of a Microscope

Without a Substage Condenser

1. Place slide on stage and center the field to be examined over opening in stage.
2. Turn low-power objective over specimen a short distance above it—one-half inch will do.
3. Adjust concave mirror, moving it back and forth, until light is as uniform as possible through the hole and onto the specimen.
4. Raise the body tube by coarse adjustment until the specimen is in focus. Check mirror, adjusting for better light.
5. Higher powers may be swung into position and light adjusted if necessary for greater magnification.

With Substage Condenser and Lamp without Lenses

1. Place slide on stage as above. Adjust objective, plane mirror and body tube for focus as above.
2. Remove ocular eyepiece and while looking down the tube open iris diaphragm of the substage condenser until it coincides with the margin of the back lens of the objective, just filling it with light, no more. Focus the condenser up and down until the light is uniform through the objective.
3. Replace ocular eyepiece. Make similar adjustments for all objectives.

To adjust both parts of a *binocular microscope,* close the left eye and focus with the fine adjustment until the image is sharp for the right eye. Leave the fine adjustment alone and focus for the left eye with the focusing adjustment on the tube outside the ocular eyepiece. Between the two eyepieces is an adjustment for changing the interpupillary distance between the eyes. Turn the adjustment slowly until the right and left images blend and a single field is seen with both eyes.

Critical Illumination (Köhler method) Using a Lamp with Condensing Lenses and an Iris Diaphragm

Lenses and an Iris Diaphragm

1. Place a slide with fine-detailed specimen in position on microscope stage. Center the condenser in relation to the stage aperture.

2. Place the lamp so the diaphragm is about 10 inches from the microscope mirror and line it up with the microscope so the light filament centers on the plane surface of the mirror. Insert a neutral filter.

3. Using a 10X ocular and 16 mm. objective, adjust the mirror until the light passes through the substage condenser to the slide. Focus microscope on the specimen and center the light.

4. Rack up the substage condenser until it almost touches the slide and close the substage diaphragm. Close the lamp diaphragm about halfway and adjust the lamp condenser until an image of the filament is focused on the closed substage condenser diaphragm. This can be observed in the microscope mirror or with a small hand mirror. Partially open the substage iris diaphragm.

5. Focus with the substage condenser until a sharp image of the lamp diaphragm coincides with the specimen on the slide. With the mirror center the diaphragm image.

6. Take out the ocular eyepiece, and, looking down the tube, observe the back lens of the objective. Open substage diaphragm until its image edge almost disappears in the back lens, but remains just visible. The back lens should be filled with light—full cone illumination. Because the light source is imaged on the diaphragm of the substage condenser, the light source is in focus at the back focal plane of the objective and the filament of the lamp can be seen.

7. Replace the ocular eyepiece. If the tube length has to be adjusted, do so (usually 160 mm. for American objectives).

Certain precautions are imperative for good illumination and bear repetition. The back lens should always be filled with even light and the aperture of the substage diaphragm should be closed to a minimum to furnish as wide a cone of light as the specimen will take. Closing down the diaphragm to reduce light intensity and thereby increase contrast in transparent objects is poor technique. Light intensity should be controlled by the kind of bulb, use of filters, or a rheostat or variable transformer inserted in the lamp system.

Unless you have had previous experience with a certain microscope, when changing from one objective to another of higher power (high dry or oil-immersion) do not take it for granted that the microscope is **parfocal** (focal planes of all objectives lie in same position on the tube). The higher power may crush a valuable specimen. Proceed as follows: examine slide with naked eye for approximate part to be examined. Center the area over the stage aperture. Check with low power, then middle power for the particular area of interest, then change to high power, but raise the tube $\frac{1}{4}$ to $\frac{1}{2}$ inch at least before revolving the nosepiece. Then, while watching the bottom of the objective from the side, lower the tube until the objective almost touches the cover glass. Look into the microscope and rack up the tube until the specimen is in focus. Remember, when an objective of a different numerical aperture is used, the condenser diaphragm must be adjusted (step 6 above). The numerical aperture (**N.A.**) number is used to compare the resolving power of the lenses; the higher the numerical aperture, the greater the resolving power and the condenser diaphragm will have to be opened wider.

Use of Oil-immersion Objective

The working distance with this objective is short and great care must be taken to prevent crushing a cover glass. Thin cover glasses must be used or the specimen mounted on the cover glass itself (page 385). Greater illumination is required than with the dry objectives and a wider cone of light is needed. The space between the objective and the cover glass, also frequently between the slide and the condenser, must be filled with a suitable medium of a refractive index and dispersion like that of the glass of the lenses. This medium is provided by **immersion oil** (cedarwood oil, crown oil).

1. Using a dry objective locate and center the area to be examined.
2. Raise microscope tube, swing oil-immersion objective into position.
3. Place a drop of immersion oil on the cover glass over the area to be examined. Watching (from the side) the lower edge of the objective, lower it slowly until it makes contact with the oil.
4. Observing through the microscope, very slowly lower the objective with the coarse adjustment until the specimen is in focus. Make more critical focus with the fine adjustment.
5. Remove ocular eyepiece and adjust the light on the back lens of the objective; the condenser diaphragm will have to be opened.

After use, clean oil-immersion objective; never leave oil on it. Wipe it with clean lens paper, then with a little xylene or chloroform on lens paper, finally drying it with clean dry lens paper. Do not leave xylene or chloroform on the lens.

Other Hints for Efficient Microscopy

Always keep oil surfaces clean, free from dust and grease. This includes the lamp condenser, filters, mirror, lenses of the substage condenser, lenses of objectives, slides, cover glasses, binocular prisms, lens of ocular eyepieces. Use a good grade of lens paper and a fine camel hair brush.

If glasses are worn, protect them from scratching by mounting a rubber band around the top of the ocular. (Fingers of old rubber gloves can be cut to fit the oculars.)

If, instead of a mechanical stage, *clips* are present on a fixed stage, place one clip over one end of the slide. Then with two fingers of one hand controlling the loose end of the slide, move the slide for examining, while manipulating the fine adjustment with the other hand. Individual preferences will determine which hand to use for which motion. With a mechanical stage the right hand has to control the knobs and the left hand the fine adjustment.

If it is convenient to have a *pointer* in the eyepiece, unscrew and remove the top lens of the ocular eyepiece. Inside, about halfway down its tube is a circular shelf. Place a small drop of Permount (or other quick-drying mountant) on this shelf and, with small forceps, place an eyelash in this drop. Arrange the eyelash to lie flat and project a little short of center of the hole formed by the circular shelf. Screw lens back in place.

When *carrying a microscope,* carry it upright, preferably with both hands. Never tilt it; the ocular eyepiece can fall out. If using a microscope for checking staining effects, or any wet mounts, place a thin piece of glass on the stage. A lantern-slide cover glass ($3\frac{1}{4}$ x 4 inch) is usually available and is an ideal size for most microscope stages. Clean it after use to prevent contamination of future slides or material.

Measuring Devices Used on a Microscope

Reading a Vernier

Most mechanical stages are equipped with a **vernier**—a device for the purpose of relocating the same spot previously examined on a slide. Two numerical scales run side by side, a long one constructed on a millimeter scale and a short one constructed on a scale of nine millimeters divided into ten equal divisions. When the area of reference on the slide is centered in the objective, read the vernier. Check the point of coincidence of the zero of the short scale against the long scale. Read the lower whole figure on the latter, to the left of the zero on the short scale. This determines the whole number, the number to the left of the decimal point in the final reading (21. of the long scale in Fig. 22). *Exception:* If the zero of the short scale coincides exactly with a whole

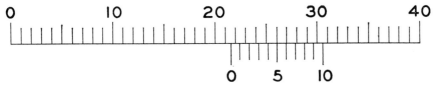

Figure 22. *A vernier scale.*

number on the long scale, then the number is recorded as a whole number with no decimals following it. The decimal is determined by the point of coincidence of the line of the short scale which perfectly coincides with any line on the long scale (.5 of the short scale in Fig. 22). The reading, therefore, in Fig. 22 will be 21.5.

Measuring Objects with an Ocular Micrometer

The measurement of slide specimens usually is done with a **micrometer disc** placed in the ocular, but first the disc's actual value with respect to the magnification at which it is being used has to be calibrated against a **stage micrometer**. Stage micrometers usually have a 2 mm. scale divided into .01 mm. divisions, or a 0.2 inch scale divided into .001 inch divisions. The ocular micrometer has a 5 mm. scale divided into 50 (0.1 mm.) divisions or 100 (.05 mm.) divisions.

Unscrew the top lens of the ocular, place the ocular micrometer on the circular shelf inside and replace the lens. Focus on the stage micrometer, moving it until the zero line of both micrometers coincide. Then a definite distance on the stage micrometer will be made to correspond to a certain number of divisions on the ocular micrometer.

The rest is simple; for example:

The ocular micrometer has 100 divisions.

Suppose that 30 divisions (each measuring .01 mm.) of the stage micrometer equal the 100 ocular micrometer divisions. Then 30 × .01 mm. = .30 mm., the length of the 100 divisions on the ocular micrometer.

Next, .30 ÷ 100 = .003 mm. (3.0 μ), the value of each single division.

Therefore, when the ocular micrometer (each division measuring 3.0 μ) is focused on a specimen, and if the specimen requires 9 divisions to meet its length, multiply 9 by 3.0 μ to equal 27.0 μ (.027 mm.), the total length of the specimen.

Obviously every combination of oculars and objectives, also different tube lengths, must each be calibrated in this fashion.

Specialized Microscopy

The image of a biological specimen can be formed and used in several ways. The most common form, known in all laboratories, is the use of color images, either natural color in the specimen or differential color applied to it. But, with the exception of a few vital stains, the latter method cannot be used on live material. Most living material is transparent to light; that is, the light wave passes through it with very little loss of intensity, so other means for examining it must be employed.

Dark Field Microscopy

In dark field, the objects themselves turn the light into the microscope by reflecting it or scattering it, and the object appears luminous on a dark background. No light from an outside source reaches the eye. A stop in the substage condenser blocks out the central part of the solid cone of light formed in the condenser, and only oblique rays in a hollow cone of light, striking from the sides, illuminate the object.

The simplest form of dark field can be developed with a black central patch stop inserted in the carrier under the condenser. Dark field elements in a threaded mount can be used in place of the upper lens of an Abbe condenser. This is practical with all objectives if the numerical aperture does not exceed 0.85 and immersion is used with the slide.

Dark field can be modified with colored stops and outer rings below the substage condenser, instead of black stops, to produce optical staining. The central stop determines the background color and the outer ring the color of the object, giving optical coloring to unstained objects and helping to reveal detail and structure.

Dark field and optical staining can be useful for examining: 1. bacteria, yeasts, and molds; 2. body fluids, plant or animal; 3. colloids; 4. living organisms in water; 5. foods, fibers, and pigments; 6. insects and scales; 7. crystals; and 8. bone, plant, and rock sections.

It is a common means of studying the results of microincineration, the investigation of minerals present in different parts of tissues. Paraffin sections of tissue fixed in a solution of formalin and alcohol are mounted on slides and placed in an electric furnace. The temperature is then slowly raised until all organic matter is burned away and only the mineral skeleton of the tissue is left. This appears white under dark-field observation.

Phase and Interference Microscopy

Although most living material is transparent to visible light, different components of tissue do alter to a different extent the **phase** of light waves passing through them. That is, the light velocity is altered, advanced or retarded and its vibration is said to be changed in phase. When two waves come together and are in phase, brightness increases, but if out of phase and of equal amplitude, interference occurs and the eye sees black, not light. Waves of intermediate difference in phase produce a series of grays. It is the aim of the phase microscope, to change slight phase differences into amplitude differences and produce a variation in intensity from light to dark contrast observable in the specimen under the microscope.

Both phase and interference microscopes follow this principle of interference phenomenon—combining light waves that are out of phase with each other to produce combined waves of greater and lesser amplitude. The means of applying the principle is different.

PHASE MICROSCOPY

The cost of phase microscopy is not excessive and the parts can be adapted to any brightfield microscope. The system requires phase contrast objectives (achromatic objectives with fixed-phase plates and a two-lens Abbe condenser with an iris diaphragm and a revolving ring below the condenser to carry four **annular ring diaphragms** (stops that produce different-sized cones of light). The correct annular ring diaphragm must be centered to the phase ring of the correct objective and match its numerical aperture. The annular diaphragm causes the light to strike the object in the shape of a hollow cone and gives rise to two types of waves; one type passes straight through the object (undiffracted), the others are diffracted into a different course. Different components in the tissue diffract differently producing the differences in intensity.

Images under phase microscopy exhibit a "halo" as a result of the diffraction of light at the phase-changing **annulus** (annular ring). The light which has passed straight through the specimen is made to interfere with the light diffracted sideways by it. Only the refracting structures are observed, and these edges and abrupt changes of refractive index produce the "halo" around the images.

INTERFERENCE MICROSCOPY

A more sensitive and accurate instrument is the interference microscope, which is better adapted to measuring the refractive indices of a specimen. In this microscope, the light splitting and recombining is carried out externally to the specimen. **Birefringent plates** (doubly refracting) are cemented to the top lens of the condenser and to the front lens of the objective. One set of rays passes through the object, the other set passes through a clear region at one side, and they are then recombined. Any phase differences between them remain constant and can interfere to give light or dark. A refractile object in one beam causes a change in light intensity.

Phase versus Interference

Both operate on the same principle—the interference phenomenon which changes phase difference into amplitude difference.

PHASE: (1) Light passing through the specimen is made to interfere with light diffracted sideways by it. (2) Only shows up diffracting structures in the specimen; produces a "halo." (3) Apparatus is simple, reasonable in cost, easy to operate and can be added to any conventional microscope. (4) Can be used to study living material, cytoplasm, cell inclusions, nucleus, action of physical and chemical agents on living cells. (5) Adequate for routine examination.

INTERFERENCE: (1) Light splitting and recombining carried out on outside of specimen and under control of experimenter. (2) No "halo"; variations in the optical path through the object are easily interpreted. Phase change can be measured. (3) Apparatus is expensive and complicated. Requires constant checking and adjusting. (4) Can be used on living material to determine dry mass: for example, changes in mass during cell activity; protein distribution, both in cytoplasm and nucleus.

Polarizing Microscopy

Closely related to the above types of observation is the use of **polarizing** attachments. These may be used on most types of microscopes, but for continued use a polarizing microscope is preferable. When a ray of **plane-polarized light** (vibrating in one plane) falls on the object, it is split into two rays: one obeys laws of refraction and the other passes through the object with a different velocity. After emerging from the object, the two rays are recombined, but because their velocity is different, they will be out of phase. This phase difference is the quantity measured in a polarizing microscope.

A **polarizing** (prism) in the fork substage instead of a condenser, or a polaroid disc in the condenser slot polarizes the light so it vibrates in one plane only. Part of the light (ordinary ray) is reflected to the side of the prism and does not illuminate the object; the other part (extraordinary ray) continues straight through the prism to emerge as polarized light. (There obviously is a loss of light, so plenty of it must be used.) If the polarizer is a prism, it usually can be rotated 360° and the amount of rotation in the field checked.

In or above the ocular is fitted another polarizing prism, the **analyzer,** whose vibration direction is set at 90° to that of the polarizer. The extraordinary ray from the polarizer becomes the ordinary ray in the analyzer and is reflected out of the field, unless an **anisotropic substance** (doubly refracting when placed between the analyzer and polarizer) rotates the plane of polarization and interferes with the path of light. Such a substance divides the light from the polarizer into two beams, one of which passes through the analyzer, making the object appear to glow against a dark background. **Isotropic substances** (singly refracting) do not polarize and therefore do not divide the beam of light and do not glow.

SOME USES OF POLARIZING MICROSCOPY

1. Determines whether an object is isotropic or anisotropic (if it rotates the plane of polarization).
2. Can be used for differences in physical properties in different directions; study of mitotic spindles.
3. Can be used on fresh unfixed material.
4. Reveals molecular orientation of structures, chemical constitution, chemical and physical intervention in the cell, pressures or tensions; all can produce anisotropic effects.
5. Can be used on natural and artificial fibers, cellulose fibrils, lamellar plasm differentiation, pseudopodia, spindles and asters, nerve fibers, muscle fibers, chromosomes, chemical and mineral crystals, crystallized hormones and vitamins, dust counts, starch grains, horn, claw and bone sections.
6. Can be used for determination of refractive indices.

X-Ray Diffraction

All forms of matter scatter X-rays and form diffraction patterns. From these patterns information concerning the materials can be ascertained; crystalline proteins show an X-ray diffraction of great complexity, fibrous proteins show less detail. Information can be obtained concerning molecular orientation, particle and molecular size and sometimes detailed molecular structure. The image recorded can be related to simple absorption processes and thus be interpreted chemically.

The simplest method with X-rays is to place a tissue section in contact with a fine-grained photographic emulsion and expose it. Magnification is obtained in an X-ray projection microscope by separating the sample and film. This requires very fine focusing. One of the principal disadvantages of the method is that vacuum is required; therefore material has to be dry, no water can be present. Freeze-dried tissue can be used.

USES OF X-RAY

Tissues with relatively high X-ray absorption are bone and tissues impregnated with heavy metals. The distribution of mineral salts in undecalcified sections of bone can be clearly shown and quantitative information obtained. Substances containing high percentage of elements of high atomic numbers can be injected into blood vessels, or the lymphatic system, and photographed with fine-grain film. Recorded images can be related to simple absorption processes and then be interpreted chemically. By using the oblique incidence of X-rays, it is possible to determine the thickness of bone tissue or nerves.

The determination of dry weight (mass) of cellular structures can be made with X-rays, but the interference microscope can also be employed for mass determination. In the latter case, the material can be alive and in fluid. Sometimes it is advantageous to compare both methods as counterchecks on artifacts: is either or are both producing artifacts?— the interference microscope because of fluid being present, or the X-ray product because the material is fixed or dried.

Ultraviolet Microscopy

Short waves beyond the visible spectrum have a profound effect upon living matter and are useful for the physical analysis of such matter. Some living material under the influence of ultraviolet radiation visibly radiates, glows and fluoresces. Some does not and remains dark. A microscope for this type of observation has been designed with optical glass in the objectives but is equipped with a quartz substage condenser. A quartz lamp condenser is part of the system to help concentrate the maximum amount of near violet on the specimen. The object itself should not fluoresce, but will absorb, partially absorb or transmit the ultraviolet and thereby reveal structural differences in a photographic image without the use of stains. The specimen must be mounted in a nonfluorescent medium: water, glycerol or mineral oil. Glass fluoresces and will reduce contrast and possibly obscure some detail in the specimen, so quartz cover glasses and slide should be used for best results, also fluorescent-free immersion oil.

Resolution is increased over that of the conventional microscope and differences in structure in the specimen are enhanced by the ultraviolet absorption. The technique is not complicated, nor expensive.

But for greater resolution and higher selective absorption, a *quartz ultraviolet microscope* is better than the above. It is, however, more difficult to handle and focus, also more costly. The quartz microscope is equipped with fused quartz objectives, crystalline quartz eyepieces, quartz substage condenser, and quartz right angle prism. Quartz slides and cover glasses should be used. The light source must be ultraviolet.

Some cells are immune to ultraviolet, others are only mildly affected and can be used with excellent results under this microscope. But in the case of those that are killed by ultraviolet, formation of artifacts should be expected. Because of the possibility of damage to these cells, focusing can be done with visible radiation and then ultraviolet used only during photography or photoelectric measuring. Tissue cannot be fixed for ultraviolet—this decreases absorption—but ice solvent or freeze dry techniques can be used. Ultraviolet photomicrographs are difficult to interpret at times and require considerable experience.

The ultraviolet microscope, therefore, has become a useful instrument for measuring the selective absorption of cellular components (measured at specific wavelengths). Its chief uses have been for the measurement of cellular concentration and localization of nucleic acids, **RNA** (ribonucleic acid) and **DNA** (desoxyribonucleic acid) content, observations on normal and **neoplastic** (tumoring) tissue (in the latter the nuclear RNA content is high). Some substances can interfere with such observations. Perhaps among the more interesting are the barbiturates, which absorb heavily and should not be used for sedation or anesthesia in animals to be prepared for this technic.

Fluorescent Microscopy

An object fluoresces when it absorbs ultraviolet light reflected on it or transmitted through it and then emits the energy as visible light of a specific violet, blue, green, yellow, orange, or red color. Secondary fluorescence can be induced by the use of **fluorochromes** (strongly fluorescent dyes or chemicals) applied to the specimen. Even though many objects fluoresce naturally, fluorescence can be intensified in them or induced in others by the use of fluorochromes which are simple to use. As with all ultraviolet preparations, nonfluorescent solutions, mounting media and oil immersion must be used. Quartz slides and cover glasses can be used, but are not essential for the technics included in this manual.

APPARATUS REQUIRED FOR FLUORESCENT MICROSCOPY

Fluorescent microscopes can be purchased from several of the optical companies (*Reichert, Zeiss-Winkel, American Optical*). In addition to a compound microscope with a focusable condenser (*Abbe* is satisfactory) minimum equipment includes: a mercury lamp and filter and yellow check filters for each ocular eyepiece. Although some technicians feel that a front surfaced aluminized mirror should be used, this is not essential. A monocular microscope gives a brighter image than a binocular microscope.

AMERICAN OPTICAL EQUIPMENT

1. A merc-Arc illuminator (lamp housing and optics are separate from the power supply), complete with glass optics. Osram HBO-200 lamp and power supply.
2. Multiple filter holder for use with the illuminator.
3. Exciter filter for higher light transmission (between light source and microscope condenser) .
4. Barrier (check) filter for ocular.

ZEISS SMALL EQUIPMENT

1. Lighting unit: lamp housing, transformer, mercury burner Osram HBO 74, Schott BG 12 filter, and gives ultraviolet in 350 mμ—450 mμ ranges.
2. Barrier filter (OG 5) for eyepiece.

ZEISS LARGE EQUIPMENT

1. Osram HBO 200 lamp ($4\frac{1}{2}$ times brighter than above), 2 Schott BG 12 filters.
2. Zeiss OG 4 and OG 5 filters for eyepiece.

Keep all equipment free from grease, which is opaque to ultraviolet light.

Fluorescent microscopy differs from ultraviolet microscopy in that the former observes the specimen directly by innate autofluorescence or by secondary fluorescence induced by fluorochromes, while the latter records specific absorption of the ultraviolet light by certain structures in the specimen.

USES FOR FLUOROCHROMES

Granules of islets of Langerhans: *Hartroft (1951)*; mucin: *Hicks and Matthaei (1958)*; blood vessels and lymphatics: *Schlegel (1949)*; mucopolysaccharides: *Kuyper (1957)*; bone marrow: *Werth (1953)*; amyloid and connective tissue: *Vassar and Culling (1959)*; nerve cells: *Zeiger et al. (1951)*; fat: *Metcalf and Patton (1944)*; nucleic acids, nucleoproteins: *Armstrong (1956), deBruyn et al. (1953)*; cancer: *Vinegar (1916), von Bertalanffy and von Bertalanffy (1960)*, and *Umiker and Pickle (1960)*; alkaline phosphatase: *Burstone (1960)*. This bibliography will easily lead to many others.

Electron Microscopy

In the electron microscope magnets focus an illuminating beam of electrons onto the specimen. The scattering of the electrons by the specimen forms shadows that can be photographed on film. Discussion concerning this method is found on page 397.

Microscopy References

Barer (1956, 1959); Beck (1938); Belling (1930); Bennett (1950); Davis (1958); Dempster (1944A and B); Engström (1956, 1959); Gage (1943) ; Ham (1957); McClung-Jones (1950); Munz and Charipper (1943); Needham (1958); Nurnberger (1955); Oster (1955); Popper and Szanto (1950); Richards (1954); Ruch (1955); Scott (1955); Shillaber (1944); Vickers (1956) and Walker (1958).

Chapter 10

Stains and Staining

Stains and Their Staining Action

Most tissues after processing do not retain sufficient color to make them and their components visible under a brightfield microscope. It is therefore expedient to add colors to tissues by staining (coloring, dying) them with the proper stains (dyes).

Baker (1958) argues logically against the nomenclature "stains and staining," saying that they are not accurate terms. For example: "basic fuchsin 'stains' chromatin; silver compounds 'stain' nerve fibers and sudan black 'stains' lipids," yet from a physical and chemical point of view the three processes differ markedly. He suggests that the terminology "colour and colouring agent or colourant" (British spelling) be applied to methods of imparting color on or in organic material. At present it does not seem advisable to depart in this direction. Supply houses still list their products as dyes or stains and specify dye content. The Biological Stain Commission has not seen fit to change its name. To the author, therefore, it appears politic to continue to use "dye," "stain" and "staining" until such a time as Baker's suggestion has taken hold. When a colored substance which is not a dye is formed, as is true of many histochemical tests and silver impregnation, the appropriate terminology will be applied.

Natural Dyes

Cochineal and Carmine

These are members of a group of dyes called "natural" stains. Unlike other natural stains, cochineal and carmine are derived from an animal source—a minute insect, the cochineal insect, *Coccus cacti*, living on spineless cacti. The dye is present as a purple sap in the females, which are harvested, dried and pulverized to produce *cochineal*. This dye by itself has little affinity for tissue unless iron, aluminum or some other metal is present. With the salt of one of these metals as a mordant (see page 107), staining will result. Alum cochineal, a commonly used form of this dye with mordant, can be an efficient nuclear stain. The dye *carmine*, is derived from cochineal by boiling the latter with a salt, usually alum, to produce a precipitate. This precipitate is insoluble in water and before it can be used as a stain must be converted into a soluble compound such as ammoniacal carmine or aceto-carmine, a process that will be described under Mordants, below.

Hematoxylin

In many respects, hematoxylin can be regarded as most important among the natural dyes. It was one of the first histological dyes, and still remains one of the most widely known and used dyes. Hematoxylin is extracted from the heartwood of logwood trees from South and Central America and the West Indies. The tree is *Hematoxylon campechianum*, one of the legumes (*Conn, 1953*), similar to acacia or cassia trees. The crude material is exported as logs, chips or as dried aqueous extract of the heartwood. This then is extracted with ether in a continuous extraction apparatus, evaporated to dryness, dissolved in water, filtered and crystallized out of solution. All of these steps are slow and difficult to handle and require costly apparatus, thus making hematoxylin one of our most expensive dyes.

In this condition it is not yet a dye, and its color must be allowed to develop by oxidation into **hematein** (color acid—no relation to *hematin*, the colored constituent of red blood cells). Oxidation may be accomplished in either of two ways: "naturally"—a slow process of exposure to air for 3 to 6 weeks, as in *Heidenhain's* hematoxylin—or artificially by the use of mercuric oxide, hydrogen peroxide, or other oxidizing agent—a more rapid process as in *Harris'* hematoxylin. Used alone, hematein is only a weak and diffuse dye with little affinity for tissues.

A weak acid will not combine with nuclear elements in sufficient quantity to produce efficient staining. Some form of mordanting (page 107) is required to form a base from this dye, which will then stain the acidic nuclear elements. The most commonly used mordants are alum salts of aluminum, potassium or iron, as already mentioned.

Baker (1958) recommends oxidation with sodium iodate for preparing hematoxylin solutions. Start with a wholly unoxidized hematoxylin dye powder, not hematein powder. Solutions started with the latter tend to lose their strength by **flocculation** (sedimentation) of the products of oxidation. The hematoxylin dye when in solution should be only partly oxidized by the sodium iodate. Use less chemical than would be required for complete oxidation; about one fourth to one half of the full amount of oxidizer is adequate. The solution will then continue to gradually ripen by atmospheric oxygen and thereby maintain its strength. Such solutions are allowed to ripen slowly, six weeks or more. (*Mayer's* hematoxylin is an example of this type.) They will produce brilliant staining for many months.

The rate of oxidation is also affected by the solvent. A neutral aqueous solution forms hematein in a few hours; an acid solution does this more slowly and an alkaline solution more rapidly. Alcoholic solutions are slow, and the addition of glycerine retards them even more. Color changes which take place in a stock solution indicate its efficiency. The changes, with no mordant present, are from water white through lilac, bright purple, deep purple, red, orange red, orange brown to brown. At the purple stage, the solution is most vigorous; at the red stages less so; and at the brown stage it is no longer useful. The lifetime of alcoholic solutions is five times greater than that of aqueous ones. (*Cole, 1943*)

Hematoxylin is an exceedingly powerful dye with various shades of staining from purples, through blues and into blue-blacks. The iron-mordanted form is one of the most valuable dyes for mitotic study, and gives to the chromatin a precise black or blue-black color. This black color is the result of the presence in hematoxylin of some tannin, and the latter in combination with iron salts produces a lasting black color.

Other natural dyes are SAFFRON from stigmas of *Crocus;* INDIGO from plants of the genus, *Indigofera;* BERBERINE from barberry; ORCEIN and LITMUS from the lichens, *Lecanora* and *Rocella;* and BRAZILIN from brazilwood—a redwood tree of the tropics. Orcein, a specific dye for **elastin** (present in elastic fibers), is prepared by boiling the plants in water. The lecanoric acid in them splits to produce **orcinol**—a resorcinol with a methyl group attached to it. Orcinol with NH_3 (ammonia) and atmospheric oxygen forms orcein.

Mordants

Carmine, dissolved in a solution of aluminum sulfate, becomes positively charged and acts as a highly basic dye. Such a compound, formed by a dye radicle with the salt or hydroxide of a divalent or trivalent metal serving to attach it to tissues, is called a **lake.** The salt used for this purpose is called a **mordant** (meaning "to bite"). Lakes may be unstable or insoluble. Usually the tissue is treated first with a solution of the mordant and then placed in the dye, and the lake forms in the tissue. The term *mordant* should not be used for all substances that increase staining action—only when salts and hydroxides of di- and trivalent metals are used.

The use of mordants has many advantages. Once the mordant-dye has combined with the tissue, the dye is relatively permanent, is insoluble in neutral solutions, and can be followed by many forms of staining. Dehydration will not decolorize them. There are three methods of use:

1. Mordant preceding dye.
2. Mordant and dye together.
3. Mordant following dye (rare).

For carmine and hematoxylin the mordants commonly used are aluminum, ferric and chromium salts, and alums (potassium alum, ammonium alum, iron alum and chrome alum). Ferric chloride also may be used as a mordant for hematoxylin, causing the tissues to stain more rapidly and more intensely than after iron alum. A 4% solution of ferric chloride can be used in place of the 4% solution of iron alum, and Cole (1933) recommends the use of a phosphate-ripened hematoxylin with it.

For long-lived solutions of combined mordant and dye, mordants with little or no oxidizing action must be used: ammonium alum, potassium alum, phosphotungstic acid, phosphomolybdic acid and iron alum-ferrous sulfate. If a long life is not requisite, mordants with vigorous oxidizing action can be used. Since their usefulness is only a matter of hours, these solutions must be prepared immediately before use: ferric chloride, ferric acetate and ferric alum. (*Cole, 1943*).

When using two separate solutions, a mordant of any kind can be used if followed by a well-ripened hematoxylin. If the solution is un-ripened, then the mordant should include a substance of considerable oxidizing power, a ferric or chromium salt. The value of two solutions lies in the fact that the dye can be preceded by a salt, which can not be used in combination with the dye in a single solution. Ferric chloride, when added to an ammonia-ripened hematoxylin, will throw down a precipitate of ferric hydroxide. Double mordanting can be profitable. A mordant followed by a solution of hematoxylin containing a mordant gives excellent results. The mordants for separate use are: ammonium or potassium alum, ferric ammonium alum (2–3 drops of HCl increases contrast), and ferric chloride (HCl increases contrast). They yield the following colors with hematoxylin: ammonium alum, bright blue nuclei; potassium alum, lilac or violet; chrome alum, cold gray blue; iron alum, blue to black. (*Cole, 1943*)

Relative to the use of metals with hematoxylin, the following list of tissue elements and the metals effectively used on them may be of practical interest. (*Mallory, 1938*)

Nuclei: aluminum, iron, tungsten
Myelin sheaths: chromium, iron, copper
Elastic fibers: iron
Collagen: molybdenum
Fibroglia, myoglia, neuroglia, epithelial fibers: tungsten
Axis cylinders: lead
Mucin: iron
Fibrin: tungsten

Lakes, formed by mordant and dye, can be used progressively, but when mordant and dye are used separately, regressive staining usually is more effective. In *progressive staining* the stain is added to the tissue until the correct depth of color is reached. In *regressive staining*, the sections are overstained and excessive amounts are removed by one of the following methods.

Method 1: By Use of Excess Mordant

With an excess of free mordant present outside of the tissue, the mordant-dye complex in the tissue is broken up, and, since the amount of mordant in the tissue is small in comparison with that in the differentiating fluid, the dye moves out of the tissue into the latter. (If the tissue is left long enough in the fluid, it is conceivable that most of the dye could move out of it into the excess mordant and the sections become colorless.) Because the nuclei hold considerably more dye than the cytoplasm, the dye is lost more completely from the latter, while some still remains in the former. At the proper point of extraction from the cytoplasm and when correct intensity is left in the nuclei, the slides are taken out of the mordant and thoroughly washed, usually in running water, to remove excess mordant. Remaining traces can cause the stain to fade in time.

Method 2: By Use of Acids

Acids are effective differentiators for some dyes, but a completely adequate explanation for their action is not available.

Method 3: By Use of Oxidizers

Oxidizers furnish a third method of regressive staining, and by this method the dye can be oxidized to a colorless condition. Oxidizers are slow in action; the parts of the cell which hold only a small amount of dye will be bleached before those possessing greater quantities of it. A complete explanation is not available in this case. Picric acid, a commonly used chemical in this category, has both a moderate oxidizing and a weak acidic action.

Not to be confused with mordants are accentuators and accelerators. **Accentuators** are substances which, contrary to the action of mordants, do not become a part of the dye complex or lake. Instead they increase the selectivity or stainability of the dye (example: phenol in carbolfuchsin). **Accelerators,** as their name implies, accelerate the action—usually of importance here in silver impregnation (chloral hydrate).

Synthetic Dyes

Natural dyes had no competition until the middle of the nineteenth century when William Perkin worked out the processes for making aniline or coal-tar dyes.

Synthetic dyes, like natural ones, can be used either progressively or regressively. An acid solution often is used to remove excess basic dye; an alkaline solution is used to remove excess acidic dye. In some cases, alcohol can act as a differentiator, particularly for basic dyes; but in general a sharper differentiation is achieved by using an acid.

The real importance of synthetic dyes lies in their use for double and triple staining, the use of two or more stains on the same slide. By placing several different contrasting colors in a tissue, this type of staining has definite advantages. The dyes, if properly chosen, will stain **histologically;** that is, each dye because of a known specificity will elect to stain only specific parts of the cells. Due to their chemical nature synthetic dyes make this kind of staining possible. By being synthesized, their formula can be controlled and the significant part of the dye is either **anionic** (acid) or **cationic** (basic) in action. Actually dye powder as purchased is a salt, but the salts of the so-called basic dyes give up OH^- ions and act as cations, while the acidic dyes give up H^+ ions and act as anions. Therefore an acid dye is the salt of a color acid, usually a sodium salt; a basic dye is the salt of a color base, usually a chloride. Basic dyes have an affinity for nuclei, which are **basophilic** (readily stained by basic dyes) and acidic dyes have an affinity for the cytoplasm, which is **acidophilic** (readily stained by acidic dyes). Also acid and base dyes may be combined to form "neutral dyes" which give results differing from those obtained with ordinary double staining using separate acid and base dyes. The action of neutral dyes is an example of **polychroming,** a process in which a dye forms other dyes spontaneously— the basis of the development of modern blood staining (*Romanowsky stains*) in which methylene blue and eosin combine in a polychroming mixture. Through polychroming, a new group of dyes, **azures,** is produced for the multiple-staining action which is so desirable in the differentiation of white blood cells.

Polychroming must not be confused with another type of staining, **metachroming,** in which certain substances are stained in one color and others in another color by the same dye. In the case of the dye *thionin,* the explanation for this reaction may be as follows:

Thionin stains chromatin blue; it stains mucus, ground substance of cartilage, and granules of mast cells, red. The dye seems to exist in aqueous solution in two forms: (1) the normal color, blue; and (2) the metachromatic color, red. Both forms are always present, but the red is in a polymerized form of the blue. The blue form is favored by increase of temperature, a lowering of pH, a decrease of dye concentration, and addition of salts, alcohol, or acetone. The red form is favored by a decrease of temperature, a raising of pH or increase in concentration of dye (*Bergeron and Singer, 1958*). Also certain substances, sulfuric esters of high molecular weight and their salts, increase the production of the red form. Mucin, the ground substance of cartilage, and the granules of mast cells contain substances of this nature, and therefore take up the metachromatic form.

The majority of dyes do not stain metachromatically, but are **ortho-chromatic** in action. This means that their action is direct and predictable under normal conditions; if it is a blue dye, it stains blue, if it is a green one it stains green, and so forth.

Structure of Synthetic Dyes[1]

The synthetic (coal tar or aniline) dyes are derivatives of benzene, all built on the **benzene ring.** When certain chemical groups, called **chromophores,** are attached to a benzene derivative, the compound acquires the property of color and is known as a **chromogen.** A chromogen, however, still is not a dye. It has no affinity for tissues, will coat them only mechanically, and can be easily removed by mechanical means. The compound must also contain a group which gives it the property of **electrolytic dissociation** (the formation of cations and anions in solution). This auxiliary group, known as an **auxochrome,** furnishes the required salt-forming properties. As mentioned above, most of the dyes are sold as salts and are stable powders until put into solution, then becoming acidic or basic by dissociation.

Nomenclature of stains has no absolute conformity. The color may be used—orange *G*, Martius yellow; or perhaps some chemical term—methyl green and so forth. If the term is followed by a letter or numeral (Sudan III, IV, ponceau 2R, 4R), one dye is being distinguished from a related one. *B* indicates a more bluish color, *Y* or *G* a more yellowish color, *WS* means water soluble; and *A, B, C* distinguish among certain azures.

Nature of Staining Action

Biologists and biochemists argue concerning the nature of staining action—is it chemical, physical or a combination of both? If chemical, this can mean that some parts of the cells are acid and others alkaline, the former tending to combine with cations and the latter with **anions.** There is an **absorption** and diffusion of the dye penetrating the cellular elements, combining with them and remaining there in a state of more or less chemical combination. This action can be combined with physical action, where there is an **adsorption** of the dye, an attraction of plus and minus charges for each other and a condensation of the dye on the surface of the cell parts. Minute particles of the dye are deposited on

[1] For a complete discussion of dyes, consult Conn, 1953 or Gurr, 1960.

the surface of the tissue by selective adsorption and then enter into combination with the tissue. The proteins, nucleic acids, and other components of the protoplasm proceed along lines of chemical laws by exchanging ions. The Stearns (1929, 1930) maintain that the confusion lies in the term *adsorption,* that it may be either a chemical or a physical force, and the adsorbent can form ions and then proceed along chemical lines.

In any case, the staining properties depend on these three factors:

1. strength of dye
2. rate of ionization of tissue proteins and dyes
3. pH value of dye solution and tissue proteins

In addition, staining can be affected by other conditions:

1. alcoholic or aqueous solution of dye
2. low or high temperature during reaction
3. simple or multiple combinations of dyes
4. strong or weak concentration of dye in solution

Standardization of Stains

In the early days of tissue staining it was difficult to secure reliable dyes. The textile dye industry was the sole source of dyes and products received were often unsatisfactory. Standardization was crudely done as to color, and this was no standardization as to chemical content. The impurities were extremely variable in quantity and quality. Grübler in Germany was the first to try to standardize dyes and he built a highly specialized business in this field. He did not actually manufacture dyes, but he bought up batches from other firms and tested them for technical use. After the beginning of the twentieth century, certain events changed Grübler's hold on the business of standardization. Perhaps of greatest influence were two world wars, causing Germany to lose its monopoly in the dye industry. No country could afford to remain dependent on another country for its source of dye if that country was likely to remain an enemy.

The lack of German dyes led to a new form of standardization in the United States. A body was organized called the Commission on Standardization of Biological Stains, later to become the present Biological Stain Commission. The object of this commission is to work with the manufacturers showing them what the biologists require, testing their products and permitting approved batches to be put on the market with the stamp of the commission on them. Specifications of the most important dyes now have been drawn up by the commission putting these dyes on a certification basis. The specifications are partly chemical and partly spectrophotometric and contain detailed statements as to how the dyes should be tested for their behavior with the results to be expected from their tests. Batches of dyes approved by the commission bear a special label furnished by the commission and known as a *certification label.* On it is a **C.I. number** (Colour Index number) indicating the certification number of that particular batch. This number means that (1) a sample of that batch was submitted to the commission for testing and a portion of it is on file; (2) the sample proved true to type by spectrophotometric tests; (3) its dye content met specifications and is correctly indicated on the label; (4) it was tested by experts in the procedure named on the label and found satisfactory; and (5) no other batch can be sold under the same certification number. Any description of the use of the stain should be followed by its C.I. number or a **C.C.** indicating that it is Commission Certified.[2]

Unless otherwise specified, dyes can be purchased from most of the scientific supply houses with chemical outlets: *Coleman and Bell Co., Hartman-Leddon Co., Fisher Scientific Co., Allied Chemical Corporation (National Aniline Division)*, and others.

Sources of foreign stains:

G. Grübler and Company, West Berlin, Germany.
Esbe Laboratory Supplies, 459 Bloor St. W., Toronto, Canada, outlet for *Gurr Stains (Michrome Stains).*

References: Baker (1945, 1958); Cole (1933, 1943); Conn (1946, 1948, 1953); Holmes (1929); Singer (1952); and Stearn and Stearn (1929, 1930).

[2] C.I. numbers used in this text are from the new revised list.

Chapter 11

Staining
Procedures

Usually certain standard principles apply to the processing of tissue on slides, but many exceptions and variations occur and will have to be handled individually.

The sections first must be deparaffinized, because most stains are applied in either aqueous or alcoholic solutions and would not penetrate efficiently through paraffin-infiltrated tissues. The customary solvent for paraffin is xylene. This is followed by the removal of the xylene with absolute alcohol because stains rarely can be applied successfully in a xylene medium. After the removal of the xylene, a general rule is to transfer the slides to a medium comparable to the solvent of the dye being used. That is, if the dye is a water solution, the slides are hydrated through a series of decreasing alcoholic and increasing aqueous dilutions, such as 95%, 80%, 70% and 50% alcohol, or the like, and finally they go into water. If the dye is dissolved in a 50% alcoholic solution, then the slides are carried only to 50% alcohol before going into the staining solution.

During the hydration process, undesirable pigments or other materials (mercuric chloride crystals, formalin pigment, etc.) are removed and the slides washed well to remove the responsible reagent. **Counterstains** (background color) or other special treatments must be applied in their proper sequence, to allow each dye or chemical to maintain its specific effect on the tissue elements. Improper sequence of staining, decolorizing, and other solutions can result in a poorly stained slide. Hematoxylin-eosin staining (page 130) provides a simple example. If the eosin (counterstain) is applied before the hematoxylin (nuclear) stain, the former stain will be completely removed during the action of the latter stain.

If slides are to be transported in quantity, rather than individually, several types of holders are useful and are on the market. *A.H. Thomas* has one holding 50 slides; *Wards* has one for six slides. Some are baskets, others are clips, and fit into special staining dishes. The tissue-processing machines are equipped with slide carriers to fit the instrument. Phosphor-bronze spring wire, 0.05 inch diameter, can be fashioned into coils of $\frac{3}{4}$ inch diameter and cut into any length to hold anywhere from 3 or 4 slides up to 15 or 20. (Fig. 23) This combination of slides and coil can be used in rectangular staining dishes with the slides resting on their long edges, or standing upright in tall sterner dishes.

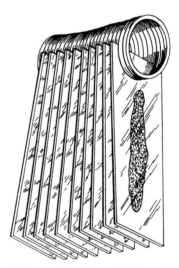

A final processing of slides is necessary to make permanent preparations for examination and storage without deterioration. All alcohol and water must be extracted (with certain exceptions) and a medium applied which maintains the tissues in a clear and transparent condition, does not alter the color or intensity of the stains, and holds a cover glass in

Figure 23. *A staining coil carrying multiple slides.*

place. The water is removed through increasing concentration of alcohol until absolute alcohol is reached. The final reagent is xylene (or the like) to remove the alcohol and make the sections lose their opacity and thereby become clear. Finally a mounting medium (**mountant**) is applied and the cover glass lowered into place completely covering the sections. (The solvent of the mounting medium usually is either toluene or xylene.)

Mounting a Cover Glass

The tidiest method for mounting a cover glass is this: (1) apply a thin streak of medium on the cover glass (Fig. 24); (2) turn cover glass over and rest on edge (shortest side of rectangles) on the slide, to left of sections (unless technician is left-handed) (Fig. 25); ease cover glass into place slowly to allow air to displace from under cover glass; press firmly from center outwards, to evenly distribute the medium. An alternate method is to apply mounting medium along one edge of sections on slide; rest one edge of cover glass adjacent to mounting medium and lower gradually to ease out air without bubble formation; press gently in place.

If, during microscopic examination of stained and mounted slides, dull black spots replace nuclear detail, the clearing solution partially evaporated out of the sections before the cover glass was in place. Return such slides to xylene, dissolve all mounting medium to allow the air to leave the sections, and remount. If the slides appear dull, almost milky, instead of crystal clear, water is present. Remove all mounting medium in xylene and return slides to absolute alcohol, preferably a fresh solution. Clear and remount.

Mounting Media (mountants)

Formerly natural resins were used as mounting media: *Canada balsam,* composed of terpenes, carboxylic acid and esters; *gum damar,* composed of unsaturated resin acids and a little ester; or *gum sandarac,* an unsaturated acid resin. These dried slowly, were variable in composition and unpredictable in behavior. Some developed acidity and faded stains, would turn yellow and crack after a few years. One still used, particularly for blood smears, is *Euparol,* refractive index 1.483, a **eutectic** (melts at low temperature) mixture of oil of eucalyptus, gum sandarac, salol, paraldehyde, menthol and camphor. *Euparol Vert* (green because of copper salt content) is claimed to intensify hematoxylin stains. Dried smears may be mounted directly in Euparol, but sections must be carried into 95% alcohol, and then into *Euparol Essence* before mounting. (If alcohol is carried into the Euparol, sections will fade.) Drain off excess Essence and apply Euparol.

The synthetic resins now available have proven superior to natural resins in most respects. The composition of synthetic resins can be controlled and they are stable and inert. They dissolve readily in xylene or toluene, do not require long drying, and adhere tightly to glass. They have the correct refractive indices, are pale in color, and do not yellow with age.

The most widely used synthetics are the β-pinene polymers—terpene resins, such as **Permount** (*Fisher Scientific Company*) and **Piccolyte**

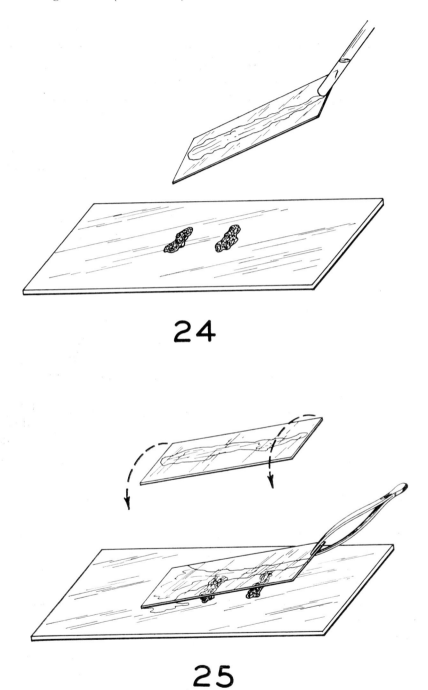

24

25

Figures 24 and 25. *Placing mountant on cover glass, turning cover over, and lowering it onto slide.*

(*General Biological Supply House*) with a refractive index of 1.51 to
1.52. *Hartman-Laddon Company* sells "**HRS**," *Harleco Synthetic Resin,*
index of refraction 1.5202; *Will Corporation* has a **Bioloid** Synthetic
Resin, index of refraction 1.5396; *Ward's* sells **Kleermount;** also the
Technicon Company sells one. The resins should have refractive indices
of 1.53 to 1.54 or better. (*Lillie et al., 1953*) There is no reason to
recommend one of the above products over the others; all are equally
efficient. They are soluble in xylene, toluene, aromatic hydrocarbon
solvents, and in chlorinated hydrocarbons such as chloroform, but not
in Dioxane.

Hyrax (*Fisher Scientific Company*), refractive index 1.71, is a permanent, neutral synthetic naphthalene resin, formulated by *Dr. G. Dallas
Hanna* for *mounting* diatoms. It is good for some unstained botanical
and parasitological materials which lose detail in other synthetics because they become too clear. Hyrax brings out structure of colorless
fibers and spines.

Lillie et al. (1950) recommend **Lustron 2020** for good preservation of
Prussian blue mounts, which tend to fade in some resins. Lustron is a
polystyrene manufactured by *Monsanto Chemical Corporation* and has
a refractive index of 159. It is water resistant and soluble in varying
degrees in aromatic and chlorinated hydrocarbons. The above authors
used it in diethylbenzene as solvent. The present author has had excellent results using toluene or xylene without the formation of air bays
as the xylene evaporated. If such trouble is encountered, diethylbenzene
is recommended; Lillie *et al.* suggest adding 5 ml. dibutylphthalate to
70 ml. xylene and 25 gm. polystyrene. This does not delay hardening.

There are also the German synthetics, **Caedax** and **Rhenohistol,** and
the British ones—**Xam, Cristalite** and **Clearmount.** These are similar
in most respects to American products.

Most synthetic mountants are allowed to air dry, but if quick drying
is a must, try this method of *Manikas and Umiker (1959)*: After slides
are covered, place them on metal trays in a drying oven, 160–170°C, 3
minutes. Remove and chill in freezing compartment of refrigerator, 2
minutes. Slides can be cleaned, marked with ink and stored without
dislodging cover glasses.

Aqueous mounting media are indispensible for the preservation of
tissue elements which are soluble in alcohol or hydrocarbons, or are
demonstrated by the use of dyes soluble in these fluids. A number of
media have been proposed using (1) gelatine and gum arabic as solidifying agents with water, (2) sugars and salts for increasing the refractive

index, and (3) glycerols and glycol as plasticizing agents. Gum arabic slowly hardens by drying, gelatine sets by cooling, and the glycerol keeps them from cracking or overfrying. The addition of phenol, thymol, merthiolate, or Zephiran prevents mold growth.

Kaiser's Glycerol Jelly

water	52.0 ml.
gelatine	8.0 gm.
glycerol	50.0 ml.

Preserve with either (1) carbolic acid (phenol), 0.1 gm.; (2) merthiolate, 0.01 gm.; or (3) Zephiran 0.1 ml.

Allow gelatine to soak for 1–2 hours in water, add glycerol and preservative. Warm for 10–15 minutes (not over 75°C) and stir until mixture is homogeneous. This keeps well in covered jar in refrigerator. If heated above 75°C, the gelatine may be transformed into metagelatine and will not harden at room temperature.

Apathy's Gum Syrup

gum arabic (acacia)	50.0 gm.
sucrose (cane sugar)	50.0 gm.
distilled water	50.0 ml.
formalin	1.0 ml.

Dissolve lumps of gum arabic in warm water; add sucrose. When dissolved, filter and allow to cool. Add formalin. Do not use powdered form of gum; it makes a milky solution, whereas the lump form produces a clearer medium. The cover glass does not have to be sealed as it does with Kaiser's glycerol jelly above.

Farrant's Medium

distilled water	40.0 ml.
gum arabic (acacia)	40.0 gm.
glycerol	20.0 ml.
carbolic acid (phenol)	0.1 gm.
(or merthiolate or Zephiran)	

It is difficult to obtain a good quality of gum arabic to make a clean and clear solution, so purchasing of the finished product from *Amend Drug and Chemical Company* is preferable.

Gray and Wess' Medium (PVA) (1952)

PVA (polyvinyl alcohol) 71–24[1]	2.0 gm.
70% acetone	7.0 ml.
glycerol	5.0 ml.
lactic acid	5.0 ml.
distilled water	10.0 ml.

Make a paste of the dry alcohol with acetone. Mix half of water with glycerol and lactic acid; stir into paste. Add rest of water drop by drop with stirring. Solution will be cloudy but becomes transparent as warmed in water bath about 10 minutes.

PVA (polyvinyl alcohol) Mounting Medium

Add 15.0 gm. PVA 71–24 powder (DuPont. See note below) slowly to 100.0 ml. cold water. Heat in water bath (80°C) with stirring until the solution becomes as viscous as thick molasses. Filter out undissolved lumps through two layers of cheesecloth. Solution will appear milky, but after standing for several hours, will clear. A thin film can be spread over stained blood smears when cover glasses are undesirable.

The following are recommended for small whole mounts, insects, worms, tiny invertebrates and the like.

Berlese Mounting Medium

1. GRAY'S FORMULA (1952).

water	10.0 ml.
glacial acetic acid	3.0 ml.
dextrose syrup	5.0 ml.
gum arabic (acacia)	8.0 gm.
chloral hydrate	75.0 gm.

Mix water with acid and syrup; dissolve gum in this. Requires week or more. Stir at intervals. When solution is complete, add chloral hydrate. This is one of the best media for insects. As was suggested for Farrant's medium, it is difficult to obtain good gum.

2. THICK FORMULA.

distilled water	40.0 ml.
saturated aqueous solution of chloral hydrate . .	30.0 ml.
gum arabic (acacia)	25.0 gm.
glycerol	5.0 ml.

[1] Obtainable from E. I. DuPont de Nemours and Co., Wilmington, Del.

Dissolve gum arabic in water, add chloral hydrate and then glycerol. Filter.

3. THIN FORMULA.

distilled water	100.0 ml.
gum arabic (acacia)	60.0 gm.
glycerol	40.0 ml.
saturated aqueous solution of chloral hydrate	100.0 ml.

Monk's Karo Medium (1938)

white Karo syrup	5.0 ml.
Certo (fruit pectin)	5.0 ml.
water	3.0 ml.
thymol for preservative	

This is recommended for mounting a group of small parts which are easily disarranged. A thin layer is spread on a slide and the parts to be mounted are removed from glycerol and immediately arranged in the medium. The mixture begins to set in about 2 minutes, and holds parts in place. Dry to hardness over heat. Cover glass can be added with a drop of mixture or with Euparol. If using mixture, use enough to prevent air pockets from forming when the medium dries.

Lacto-phenol Mounting Medium

melted phenol (carbolic acid)	3 parts
lactic acid	1 part
glycerol	2 parts
distilled water	1 part

CMC-10 Mounting Medium

This is a nonresinous mounting medium supplied by *General Biological Supply House.* It is primarily for small arthropods, such as fleas, ticks, mites, etc., but cannot be used for stained material. Small specimens containing little air can be mounted directly, but larger ones are mounted from water or alcohol.

Yetwin's Mounting Medium for Nematodes and Ova (1944)

10% bacto-gelatine, granular, Difco	150.0 ml.
glycerol	50.0 ml.
1% chromium potassium sulfate aqueous (chrome alum)	100.0 ml.
phenol (carbolic acid), melted	1.0 ml.

Dissolve gelatine in boiling water, add glycerol. After mixing add chrome alum solution and phenol. Liquefies in 15 minutes at 65°C. May transfer from glycerol or formalin directly. Hardens to form permanent mount.

Abopon

This mounting medium is water miscible and can replace glycerol jelly in several special staining techniques. It can be purchased from the *Glyco Chemicals Company, Williamsport, Pennsylvania,* in the form of lumps or solution. Dissolve the solid form, approximately 50 gm., in 25 ml. distilled water. The fluid form usually is too thick and is diluted with distilled water.

Diaphane

This medium is available in two forms, colorless (r.i., 1.4777) and green (r.i., 1.4792). Slides can be mounted directly from absolute, 95% or 70% alcohol. It and its solvent can be purchased from the *Will Corporation.*

Fluorescent Mounting Medium (Rodriquez and Deinhardt, 1960)

Elvanol 51-05 (DuPont. See note, p. 120)	20.0 gm.
0.14M Sodium chloride buffered with 0.01M	
$KH_2PO_4 - Na_2HPO_4 \cdot 12H_2O$, pH 7.2	80.0 ml.
add glycerol	40.0 ml.

Agitate another 16 hours

Remove undissolved particles of Elvanol by centrifuging, 12,000 rpm, 15 minutes. The pH should be between 6 and 7.

Aqueous Mounting Technics

Aqueous mounts—sections or whole mounts—are removed from the water, placed on a slide and covered with a drop of mounting medium. The cover glass, held in a horizontal position, is placed directly on the medium. Do not drop it from a slanted position. By the former method, the object can be kept centered and not carried to one side. In many cases it is not necessary to press the cover glass into place; its own weight is sufficient. The sections or objects are not attached to the slides and too much pressure may result in disarranged and broken material.

The Two-cover Glass Method

The material is mounted out of glycerol into glycerol jelly between two cover glasses, one of which is smaller than the other. Clean away excess jelly and air dry overnight. Invert the pair of cover glasses on a drop of resinous medium, such as Permount or Piccolyte, on a slide. This will permanently seal the mount, and it can be treated like any resin mount.

Ringing Slides

If the mountant contains a volatile substance like water and the slides are to be rendered relatively permanent, the cover glass must be sealed with a ringing material. Ringing cements are sold by supply houses, such as *General Biological's* "Turtox Slide Ringing Cement." Others easily obtainable are Duco cement, colorless nail polish, gold size and asphaltum. *Lustron 2020 (Monsanto Chemical Corp.)* dissolved in xylene can be used. Orange shellac in alcohol can ring a cover glass and then be covered with black asphalt varnish. Prepare the ringing shellac by dissolving flake orange shellac in 95% alcohol. It dissolves slowly, so keep the bottle in a warm place, and shake it occasionally. By adding 1 drop castor oil to each ounce of liquid, the ring will not dry out completely. (Needham, 1958)

Conger (1960) recommends *Dentists' Sticky Wax (Kerr Manufacturing Co., Detroit, Mich.).* It is solid and slightly tacky at room temperature, but flows easily when melted. It adheres well and does not leak, but will crack off cleanly if frozen with dry ice or liquid air. Good for acetocarmine preparations.

A firm and reasonably permanent ringing cement is cover glass cement "Kronig" from Riedel-de-Häen AG, Seelze-Hannover, Germany. At present it is not handled by American importers, but it can be purchased from George T. Gurr, London.

For temporary mounts, melted paraffin can be used to ring a cover glass, but it is susceptible to temperature damage and will crack away from the cover. It, therefore, is not recommended for slides subject to hard usage and the passage of time.

If the cover glasses are round, a turntable rotating on a steel pin or ball bearing facilitates the ringing operation. (*Watson and Sons, London*) The turntable spins rapidly and, with the ringing cement on a brush, a neat seal can be made by following concentric guide lines.

Chapter 12

Hematoxylin
Staining

SUBSTITUTES AND COUNTERSTAINS

Single Solutions

Delafield's Hematoxylin (CARLTON, 1947)

Dissolve 4 gm. hematoxylin in 25 ml. absolute ethyl alcohol. Mix gradually into 400 ml. ammonia alum, $Al_2(SO_4)_3(NH_4)_2SO_4 \cdot 24H_2O$, saturated aqueous (approximately 1 part alum to 11 parts distilled water). Leave exposed to light in a flask with a cotton plug for 3–5 days. Filter. Add to the filtrate, 100 ml. glycerine and 100 ml. methyl alcohol. Ripen for at least 6 weeks. The ripened solution will keep for years in a stoppered bottle.

Ehrlich's Hematoxylin (GURR, 1956)

hematoxylin	2.0 gm.
ammonia alum, $Al_2(SO_4)_3(NH_4)_2SO_4 \cdot 24H_2O$ . .	3.0 gm.
alcohol, methyl or ethyl	100.0 ml.
glycerol	100.0 ml.
distilled water	100.0 ml.

Ripens in 6–8 weeks, or may be ripened for immediate use with 2.4 gm. sodium iodate.

Add 10 ml. glacial acetic acid. Keeps for years.

Harris' Hematoxylin (MALLORY, 1944)

Dissolve 1.0 gm. hematoxylin in 10 ml. ethyl alcohol. Dissolve 20 gm. potassium or ammonia alum, $Al_2(SO_4)_3K_2SO_4 \cdot 24H_2O$ or $Al_2(SO_4)_3$ $(NH_4)_2SO_4 \cdot 24H_2O$, in 200 ml. water and boil. Add hematoxylin and boil $\frac{1}{2}$ minute. Add 0.5 gm. mercuric oxide. Cool rapidly. Add few drops of glacial acetic acid to keep away metallic luster and brighten nuclear structure. Does not keep longer than a month or two.

Mayer's Hematoxylin (MALLORY, 1944)

Add 1 gm. hematoxylin to 1 liter distilled water. Heat gently and add 2 gm. sodium iodate and 50 gm. potassium alum, $Al_2(SO_4)_3K_2SO_4 \cdot 24H_2O$. Heat until dissolved and add 1 gm. citric acid and 50 gm. chloral hydrate. Preferably ripen for 6–8 weeks, but can be used within 1–2 weeks.

Papamiltiades Hematoxylin (1953)

hematoxylin, 1% aqueous	100.0 ml.
aluminum sulfate, 5% aqueous	50.0 ml.
zinc sulfate, 5% aqueous	25.0 ml.
potassium iodide, 4% aqueous	25.0 ml.
glacial acetic acid	8.0 ml.
glycerol	25.0 ml.

Ready for immediate use; keeps approximately 2 months.

Phosphotungstic Acid Hematoxylin (LIEB, 1948)

phosphotungstic acid	10.0 gm.
hematoxylin	0.05 gm.
red mercuric oxide	0.025–0.05 gm.
hydrogen peroxide	2.0 ml.
distilled water	500.0 ml.

Dissolve hematoxylin in a little water with heat. Dissolve phosphotungstic acid in rest of water with heat; add hematoxylin solution. Bring to boil. Cautiously add mercuric oxide, and remove from flame. Cool. Add hydrogen peroxide. Ready for use in 5–7 days; should be brownish red in color.

Double Solutions

Weigert's Iron Hematoxylin (MALLORY, 1944)

SOLUTION A.

iron chloride, $FeCl_2$, 29% aqueous	4.0 ml.
distilled water	95.0 ml.
hydrochloric acid (sp.gr. 1.88–1.92, 37–38% HCl)	1.0 ml.

SOLUTION B.

hematoxylin	1.0 gm.
95% ethyl alcohol	100.0 ml.

Mix equal parts of *A* and *B*. This is best prepared each time, but will keep for 7–8 days once mixed.

Groat's Variation of Weigert's Hematoxylin (1949) (a single solution)

distilled water	50.0 ml.
sulfuric acid (sp.gr. 1.84, 94% H_2SO_4)	0.8 ml.
ferric alum, $Fe_2(SO_4)_3(NH_4)_2SO_4 \cdot 24H_2O$	1.0 gm.
95% ethyl alcohol	50.0 ml.
hematoxylin	0.5 gm.

Mix in order given at room temperature. Filter. Groat recommends his solution as better than Weigert's; it stains well within 10 minutes.

Lillie's Variation of Weigert's Hematoxylin (LILLIE AND EARLE, 1939A)

SOLUTION A.

ferric alum, $Fe_2(SO_4)_3(NH_4)_2SO_4 \cdot 24H_2O$	20.0 gm.
distilled water	200.0 ml.

SOLUTION B.

hematoxylin	2.0 gm.
absolute methyl alcohol	60.0 ml.
glycerol	60.0 ml.

Janssen's Hematoxylin (LILLIE AND EARLE, 1939A)

SOLUTION A.

ferric alum, $Fe_2(SO_4)_3(NH_4)_2SO_4 \cdot 24H_2O$	15.0 gm.
ferrous sulfate, $FeSO_4 \cdot H_2O$	15.0 gm.
distilled water	100.0 ml.

SOLUTION B.

hematoxylin	1.0 gm.
95% ethyl alcohol	50.0 ml.
glycerol	50.0 ml.

Mix *A* and *B* in equal amounts. Can be kept unchanged for several months, but if solution has turned brown, it is no longer usable. Keeps better than Weigert's.

Hansen's Iron Trioxyhaematin (PANTIN, 1946)

SOLUTION A.

ferric alum, $Fe_2(SO_4)_3(NH_4)_2SO_4 \cdot 24H_2O$	10.0 gm.
ammonium sulfate	1.4 gm.
distilled water	150.0 ml.

SOLUTION B.

hematoxylin	1.6 gm.
distilled water	75.0 ml.

Dissolve both solutions with gentle heat. Cool. Pour solution *B* in a porcelain evaporating dish. Add *A*, stirring constantly. Heat slowly without stirring just to boiling point. Cool rapidly by floating dish on cold water. A deep violet color turns brown. Filter into stoppered bottle with little air space above solution. Keeps 6–8 months, but if it develops a green sheen it is unsatisfactory. Can be used progressively or regressively.

Double Solutions, Never Mixed Before Use

Heidenhain's Iron Hematoxylin

SOLUTION A.

ferric alum, $Fe_2(SO_4)_3(NH_4)_2SO_4 \cdot 24H_2O$	4.0 gm.
distilled water	100.0 ml.

Keep in refrigerator to prevent precipitation on sides of bottle.

SOLUTION B.

hematoxylin	10.0 gm.
95% ethyl alcohol	100.0 ml.

Let stand until a deep wine-red color; 4–5 months is not too long. Add 4–5 ml. of this stock solution to 100 ml. distilled water; this gives a practically aqueous solution and is already ripe. Saturated aqueous lithium carbonate—3 drops—added to the working solution improves color.

Never mix *A* and *B*. *A* is used as a mordant solution, and precedes *B*.

Mallory's Iron Chloride Hematoxylin (1944)

SOLUTION A.

iron chloride, $FeCl_2$	5.0 gm.
distilled water	100.0 ml.

SOLUTION B.

hematoxylin	0.5 gm.
distilled water	100.0 ml.

Prepare fresh each time. These solutions are never mixed. *Rawlins and Takahashi (1947)* say that bubbling air through hematoxylin solutions ripens them more rapidly. American hematoxylin solutions may ripen in 2–3 weeks. *Hance and Green (1959)* ripen solutions even more rapidly by bubbling oxygen from a tank into the bottom of a container of hematoxylin.

Testing Hematoxylin Solutions

Add several drops of the solution to *tap* (not distilled) water. If it turns bluish purple immediately it is still satisfactory, but if it changes slowly, stays reddish or brownish, it has weakened or broken down and should be discarded.

Substitutes for Hematoxylin Solutions

Gallocyanin

gallocyanin	0.15 gm.
chrome alum, $Cr_2(SO_4)_3K_2SO_4 \cdot 24H_2O$ 5%	
aqueous	100.0 ml.

Boil 2–3 minutes. Filter. Keeps about a week, then deteriorates slowly. An iron lake may be prepared by substituting 5% aqueous iron alum for the chrome alum. (*Proescher and Arkush, 1928*)

Hematein (Hemalum) (KORNHAUSER, 1930)

hematein	0.5 gm.
95% ethyl alcohol	10.0 ml.

Grind hematein with alcohol in glass mortar;
Add to potassium alum, $Al_2(SO_4)_3K_2SO_4 \cdot 24H_2O$

5% aqueous	500.0 ml.

Immediately ready for use.

Counterstains for Hematoxylin, Gallocyanin and Hematein

Eosin

eosin Y, C.I. 45380	1.0 gm.
70% ethyl alcohol	1000.0 ml.
glacial acetic acid	5.0 ml.

Dilute with equal volume of 70% alcohol for use and add 2–3 drops of acetic acid.

Eosin (PUTT'S, 1948)

eosin Y, C.I. 45380	1.0 gm.
potassium dichromate	0.5 gm.
saturated aqueous picric acid	10.0 ml.
absolute ethyl alcohol	10.0 ml.
distilled water	80.0 ml.
glacial acetic acid (optional)	1 drop

Eosin-Orange G

1% eosin Y, C.I. 45380, in 95% ethyl alcohol	10.0 ml.
orange G, C.I. 16230, saturated solution in 95% ethyl alcohol (approximately 0.5 gm. per 100 ml.	5.0 ml.
95% ethyl alcohol	45.0 ml.

Other Acceptable Counterstains

1. Acid fuchsin, C.I. 42685, 5% aqueous (slightly acidified improves stain). If overstained, rinse with tap water.

2. Orange *G*, C.I. 16230, saturated in 95% ethyl alcohol.
3. Van Gieson or substitute, page 165.
4. Bordeaux red, C.I. 16180, 1% aqueous.
5. Biebrich scarlet, C.I. 26905, 1% aqueous, a good counterstain.
6. Additional "eosins"
    a. Eosin *Y*, C.I. 45380, 0.1–0.5% in 95% ethyl alcohol.
    b. Erythrosin *B*, C.I. 45430, 0.1–0.5% in 95% ethyl alcohol.
    c. Phloxine *B*, C.I. 45410, 0.5% aqueous, plus a few drops of acetic acid, page 229.
7. Congo red, C.I. 22120, 0.5% aqueous.
8. Light green *SF*, yellowish, C.I. 42095, 0.2–0.3% in 95% ethyl alcohol.
9. Aniline blue *W.S.*, C.I. 42780, pages 147, 149, 150, 160.
10. Fast green *FCF*, C.I. 42053, similar to light green or aniline blue.

Hematoxylin Staining Procedures

Delafield's (or Harris) Hematoxylin

Progressive Method

FIXATION: any general fixative or one specific for nuclear detail.

SOLUTIONS:
   Hematoxylin, page 124.
   Counterstain, page 129.

PROCEDURE: The slides are passed through a "down" series of jars, a process often termed **running down** slides to water (or **hydration**) because a series of alcohols of decreasing strength is used. (From left to right, top row of Fig. 26) Never at any time during this procedure allow the slides to dry.

1. xylene (or toluene) .... 2–3 minutes or longer.

   (2 changes may prove profitable to insure complete removal of paraffin.)

2. absolute alcohol .... 2–3 minutes or longer.
3. 95% alcohol .... 2–3 minutes or longer.
4. 70% alcohol .... 2–3 minutes or longer.

   If mercuric chloride was absent from fixative, skip steps 5 through 7 and proceed into step 8.

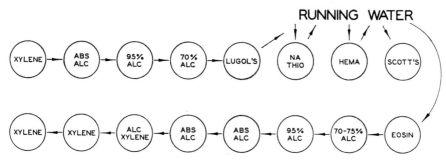

Figure 26. *A suggested arrangement of staining jars. An alternate arrangement can include two jars of xylene in the "down series" (left to right) when many slides are being stained. An absolute alcohol-xylene in "up series" (right to left) is optional.*

5. Lugol's solution (page 410) 3 minutes.
6. running water . . . . 3 minutes.
7. 5% sodium thiosulfate, Na$_2$
   S$_2$O$_3$ . . . . 2–3 minutes.
8. running water . . . . 3–5 minutes.
9. hematoxylin, Delafields's . . . 2–5 minutes, check after 1 minute
   for stain intensity. Fresh solutions stain faster than old ones. If
   not dark enough, return slides to stain. Rinse off stain in tap water before checking under microscope. If slide becomes too dark,
   convert to regressive type of stain, page 000.

10. running water . . . . 3–5 minutes.
11. Scott's solution (page 412) . 3 minutes.
12. running water . . . . 3–5 minutes.
13. counterstain . . . . 1 or more minutes, depending on
    stain used.

Transfer slides through "up" series, termed **running up** slides (or
dehydration) using a series of alcohols of increasing strength. Steps
14 and 15 can control intensity of counterstain. Carefully watch timing in these solutions. (From right to left, bottom row, Fig. 26)

14. 70% alcohol . . . . 1 or more dips.
15. 95% alcohol . . . . few dips.
16. absolute alcohol . . . . 3 minutes or longer.
17. absolute alcohol . . . . 2–3 minutes or longer.
18. absolute alcohol-xylene (1:1)
    optional . . . . 2–3 minutes or longer.

19. xylene .... 2–3 minutes or longer.
20. xylene .... 2–3 minutes or longer.
21. mounting medium; keep sections moist with xylene during this process. They must not dry. Add cover glass, page 115.

RESULTS:

nuclei—deep blue

cytoplasmic structures—pink, rose, etc., depending on counterstain

COMMENTS:

1. Slides may be left in higher alcohols and xylene longer than scheduled (indicated by "or longer"), but do not leave them indefinitely in any solutions weaker than 80 or 95% alcohol. Lower alcohols and water can loosen the sections from the albumen.
2. Isopropyl alcohol can be substituted for ethyl alcohol in this schedule, but cannot be used as a stain solvent.
3. Two to five minutes for Delafield's (step 9) is an approximate time only. This may have to be varied according to the tissue used. Tissues can be individualistic, often due to the type of fixative employed on them, and a certain amount of trial and error may be required to develop the exact timing schedule.
4. The cause of some difficulties can be problematical. Poor staining can result from improper fixation, leaving gross tissues too long in alcohol or iodine, faulty processing during preparation for embedding, or careless handling of the slides in preparation for staining. In many instances no amount of trial and error will produce a perfect stain. The only correctable faults are those made during deparaffinization and hydration of the slides and the slides should be reversed through the solutions, back to xylene. Change to fresh solutions and try again.
5. Sometimes too many slides have been taken through the fluids and they are contaminated. If as many as 20–40 slides are being stained, use two changes of xylene in step 1 and follow step 20 with a third change. Prevent further contamination by draining slides properly. On removing them from a solution, touch the edges against the inner surface of the staining jar, and then against paper toweling. But do not be too thorough and let the slides dry. Merely drain off excess liquid.
6. Hematoxylin staining must be left in a "blued" condition. The original pinkish color of the hematoxylin, like Delafield's, must be converted to a blue color by alkalinity. In the progressive method this is accomplished in running water to remove excess dye and start the

bluing action. Then use Scott's solution (step 11), a couple of drops of ammonia in a final wash, or a weak solution of sodium bicarbonate, to insure teh alkaline condition. In the regressive method (below) the same applies, and as a precaution against neutralization caused by carrying one solution over into the other (step 5), after several exchanges of slides, add a drop or two of acid and base to them. If there is any pinkness left in the nuclei, they are not adequately blued.

Regressive Method

PROCEDURE:

1. Deparaffinize and run slides down (hydrate) to water, removing $HgCl_2$ if present.
2. Stain in Delafield's hematoxylin, until slides are well overstained: 15–20 minutes.
3. Wash in running water: 3–5 minutes.
4. Transfer to 70% alcohol.
5. Destain in 0.5% (app.) HCl (2–3 drops in 60.0 ml. of 70% alcohol) few seconds. Remove to 70% alcohol with drop of ammonia added until sections turn blue. Examine under microscope. If nuclei are too dark, repeat above procedure. When nuclei stand out sharply blue against colorless background, blue slides thoroughly in alkaline solution: 3–5 minutes.
6. Transfer to 70% alcohol.
7. Counterstain.
8. Dehydrate as for progressive staining.
9. Clear and mount.

RESULTS:

nuclei—deep blue, sharper than in the progressive method
other elements—colors of counterstain

Mayer's Hematoxylin

FIXATION: any general fixative or one specific for nuclear detail.

SOLUTIONS:

Hematoxylin, page 125.
Counterstains, page 129.

PROCEDURE:

1. Deparaffinize and run slides down (hydrate) to water, removing $HgCl_2$ if present.

2. Stain in Mayer's hematoxylin: 11 minutes.
3. Wash in running water: 3 minutes.
4. Blue in Scott's solution: 3 minutes.
5. Wash in running water: 3–5 minutes.
6. Counterstain.
7. Dehydrate quickly through 70 and 95% alcohols.
8. Finish dehydration, absolute alcohol.
9. Clear and mount.

RESULTS:

nuclei—deep blue
other elements—colors of counterstain

Heidenhain's Iron Hematoxylin

FIXATION: any general fixative, preferably one containing $HgCl_2$.

SOLUTIONS:

Hematoxylin and iron alum, page 127.
Counterstains, page 129.

PROCEDURE:

1. Deparaffinize and run slides down (hydrate) to water, removing $HgCl_2$.
2. Mordant in 4% iron alum: 15–30 minutes (or overnight, see comments below).
3. Wash in running water: 5 minutes.
4. Stain in hematoxylin: 15–30 minutes (or overnight).
5. Wash in running water: 5 minutes.
6. Destain in 2% aqueous iron alum or saturated aqueous picric acid (see comments below) until nuclei stand out sharp and clear against colorless background. Dip slides in water containing couple of drops of ammonia before examining them. *Warning:* too much ammonia will loosen sections.
7. Wash in running water: 15–30 minutes or longer.
8. Counterstain, if desired.
9. Run slides up through alcohols (dehydrate), clear and mount.

RESULTS:

nuclei—blue black to black
muscle striations—blue-grey
other elements—colors of counterstain, or very light grey to colorless if no counterstain used

COMMENTS:

The shorter staining schedule produces blue-black nuclei and the overnight staining a truer black. The latter is recommended for mitochondria. Picric acid usually perfects a more sharply differentiated nucleus than destaining with iron alum. Prolonged destaining in the latter case can leave a tan or yellow tinge in the cytoplasm. Yellow color left in the tissue after picric acid is due to insufficient washing following the destaining. Striations of muscle and some protozoan structures are better differentiated by iron alum. After either method thorough washing is essential or the sections will continue to destain slowly and fade after a time. (Picric acid destaining, *Tuan, 1930*)

The destaining agents act both as an acid and an oxidizer, reacting in two ways: (1) as an acid they extract stain faster from the cytoplasm than from the nucleus; and (2) as an oxidizer they bleach the stain uniformly. If an acid is used alone, the staining of the nuclei can be favored, and if the oxidizer is used alone, the staining of the cytoplasm can be enhanced.

Hutner (1934) recommends for nuclei:
1. Mordant in 4% iron alum: 1 hour.
2. Stain hematoxylin: 1 hour.
3. Destain in saturated aqueous picric acid.
4. Wash and blue by adding 1–2 drops ammonia to 70% alcohol.

Hutner recommends for cytoplasm:
1. Mordant in iron alum: 30 minutes.
2. Stain in hematoxylin: 30 minutes.
3. Destain in freshly made 95% alcohol 2 parts, Merk's superoxol (30% H_2O_2) 1 part.
4. Rinse in 1 change 70% alcohol, 10 minutes.

For brevity, intermediate steps were omitted in the above. Oxidizer and acid can be combined to approximate iron alum destaining effects:
0.25% HCl in 95% alcohol, 2 parts; Superoxol, 1 part.
Wash in 70% alcohol and blue.

Iron Hematoxylin GROAT'S SINGLE SOLUTION (1949)

FIXATION: any general fixative, preferably containing $HgCl_2$.

SOLUTIONS:
Hematoxylin, page 126.
Counterstains, page 129.

PROCEDURE:

1. Deparaffinize and run slides down (hydrate) to water, removing $HgCl_2$.
2. Stain in Groat's iron hematoxylin: approximately 10 minutes.
3. Rinse off excess stain with running water: 10 minutes.
4. Counterstain, if desired.
5. Dehydrate, clear, and mount.

RESULTS:

nuclei—black

other elements—color of counterstain

COMMENTS:

The 10-minute timing is approximate: check under the microscope for depth of color. If the background is too grey it may be decolorized in:

distilled water	50.0 ml.
95% alcohol	50.0 ml.
sulfuric acid (sp.gr. 1.84, 95.5–96.5% H_2SO_4)	0.18. ml.

Follow by neutralizing in:

distilled water	50.0 ml.
95% alcohol	50.0 ml.
sodium bicarbonate	0.5 gm.

Phosphotungstic Acid Hematoxylin (AS MODIFIED BY LIEB 1948)

FIXATION: any general fixative, preferably containing $HgCl_2$. Lieb suggests if tissue is formalin fixed, mordant sections before staining in saturated aqueous mercuric chloride, rinse and treat with Lugol's.

SOLUTIONS:

Hematoxylin, page 125.

Potassium permanganate, 0.5%

potassium permanganate	0.5 gm.
distilled water	100.0 ml.

Oxalic acid, 2%

oxalic acid	2.0 gm.
distilled water	100.0 ml.

Iron alum, 4%, page 127.

PROCEDURE:

1. Deparaffinize and run slides down (hydrate) to water, removing $HgCl_2$.
2. Oxidize in potassium permanganate, freshly prepared: 5 minutes.
3. Wash in running water: 5 minutes.
4. Bleach in oxalic acid: 5 minutes.
5. Wash in running water: 5 minutes; follow with rinse in distilled water.
6. Mordant in iron alum: 1 hour.
7. Wash out excess alum in running water 10 minutes or longer, rinse in distilled water.
8. Stain in phosphotungstic acid hematoxylin: 2–24 hours. Usually complete in 2–3 hours, rarely requires overnight.
9. Transfer directly to 95% alcohol: brief rinse.
10. Dehydrate, absolute alcohol; watch that elements stained reddish brown are not destained.
11. Finish dehydration in isopropyl alcohol (99%), 2 changes: 3 minutes each.
12. Clear and mount.

RESULTS:

nuclei, mitochondria, centrioles, fibrin, fibroglia, myoglia and neuroglia fibrils, and contractile elements of striated muscle—blue collagen, reticulum, elastin, cartilage and bone—yellowish to brown red

COMMENTS:

Mullen and McCarter (1941) use a chromium-chloride mordant after formalin fixation: Deparaffinize and hydrate to water, mordant for 2 hours or longer in

chromium chloride, $CrCl_3$	5.0 gm.
distilled water	100.0 ml.
glacial acetic acid	5.0 ml.

Good for several weeks. After this mordanting, the staining will be as brilliant as following Zenker fixation.

Weigert's Iron Hematoxylin. (MALLORY 1944; JANSSEN AND LILLIE)

FIXATION: any general fixative or one specific for nuclei.

SOLUTIONS:

Hematoxylin, page 126.
Counterstains, page 129.

PROCEDURE:
1. Deparaffinize and hydrate slides to water, remove $HgCl_2$.
2. Stain in Weigert's hematoxylin: 3–5 minutes or longer.
3. Wash, running water: 5 minutes.
4. Counterstain.
5. Dehydrate, clear, and mount.

RESULTS:
nuclei—black
other elements—color of counterstain

COMMENTS: This is used progressively, check results under microscope.

Mallory's Iron Chloride Hematoxylin (1944)

FIXATION: any general fixative, or one specific for nuclei.

SOLUTIONS:
Ferric chloride, page 128.
Hematoxylin, page 128.
Counterstains, page 129.
Ferric chloride for destaining (0.25%): dilute 5 ml. of the 5% stock solution (above) with 95 ml. distilled water.

PROCEDURE:
1. Deparaffinize and hydrate slides to water, remove $HgCl_2$.
2. Mordant in ferric chloride: 1 hour or longer.
3. Wash in running water: 5 minutes.
4. Stain in hematoxylin: 1 hour or longer.
5. Wash in running water: 3–5 minutes.
6. Destain in ferric chloride, 0.25%; agitate slides, check under microscope.
7. Wash thoroughly, running water: 10–15 minutes.
8. Counterstain, if desired.
9. Dehydrate, clear, and mount.

RESULTS:
nuclei—deep blue
other elements—color of counterstain

Hematoxylin Substitute Procedures

Gallocyanin (ROMEIS, 1948)

Gallocyanin is an excellent substitute for hematoxylin and can be used in most procedures designed for the latter dye. The solution is made in a few minutes and ready for immediate use; also an iron lake can be prepared. No differentiation is required, and it is better than hematoxylin for tissues of the central nervous system. It can replace thionin for ganglia and glia cells, but not for myelin sheaths. It is good for negri bodies. The preferred fixatives are aceto-formol, Zenker's (acetic or formol) or formalin—fixatives which preserve chromophilic substance.

SOLUTIONS: page 128.

PROCEDURE:
1. Deparaffinize and hydrate to water.
2. Leave in stain overnight, or 3 hours at 56°C.
3. Wash thoroughly and proceed to counterstain.
4. Dehydrate, clear, and mount.

RESULTS:
nuclei—blue

Hematein (Hemalum). (KORNHAUSER, 1930).

FIXATION: any general fixative, preferably containing $HgCl_2$.

SOLUTIONS:
Hemalum, page 129.
Counterstains, page 129.

PROCEDURE:
1. Deparaffinize and hydrate slides down to water, remove $HgCl_2$.
2. Stain hemalum, progressively: about 5 minutes.
3. Wash in running water: 5–10 minutes.
4. Counterstain.
5. Dehydrate, clear, and mount.

RESULTS:
nuclei—blue
other elements—color of counterstain

Red Nuclear Staining

Darrow Red. (POWERS ET AL., 1960).

FIXATION: any general fixative.

SOLUTION:
Darrow Red:

darrow red [1] .... 50.0 mg.
0.2M glacial acetic acid (*p*H2.7) .... 200.0 ml.

Boil gently: 10 minutes. Cool and filter. Stable for 1 month.

PROCEDURE:
1. Use frozen sections in water, or deparaffinize paraffin sections and hydrate to water.
2. Stain in darrow red: 20–30 minutes.
3. Rinse in distilled water.
4. Differentiate and dehydrate through 50%, 70%, and 95% alcohol, not so slowly as to remove too much dye from nuclei, but just to decolorize background.
5. Complete dehydration in n-butyl alcohol; clear, and mount.

RESULTS:
nuclei—red
other elements—depending on other stains applied

COMMENTS:
This is a good nuclear stain for contrast with blue cytoplasmic stains—following luxol fast blue for example. It cannot be used with nitrocellulose because the medium stains with Darrow red.

Scarba Red (SLIDDERS ET AL., 1958)

FIXATION: any general fixative.

SOLUTIONS:
Scarba red:

melted phenol (carbolic acid) .... 2.0 gm.
neutral red .... 1.0 gm.
Mix thoroughly, allow to cool, dissolve in:
95% ethyl alcohol .... 15.0 ml.
Add:
2% aniline in water .... 85.0 ml.
glacial acetic acid .... 1.0–3.0 ml.

Mix well and filter. Keeps for at least 6 months.

[1] Matheson Coleman and Bell.

Differentiator:

70% ethyl alcohol	85.0 ml.
formalin	15.0 ml.
glacial acetic acid	15.0 drops.

PROCEDURE:

1. Deparaffinize and hydrate slides to water (remove $HgCl_2$ if present).
2. Stain in scarba red: 5 minutes.
3. Rinse in distilled water.
4. Transfer to 70% alcohol: 2–3 minutes.
5. Differentiate until nuclei are clear and sharp against colorless background.
6. Dehydrate, 95% and absolute alcohol.
7. Clear in xylene and mount.

RESULTS:

chromatin and calcium—red

SPECIFIC
STAINING
METHODS

PART II

SPECIFIC
STAINING
METHODS

Chapter **13**

Connective
Tissue

Connective tissue, so named because its chief function is to connect the other tissues of the body, also provides support for these tissues. Connective tissue is far too complex to discuss at any length in this type of book, but a few terms will be covered briefly.

Stroma is a term referring to the supporting tissues in an organ; the **parenchyma** is composed of the cells that perform the function of the organ.

Collagenic fibers (*collagen*) have tensile strength (*tendons*); they may be single or aggregate in bundles, and they do not branch.

Reticular fibers are delicate and often connected to and supported by collagenic fibers. (For silver methods, see page 179.) Reticular fibers, often forming dense networks, support cells, capillaries, nerve fibers and other tissue units, and form parts of **basement membranes** (intercellular substance lying between epithelial membranes and their supporting connective tissue).

Elastic fibers are long and narrow and are not composed of fibrils, but are homogeneous. They have the ability to stretch and are located in such places as the walls of blood vessels or in the respiratory system.

Areolar tissue lies between muscles and fasciae and contains both collagenic and elastic fibers embedded in a ground substance.

The **ground substance** is an amorphous kind of material that lies around fibrous intercellular substances; thus the fibers are seldom

145

found by themselves. In most stains ground substance is uncolored, but it contains mucopolysaccharides and can be shown by metachromatic staining (page 280) .

Hyalin(e) is a descriptive noun or adjective meaning glassy. A substance so described is a translucent, refractile albuminoid. **Amyloid** deposits (amorphous material accumulating in intercellular spaces in certain pathologic conditions) is said to be hyaline in nature. Old collagen can become hyaline.

Fibrin (page 230) is formed from fibrinogen (a protein in blood plasma) and as it forms develops a mesh of fibers at the site of cut blood vessels.

Mast cells are numerous in areolar and other types of connective tissue. Staining of mast cells has been included with technics for cytoplasmic elements (page 276) because of their characteristic granules. The cytoplasm of mast cells is stuffed with these granules that usually are stained metachromatically.

Plasma cells are more common in **hemopoietic** (concerned with blood formation) tissue than in loose connective tissue and if numerous in the latter appear to be associated with low-grade inflammation.

Keratin is a horny material formed by the fusing together of the surface cells of dry epithelial membranes. (*Reference:* Ham. 1957)

Mallory Staining

Mallory's Triple Connective Tissue Stain

Innumerable modifications of this method appear from time to time in the literature, particularly for the use of phosphomolybdic and phosphotungstic acid. Experiments by *Holde* and *Isler* (*1958*) support the need for phosphomolybdic acid if specific staining of connective tissue is desired. The acid diminishes the background and nuclear staining, leaving only the connective tissue stained with aniline blue. They feel that the staining property of connective tissue is due to the presence of the acid on the fibers. *Baker* (*1958*) suggests that phosphomolybdic acid acts as a "colorless acid dye" in the tissue, chiefly on **collagen**. It acts as a dye excluder with acid dyes such as acid fuchsin, excluding them from collagen. Then the aniline blue stains the collagen selectively, but is excluded from other tissues. Phosphomolybdic acid should not be termed a mordant, since it also opposes the action of aniline blue. Without phosphomolybdic acid present, aniline blue stains more strongly and with very little selectivity. As to the use of phosphotungstic acid, it may be of interest to recall that certain tissue elements react more specifically to certain metals than to others; collagen to molybdenum, and fibroglia, myoglia, neuroglia and epithelial fibers to tungsten. *Lillie (1952)* writes that phosphotungstic acid intensifies plasma staining and phosphomolybdic acid the fiber staining. The acids may be used separately or together depending on the final desired effect.

Oxalic acid is often used. *Mallory (1944)* claims that it makes the aniline blue stain more rapidly and intensely. *Baker (1958)* seems to agree when he suggests that oxalic acid lowers the *p*H, seeming thereby to aid the staining of aniline blue, also of orange G.

No polychroming or metachroming takes place in the combination of dyes; they react orthochromatically in varying intensities of their own colors. In Mallory's combination of stains, aniline blue (acidic) stains connective tissue and cartilage; orange G (acidic) stains the blood cells, myelin and muscle; acid fuchsin (acidic) stains the rest of the tissue (including the nuclei) in grades of pink and red. This is not, however, an efficient method for staining nuclei and they will fade in a few years. Modifications of Mallory's using basic fuchsin, carmine or azocarmine result in more permanent nuclear staining, since the basic stain reacts more reliably than the acidic one with the nuclei. The method also may be preceded with hematoxylin staining for a brilliant permanent nuclear stain.

The final staining may be followed by an acetic acid wash (0.5–1%) for 3–5 minutes or longer, producing more transparent sections without altering the color.

Method (PANTIN, 1946)

FIXATION: any general fixative, preferably containing $HgCl_2$.

SOLUTIONS:

Mallory I:

acid fuchsin, C.I. 42685	1.0	gm.
distilled water	100.0	ml.

Phosphomolybdic acid:

phosphomolybdic acid	1.0	gm.
distilled water	100.0	ml.

Mallory II:

aniline blue, *WS*, C.I. 42780	0.5	gm.
orange G, C.I. 16230	2.0	gm.
distilled water	100.0	ml.

PROCEDURE:

1. Deparaffinize and hydrate slides to water; remove $HgCl_2$. If $HgCl_2$ is absent from fixative, mordant in saturated aqueous $HgCl_2$, plus 5% glacial acetic acid: 10 minutes. Wash, treat with Lugol's and sodium thiosulfate, wash and rinse in distilled water.
2. Stain in Mallory I: 15 seconds.
3. Rinse in distilled water: 10 or more seconds, to differentiate reds.
4. Treat with phosphomolybdic acid: 1–5 minutes.
5. Rinse briefly in distilled water.
6. Stain in Mallory II: 2 minutes.
7. Rinse in distilled water.
8. Differentiate aniline blue in 90% ethyl alcohol.
9. Dehydrate in absolute alcohol, clear and mount.

RESULTS:

nuclei—red
muscle and some cytoplasmic elements—red to orange
nervous system—lilac
collagen—dark blue
mucus, connective tissue and hyaline substance—blue
chitin—red
yolk—yellow to orange
myelin and red blood cells—yellows and orange
dense cellular tissue (liver)—pink with red nuclei
bone matrix—red

COMMENTS:

From distilled water (step 7) the slides can be run through the "up" series of alcohols, thereby controlling the blue color. Aqueous-alcoholic solutions differentiate the amount of Mallory II left in the various parts of the tissue. After the slides have remained in the absolute alcohol for a couple of minutes they should have changed from a muddy purple to a clear blue and red. An acetic acid rinse, as mentioned (page 147), following step 7 contributes to the transparency of the sections.

For better nuclear detail, Mallory I can be preceded by alum hematoxylin staining. (Results: nuclei—blue)

Landrum and McFarlane (1940) recommend addition of celestin blue. Follow step 1 with:

(*a*) celestin blue: 2 minutes

celestin blue *B*, C.I. 51050	0.5 gm.
iron alum	5.0 gm.
distilled water	50.0 ml.
Dissolve alum in water, add celestin blue: boil 3 minutes;	
add glycerol	14.0 ml.

(*b*) hematoxylin: 2 minutes
(*c*) running water: 5 minutes
(*d*) proceed to step 2

Krichesky (*1931*) proposed the following for solution (Mallory) II.

A. aniline blue, *WS*, C.I. 42780	2.0 gm.
distilled water	100.0 ml.
B. orange *G*, C.I. 16230	1.0 gm.
distilled water	100.0 ml.
C. phosphomolybdic acid	1.0 gm.
distilled water	100.0 ml.

Keep solutions *A, B* and *C* in separate bottles because the mixture deteriorates on standing. When ready to use, mix equal parts of each.

Azan Stain, Mallory Heidenhain's (MODIFIED AFTER KONEFF, 1938)

FIXATION: Zenker-formol; other general fixatives fair, but following them is improved by mordanting slides overnight in 3% potassium dichromate.

SOLUTIONS:

Azocarmine:

azocarmine *G*, C.I. 50085	0.2–1.0 gm.
distilled water	100.0 ml.
glacial acetic acid	1.0 ml.

Boil azocarmine in water 5 minutes, cool, filter and add acetic acid.

Aniline alcohol:

aniline	1.0 ml.
85–90% ethyl alcohol	1000.0 ml.

Acid alcohol:

glacial acetic acid	1.0 ml.
90–95% ethyl alcohol	100.0 ml.

Phosphotungstic acid:

    phosphotungstic acid ....   5.0 gm.

    distilled water .... 100.0 ml.

Aniline blue stain:

    aniline blue, *WS*, C.I. 42780 ....   0.5 gm.

    orange *G*, C.I. 16230 ....   2.0 gm.

    oxalic acid ....   2.0 gm.

    distilled water .... 100.0 ml.

    5% phosphotungstic acid (above) ....   1.0 ml.

Acidulated water:

    glacial acetic acid ....   1.0 ml.

    distilled water .... 100.0 ml.

PROCEDURE:

1. Deparaffinize and hydrate slides down to water; remove $HgCl_2$.
2. (aniline alcohol: 45 minutes)[1]
3. (acid alcohol: 1–2 minutes)
4. Stain in azocarmine, 56°C: 1 hour. (2 hours) Check temperature carefully; if too high, azocarmine differentiates poorly.
5. Rinse in distilled water.
6. Differentiate in aniline alcohol. Check under microscope for brilliant red nuclei and very light red cytoplasm.
7. Treat with acid alcohol: 1–2 minutes.
8. Transfer to phosphotungstic acid: 2–3 hours. (4 hours)
9. Rinse in distilled water.
10. Stain in aniline blue solution: 1–2 hours. (4 hours)
11. Rinse in distilled water.
12. Treat with phosphotungstic acid: 3–5 minutes.
13. Rinse in distilled water.
14. Rinse in acidulated water: 1–2 minutes or longer.
15. Rinse in 70% alcohol: briefly dip.
16. Dehydrate 95% alcohol, several dips in each of 2 changes.
17. Dehydrate, absolute alcohol, clear and mount.

RESULTS:

nuclei—brilliant red

collagen and reticulum—blue

muscle—red and yellow

basophil cytoplasm—light blue

---

[1] For strikingly beautiful results, particularly for pituitary, Koneff's longer method is recommended. Changes in timing are indicated in parentheses.

acidophil cytoplasm—orange-red
chromophobes—colorless or light gray

COMMENTS:

The azan method is recommended particularly for pituitary and pancreas but also is outstanding for connective tissue. If a tissue does not "take" the azocarmine, it may be due to formalin content of the fixative. To correct this condition, mordant the sections overnight in 3% aqueous potassium dichromate.

Romeis (1948) suggests the substitution of acid alizarine blue for azocarmine; this shortens the time and does not require heat.

PROCEDURE:

1. Stain in acid alizarine blue: 5 minutes.

   aluminum sulfate, $Al_2(SO_4)_3$ .... 10.0 gm.
   acid alizarine blue, C.I. 58610 .... 0.5 gm.
   distilled water .... 100.0 ml.

   Bring to boil: 5–10 min. Let cool. Fill to 100 ml. with distilled water. Filter. Red violet color.
2. Wash, running water.
3. Treat with phosphotungstic or phosphomolybdic acid, 5% aqueous: 30 minutes.
4. Wash in distilled water.
5. Proceed to aniline blue stain.

RESULTS:

After phosphotungstic acid, the alizarine color turns red, stays in nuclei and muscles, but is removed from collagen.

After phosphomolybdic acid, the nuclei and muscle will be blue.

Mallory-Heidenhain Stain: Rapid One-Step Method (CASON, 1950)

FIXATION: any good general fixative.

SOLUTION:

Staining solution:

   distilled water .... 200.0 ml.
   Dissolve each of below before adding next stain:
   phosphotungstic acid .... 1.0 gm.
   orange G, C.I. 16230 .... 2.0 gm.
   aniline blue, *WS*, C.I. 42780 .... 1.0 gm.
   acid fuchsin, C.I. 42685 .... 3.0 gm.

Keeps for several months.

PROCEDURE:

1. Deparaffinize and hydrate slides to water, remove $HgCl_2$.
2. Stain: 5 minutes.
3. Wash in running water: 3–5 seconds.
4. Dehydrate rapidly, clear, and mount.

RESULTS:

collagen—blue
ground substance of cartilage and bones—shades of blue
mucus, amyloid, other hyaline substances—shades of blue
nuclei, fibroglia, myoglia, neuroglia fibrils, axis cylinders, fibrin—red
erythrocytes, myelin—yellow
elastin—pale pink or yellow

Trichrome Staining

Masson Trichrome Stain

Masson (1928), when he developed this method, called it a trichrome stain, although it included four dyes. Since then the trichrome name has been applied to many modifications of Masson's method using many combinations of different dyes.

FIXATION: any general fixative.

SOLUTIONS:

Iron alum:

ferric ammonium sulfate	4.0	gm.
distilled water	100.0	ml.

Masson *A:*

acid fuchsin, C.I. 42685 1% aqueous	10.0	ml.
ponceau de xylidine, C.I. 16150 1% aqueous	90.0	ml.
glacial acetic acid	1.0	ml.

Lillie (1940) suggests alternate stains for ponceau de xylidine: ponceau *2R*, nitazine yellow, Biebrich scarlet, azofuchsin *3B*, G and *4G*, Bordeaux red, chromotrope *2R*, chrysoidin, eosin *Y*, orange *G* and crocein.

Masson *B:*

phosphomolybdic acid, 1% aqueous (0.5 gm./ 50 ml. water)	50.0	ml.
phosphotungstic acid, 1% aqueous (0.5 gm./ 50 ml. water)	50.0	ml.

Masson *C:*

fast green *FCF*, C.I. 42053	2.5 gm.
distilled water	100.0 ml.
glacial acetic acid	2.5 ml.

Aniline blue can be substituted for fast green. If so, after staining with Masson *C* (step 11 below), extract excess stain for 5 minutes with 1% phosphomolybdic acid, aqueous, followed by a quick rinse in distilled water and then proceed with step 12, below.

Hematoxylin, see page 124.
Acetic acid rinse.

glacial acetic acid	1.0 ml.
distilled water	100.0 ml.

PROCEDURE:

1. Deparaffinize and hydrate slides to water. Remove $HgCl_2$. Mordant formalin-fixed tissue in saturated aqueous $HgCl_2$: 5 minutes. Wash, running water: 5 minutes. Treat with Lugol's and sodium thiosulfate.
2. Mordant with iron alum: $\frac{1}{2}$ hour at room temperature or 5 minutes at 40–50°C.
3. Wash in running water: 5 minutes.
4. Stain in hematoxylin (Delafield's or the like): $\frac{1}{2}$ hour, room temperature, or 5 minutes at 40–50°C.
5. Wash in running water: 5 minutes.
6. Differentiate in saturated aqueous picric acid.
7. Wash thoroughly, running water: 10–20 minutes.
8. Stain in Masson *A:* 5 minutes.
9. Rinse in distilled water.
10. Treat with Masson *B:* 10 minutes.
11. Stain in Masson *C:* 2–5 minutes.
12. Differentiate in acetic acid rinse: 1–2 minutes.
13. Dehydrate quickly 70% and 95% alcohol.
14. Dehydrate, absolute alcohol, 2 changes: 3 minutes each.
15. Clear and mount.

RESULTS:

nuclei—blue to blue-black
collagen, mucus—blue or green
cytoplasmic elements, keratin, muscle—reds

Masson Trichrome Stain, Modified (GURR, 1956)

FIXATION: any general fixative.

SOLUTIONS:
Iron alum:

ferric ammonium sulfate	4.0 gm.
distilled water	100.0 ml.

Hematoxylins, see page 124.
Acid fuchsin:

acid fuchsin, C.I. 42685	1.0 gm.
distilled water	100.0 ml.
glacial acetic acid	1.0 ml.

Ponceau de xylidine:

ponceau de xylidine, C.I. 16150	1.0 ml.
distilled water	100.0 ml.
glacial acetic acid	1.0 ml.

Fast green:

fast green *FCF*, C.I. 42053	2.0 gm.
distilled water	100.0 ml.
glacial acetic acid	2.0 ml.

Phosphomolybdic acid:

phosphomolybdic acid	1.0 gm.
distilled water	100.0 ml.

Acidic water:

glacial acetic acid	1.0 ml.
distilled water	100.0 ml.

PROCEDURE:
1. Deparaffinize and hydrate slides to water, remove $HgCl_2$. Mordant formalin-fixed tissue in saturated aqueous $HgCl_2$: 5 minutes. Wash in running water: 5 minutes. Treat with Lugol's and sodium thiosulfate.
2. Mordant in iron alum: $\frac{1}{2}$ hour.
3. Wash in running water: 5 minutes.
4. Stain in hematoxylin (Delafield's or like): $\frac{1}{2}$ hour.
5. Wash, running water: 5 minutes.
6. Differentiate in saturated aqueous picric acid.
7. Wash thoroughly in running water: 10 minutes or longer.
8. Stain in acid fuchsin: 5 minutes.

9. Rinse in distilled water until excess stain is removed. Check under microscope.
10. Stain in ponceau de xylidine: 1–5 minutes.
11. Rinse in tap water, control under microscope for proper intensity of acid fuchsin and ponceau de xylidine.
12. Differentiate in phosphomolybdic acid: 5 minutes.
13. No rinse, transfer directly into fast green: 2 minutes.
14. Differentiate fast green in acidic water and dehydrating alcohols.
15. Dehydrate in absolute alcohol, 2 changes: 3 minutes each.
16. Clear and mount.

RESULTS:

nuclei—deep mauve blue to black
cytoplasmic elements—varying shades of red and mauve
muscle—red
collagen, mucus—green

COMMENTS:

Among the many modifications of Masson's stain, this is one of the best, because it seems to offer good control of both red dyes by the use of two separate solutions. In most cases, the full 5 minutes in the acid fuchsin is advisable, but time in the ponceau de xylidine is not quite so critical.

Pollak's Rapid Method (1944)

FIXATION: any general fixative. Formalin-fixed tissues are improved by treating slides overnight with saturated aqueous $HgCl_2$.

SOLUTIONS:

Hematoxylins, see page 124.
Trichrome stain:

acid fuchsin, C.I. 42685	0.5 gm.
ponceau 2R, C.I. 16150	1.0 gm.
light green SF, yellowish C.I. 42095	0.45 gm.
orange G, C.I. 16230	0.75 gm.
phosphotungstic acid	1.5 gm.
phosphomolybdic acid	1.5 gm.
glacial acetic acid	3.0 ml.
50% ethyl alcohol up to	300.0 ml.

Add acetic acid to alcohol; split solution in 4 parts. Dissolve acid fuchsin and ponceau in one part; light green in the second part; orange G and phosphotungstic acid in the third part; and phosphomolybdic acid in the fourth part. Mix four solutions and filter. Keeps well.

Acidified water:

glacial acetic acid	0.2 ml.
distilled water	100.0 ml.

PROCEDURE:

1. Deparaffinize and hydrate slides to water; remove $HgCl_2$.
2. Stain in Mayer's hematoxylin: 10 minutes. (Pollak uses Weigert's: 10–20 minutes.)
3. Wash in running water: 10 minutes.
4. Stain in trichrome stain: 7 minutes.
5. Rinse briefly in distilled water.
6. Differentiate in acidified water: only a few seconds; check under microscope if necessary.
7. Dip a few times in 70% alcohol.
8. Dehydrate in 95% alcohol: several seconds in each of two changes.
9. Dehydrate, absolute alcohol, clear and mount.

RESULTS:

nuclei—dark blue
muscle, elastin—red
fibrin, calcium—purple
hyalin—pale blue
collagen, mucus—blue green

Gomori (1950B) Method

FIXATION: any general fixative. Formalin-fixed tissues are improved by treating slides overnight with saturated aqueous $HgCl_2$.

SOLUTIONS:

Hematoxylins, see page 124.
Trichrome mixture:

chromotrope *2R*, C.I. 16570	0.6 gm.
fast green *FCF*, C.I. 42053 or light green *SF*, C.I. 42095	0.3 gm.
phosphotungstic acid	0.6–0.7 gm.
glacial acetic acid	1.0 ml.
distilled water	100.0 ml.

Keeps indefinitely. Aged solutions stain less red and more green than fresh ones.

Acidic water:

    glacial acetic acid .... 0.2 ml.

    distilled water .... 100.0 ml.

PROCEDURE:

1. Deparaffinize and hydrate slides to water; remove $HgCl_2$.
2. Slightly overstain with any hematoxylin.
3. Wash in running water: 5 minutes.
4. Stain in trichrome mixture: 5–20 minutes.
5. Rinse briefly in distilled water to remove some of excess stain.
6. Rinse briefly in acidic water.
7. Rinse in 70% alcohol.
8. Dehydrate in 95% alcohol, 2 changes; be careful not to remove too much green.
9. Dehydrate, absolute alcohol, clear and mount.

RESULTS AND COMMENT

There have been a number of attempts to combine the azan and Masson methods in a quicker one. Gomori considered Pollak's as a disappointingly dull color scheme, lacking real red shades. Almost any combination of an acid triphenylmethane dye with a sulfonated azo dye in the presence of phosphomolybdic or phosphotungstic acid will give good results. The former favors the green and blue shades, the latter the reds. A short staining time produces more red and prolonged staining more green and blue. Rinsing in tap water weakens the reds.

If more red is desired—in muscle and epithelial fibers, for example—before staining treat with warm Bouin's 56–60°C: 2–5 minutes. Follow by washing until yellow color disappears.

The rinse in acetic acid does not change the colors, but makes them more delicate and transparent.

Lillie (1954B) says that Gomori's trichrome gives a rather diffuse and incomplete picture of the more finely fibrillar stroma, and the reticulum of the liver and spleen are difficult to discern.

The author has had good results with most of the trichrome methods and can only recommend that the selection of a routine stain will have to be made by each individual. All of the short trichrome methods offer clearer and sharper returns on thin (5–7 microns) sections than on thicker ones. For the latter, Mallory's, Masson, or Azan methods should be used.

Churg and Prado (1956) Method

FIXATION: mercuric chloride type excellent. Improve formalin fixation by treating slides overnight in saturated aqueous $HgCl_2$.

SOLUTIONS:

Crystal violet stain:

crystal violet, C.I. 42555	0.1 gm.
distilled water	100.0 ml.
glacial acetic acid	0.2 ml.

Acidic water:

glacial acetic acid	0.2 ml.
distilled water	100.0 ml.

Phosphomolybdic acid:

phosphomolybdic acid	1.0 gm.
distilled water	100.0 ml.

Chromotrope-aniline blue stain:

chromotrope *2R*, C.I. 16570	1.0 gm.
aniline blue *WS*, C.I. 42780	0.25 gm.
HCl, 0.02N (1.7 ml. conc. HCl in 998.3 ml. distilled water)	50.0 ml.

Dissolve aniline blue in acid with gentle heat. Cool and add chromotrope. Keeps well for months.

PROCEDURE:

1. Deparaffinize and hydrate slides to water. Remove $HgCl_2$.
2. Stain in crystal violet: 2–3 minutes.
3. Differentiate in acidic water: 3–45 seconds.
4. Rinse well in distilled water.
5. Treat with phosphomolybdic acid: 3–45 seconds.
6. Rinse in distilled water.
7. Stain in chromotrope-aniline blue: 2 minutes.
8. Rinse in distilled water.
9. Dehydrate quickly through 70% and 2 changes 95% alcohol.
10. Dehydrate, absolute alcohol, clear and mount.

RESULTS:

Formalin-fixed tissue without $HgCl_2$:

nuclei—purplish
cytoplasm—pale blue to pink

muscle—red
collagen, basement membrane—brilliant blue
fibrin, serum protein—red
red blood cells, keratin—bright red
colloid, hyalins—blue to purple to red

After HgCl₂:

elastic fibers and mucus—purple

Picro-Gomori Method (MENZIES, 1959)

FIXATION: mercuric chloride type best.

SOLUTIONS:
Hematoxylins, see page 124.
Orange G-picric acid:

orange *G*, C.I. 16230	1.0 gm
picric acid, saturated aqueous	100.0 ml.

Light green-chromotrope:

light green *SF*, yellowish, C.I. 42095	0.3 gm.
phosphotungstic acid	0.6 gm.
chromotrope *2R*, C.I. 16570	0.6 gm.
glacial acetic acid	1.0 ml.
distilled water	99.0 ml.

Acidic water:

glacial acetic acid	1.0 ml.
distilled water	100.0 ml.

PROCEDURE:
1. Deparaffinize and hydrate slides down to water. Remove HgCl₂.
2. Stain hematoxylin (Weigert's, Mayer's, etc.) for correct time depending on hematoxylin used.
3. Stain in orange G-picric acid: 1 minute.
4. Wash in running water until erythrocytes are yellow: 5–10 minutes.
5. Stain in light green-chromotrope: 2 minutes.
6. Sharpen stain in acidic water, 3 changes: 1 minute each.
7. Rinse in 70% alcohol.
8. Hydrate, clear and mount.

RESULTS:
erythrocytes—brilliant orange yellow
fibrin—orange red or red

smooth muscle—deep purplish red
epithelial cytoplasm—varies, red to green
collagen—clear green

COMMENTS:

This method gives excellent differentiation between smooth muscle, collagen and fibrin.

Koneff's Aniline Blue Stain (1936)

FIXATION: any general fixative, preferably containing $HgCl_2$.

SOLUTIONS:

Iron alum:

ferric ammonium sulfate	5.0	gm.
distilled water	100.0	ml.

Hematoxylins, see page 124.
Aniline blue solution:

aniline blue WS, C.I. 42780	0.1	gm.
oxalic acid	2.0	gm.
phosphomolybdic acid	15.0	gm.
distilled water	300.0	ml.

PROCEDURE:

1. Deparaffinize and hydrate slides down to water, remove $HgCl_2$.
2. Mordant in iron alum: 10 minutes.
3. Wash in distilled water: 10 minutes, several changes.
4. Stain in hematoxylin (Delafield's or the like): 5–15 minutes. This may be progressive or regressive.
5. Wash in running water: 5 minutes; rinse in distilled water.
6. Stain in aniline blue stain: 10–15 minutes. Koneff stains overnight.
7. Rinse in distilled water; few dips.
8. Dehydrate quickly through 50 and 70% alcohol.
9. Dehydrate in 95% alcohol, 2 changes: 3 minutes each.
10. Finish dehydration in absolute alcohol; clear and mount.

RESULTS:

collagen, reticulum, mucus, hyaline cartilage—blue
nuclei, red corpuscles—violet or purple blue
cytoplasm, myelin sheaths, muscle fibers—brown
elastic fibers—reddish brown or red

Kornhauser's Quad Stain (1943, 1945)

FIXATION: any general fixative, preferably containing $HgCl_2$.

SOLUTIONS:

Orcein:

orcein	0.4 gm.
nitric acid, conc.	0.4 ml.
90% ethyl alcohol	100.0 ml.

Acid alizarine blue:

acid alizarine blue *BB*, C.I. 58610	0.35 gm.
aluminum ammonium sulfate	5.0 gm.
acetic acid, N/10 (5.8 ml. glacial acetic acid made up to 1 liter)	82.0 ml.

Boil gently in Erlenmeyer flask covered with watch crystal: 10 minutes. Cool and filter.

Phosphotungstic-phosphomolybdic acid:

phosphotungstic acid	4.0 gm.
phosphomolybdic acid	1.0 gm.
distilled water	100.0 ml.

Orange *G*-fast green:

orange *G*, C.I. 16230	2.0 gm.
fast green *FCF*, C.I. 42053	0.2 gm.
glacial acetic acid	2.0 ml.
distilled water	100.0 ml.

PROCEDURE:

1. Deparaffinize and run slides down to 85% alcohol. Remove $HgCl_2$ if present.
2. Orcein: 2–24 hours, until elastin fibers are red brown. May be omitted if no elastin is present or is not to be stained.
3. Wash out excess orcein, two changes 85% alcohol.
4. Run down to water.
5. Acid alizarine blue: 5–10 minutes.
6. Decolorize and mordant in phosphotungstic-molybdic solution, until collagen is destained: 10–30 minutes.
7. Rinse few seconds in distilled water.
8. Stain in orange *G*-fast green: 3–10 minutes.
9. Rinse in 50% alcohol: about 10 seconds.
10. Dehydrate, 95% and absolute alcohol, clear and mount.

RESULTS:

elastin—red brown
nuclei, basophilic granules—blue
cytoplasm, muscle fibers—violet
collagen, reticulum, basement membrane—green
erythrocytes, myelin sheaths, acidophilic granules, plasmosomes—orange

Movat's Pentachrome Stain (1955)

FIXATION: formol-sublimate-acetic is best: 12–18 hours.

mercuric chloride	4.0 gm.
formalin	20.0 ml.
distilled water	80.0 ml.
glacial acetic acid	5.0 ml.

Do not use a dichromate fixative; it diffuses the alcian blue staining. If 10% formalin is used, after the sections are mounted on slides and hydrated, post-fix them in formol-sublimate-acetic for 2–3 hours, or overnight.

SOLUTIONS:

Alcian blue:

alcian blue *8GS*, C.I. 74240	1.0 gm.
distilled water	100.0 ml.
Filter, and add:	
glacial acetic acid	1.0 ml.

Prepare fresh each time.

Weigert-Hart resorcin-fuchsin:
Weigert's resorcin-fuchsin (stock solution):

basic fuchsin, C.I. 42500	2.0 gm.
resorcinol	4.0 gm.
distilled water	200.0 ml.

Mix in a porcelain dish and after it comes to a boil cook for 1 minute. A scum should form. Add 25.0 ml. of 29% aqueous ferric chloride. Cool, filter, and leave precipitate on filter paper until dry. Cover and leave overnight. Place precipitate in porcelain dish and add 200.0 ml. of 95% ethyl alcohol. Bring to a boil on an electric hot plate. Add 4.0 ml. of concentrated hydrochloric acid (see Comment 1). Remove from hot plate and bring volume to 200.0 ml. by adding 95% alcohol. The solution keeps well.

Working solution:

70% ethyl alcohol	94.0 ml.
Weigert's resorcin-fuchsin	5.0 ml.
hydrochloric acid (see Comment 1)	1.0 ml.

Weigert's hematoxylin, page 000.

Woodstain scarlet-acid fuchsin:

Stock solution *A:*

woodstain scarlet N.S.[1]	0.1 gm.
distilled water	99.5 ml.
glacial acetic acid	0.5 ml.

Stock solution *B:*

acid fuchsin, C.I. 42685	0.1 gm.
distilled water	99.5 ml.
glacial acetic acid	0.5 ml.

Working solution:

Solution *A*	40.0 ml.
Solution *B*	10.0 ml.

Phosphotungstic acid:

phosphotungstic acid	5.0 gm.
distilled water	100.0 ml.

Alcoholic saffron:

saffron[2]	6.0 gm.
absolute ethyl alcohol	100.0 ml.

Place in tightly corked bottle to prevent hydration and place in incubator, 58°C for 48 hours before use. Store in an airtight bottle.

PROCEDURE:

1. Deparaffinize and hydrate slides to water; remove $HgCl_2$.
2. Rinse thoroughly in distilled water.
3. Stain in alcian blue: 15 to 30 minutes.
4. Wash in running water: 3 minutes.
5. Place in alkaline alcohol: 2 hours: (Add a few drops of ammonia to 95% alcohol until *p*H is over 8. This solution converts the alcian blue into an insoluble pigment.)

[1] Edward Gurr, London, England.
[2] Safran de Gatinais, Grübler, may be obtained from Roboz Surgical Co., Washington, D.C.

6. Wash in running water: 10 minutes.
7. Rinse in 70% alcohol.
8. Stain in resorcin solution: 16 hours.
9. Wash in running water: 10 minutes; rinse in distilled water.
10. Stain in Weigert's hematoxylin: 15 minutes.
11. Wash in running water: 10 minutes; rinse in distilled water.
12. Stain in woodstain-acid fuchsin: 5 minutes. (During its staining action this solution differentiates the hematoxylin.)
13. Rinse in 0.5% aqueous acetic acid (0.5 ml./99.5 ml. water).
14. Differentiate in phosphotungstic acid: 10 to 20 minutes, or until collagen is pale pink and ground substance bluish.
15. Rinse in 0.5% aqueous acetic acid.
16. Dehydrate thoroughly in 3 changes of absolute alcohol. Use fresh and good-grade alcohol or the tissue will not take on the collagen stain which follows.
17. Stain in saffron: 5 to 15 minutes. Use an airtight staining jar, preferably screw-cap type of coplin jar, to prevent hydration of saffron solution.
18. Transfer through 3 changes of fresh, good-grade absolute alcohol.
19. Clear and mount.

RESULTS:

nuclei—blue to black

cytoplasm—red

elastic fibers—dark purple to black

collagen and some reticular fibers—yellow to greenish yellow

ground substance (acid mucopolysaccharides) and some reticular fibers—blue to bluish green

fibrinoid—intense red

COMMENTS:

1. *Movat* says: "It is important for these staining methods to prepare solutions with HCl of specific gravity 1:124 (the *offizielle Salzaure*) and not concentrated HCl as stated in some textbooks. It is prepared by adding 50 cc. of distilled water to 100 cc. of concentrated HCl (specific gravity 1.19)."

2. Movat includes other modifications of his method using orange G and diphenyl fast red, but seems to favor the above procedure. He calls his method a demonstration of all connective tissue elements in a single section.

Picro-Ponceau Staining

Picro-Ponceau with Hematoxylin (GURR, 1956)
(Van Gieson Substitute, nonfading)

FIXATION: any general fixative.

SOLUTIONS:

Hematoxylins, see page 124.
Picro-ponceau:

ponceau S, C.I. 27195, 1% aqueous	10.0 ml.
picric acid, saturated aqueous	86.0 ml.
acetic acid, 1% aqueous	4.0 ml.

PROCEDURE:

1. Deparaffinize and hydrate slides down to water, remove $HgCl_2$.
2. Optional (see Comments): mordant with iron alum before Delafield's (or similar) hematoxylin. Follow by washing in running water.
3. Overstain in hematoxylin: 5–15 minutes.
4. Wash thoroughly in running water until slides are deep blue: 10 minutes or longer.
5. Stain in picro-ponceau: 3–5 minutes. (This may be too long for some tissues; the stain acts, in addition to staining, as a destaining agent on the hematoxylin.) Rinse for a few seconds in distilled water and check under microscope. Continue to stain and destain or differentiate in water until nuclei are sharp.
6. Dip several times in 70% alcohol.
7. Dehydrate in 95% alcohol, 2 changes, to insure complete removal of excess picric acid. Only that which has acted as a dye must be left in the tissue.
8. Dehydrate, absolute alcohol; clear and mount.

RESULTS:

nuclei—brown to brownish or bluish black
collagenous and reticular fibers—red
elastic fibers, muscle fibers, erythrocytes, epithelia—yellow

COMMENTS:

Weigert's type of hematoxylin is excellent for this method, but it is not necessary to precede it with iron mordanting. The iron mordant is present in the staining solution.

This method is so superior to the so-called Van Gieson stain which uses acid fuchsin instead of ponceau *S*, that the Van Gieson method has been omitted. Colors are identical but the Van Gieson proves unsatisfactory because it fades rapidly.

Elastin Tissue Staining

Verhoeff's Elastin Stain (MALLORY, 1944)

FIXATION: any general fixative.

SOLUTIONS:

Verhoeff's stain:

on electric hot plate, dissolve 3 gm. hematoxylin in 66 ml. absolute ethyl alcohol. Cool, filter and add 24 ml. of 10% aqueous ferric chloride ($FeCl_2$) and 24 ml. Verhoeff's iodine solution. Usefulness is limited to 1–2 weeks.

Verhoeff's iodine solution:

potassium iodide (*KI*)	4.0 gm.
distilled water	100.0 ml.
Dissolve, and add:	
iodine	2.0 gm.

Ferric chloride solution, 10%:

ferric chloride, $FeCl_2$	10.0 gm.
distilled water	100.0 ml.

Ferric chloride solution, 2%:

10% ferric chloride	20.0 ml.
distilled water	100.0 ml.

Picro-ponceau solution:

ponceau *S*, C.I. 27195, 1% aqueous	10.0 ml.
picric acid, saturated aqueous	86.0 ml.
acetic acid, 1% aqueous	4.0 ml.

PROCEDURE:

1. Deparaffinize and run slides down to 70% alcohol. Removal of $HgCl_2$ not necessary.
2. Stain in Verhoeff's stain: 15 minutes.
3. Rinse in distilled water.
4. Differentiate in 2% ferric chloride: few minutes. Elastic fibers

should be sharp black, nuclei brown. If destained too far, return slides to Verhoeff's for another 5–10 minutes.

5. Transfer to sodium thiosulfate, 5% aqueous: 1 minute.
6. Wash in running water: 5–10 minutes.
7. Counterstain in picro-ponceau: 1 minute.
8. Differentiate in 95% ethyl alcohol: few seconds in each of 2 changes.
9. Dehydrate in absolute alcohol; clear and mount.

RESULTS:

elastic fibers—brilliant blue-black
nuclei—blue to brownish black
collagen—red
other tissue elements—yellow

COMMENTS:

If elastic fibers stain unevenly, or not at all, Verhoeff's solution is too old.

Orcinol-New Fuchsin (FULLMER AND LILLIE, 1956)

FIXATION: any general fixative.

SOLUTION:

new fuchsin, C.I. 42520 .... 2.0 gm.
orcinol .... 4.0 gm.
distilled water .... 200.0 ml.
Boil for 5 minutes; add:
ferric chloride, $FeCl_3$, 29.1% aqueous .... 25.0 ml.

Boil for 5 minutes. Cool, collect precipitate on filter paper and dissolve in 100 ml. of 95% ethyl alcohol.

PROCEDURE:

1. Deparaffinize and transfer slides into absolute alcohol.
2. Stain in orcinol-new fuchsin, 37°C, 15 minutes.
3. Differentiate in 70% alcohol, 3 changes, 5 minutes each.
4. Dehydrate, 95% and absolute alcohol, clear and mount.

RESULTS:

elastic fibers—deep violet
collagen—unstained by orcinol-new fuchsin

COMMENTS:

Slides can be counterstained with hematoxylin, safranin, or picro-ponceau; of the three, safranin offers best color contrast.

Aldehyde-Fuchsin (GOMORI, 1950C) (MODIFIED BY CAMERON AND STEELE, 1959)

FIXATION: any good fixative, preferably without dichormate. Bouin's and formalin produce a colorless background.

SOLUTIONS:

Potassium permanganate, 0.3%:

potassium permanganate	0.3 gm.
distilled water	100.0 ml.

Sodium bisulfite, 2.5%:

sodium bisulfite	2.5 gm.
distilled water	100.0 ml.

Aldehyde-fuchsin:

Add 1 gm. basic fuchsin, C.I. 42500, to 200 ml. boiling water: boil 1 minute. Cool and filter. Add 2 ml. concentrated hydrochloric acid and 2 ml. paraldehyde. Leave stoppered at room temperature. When mixture has lost reddish fuchsin color and is deep purple (3–4 days), filter it and discard filtrate. Dry precipitate on filter paper in an oven. Remove and store in bottle. Makes about 1.9 gm. To make staining solution, dissolve 0.25 gm. in 50 ml. of 70% alcohol. Keeps at least six months. (*Rosa, 1953*)

PROCEDURE:

1. Deparaffinize and hydrate slides to water; remove $HgCl_2$.
2. Oxidize in potassium permanganate: 1 minute.
3. Rinse in distilled water.
4. Bleach in sodium bisulfite until permanganate color is removed.
5. Wash in running water: 5 minutes.
6. Transfer to 70% alcohol: 2 minutes.
7. Stain in aldehyde fuchsin: 5–10 minutes.
8. Wipe off back of slide and rinse in 95% alcohol.
9. Differentiate in 95% alcohol until no more aldehyde-fuchsin comes out of sections.
10. Dehydrate, absolute alcohol; clear and mount.

RESULTS:

elastin—deep purple
mast cells, chief cells of gastric mucosa, beta cells of pancreas, basophils of pituitary and some kinds of mucin also stain purple.

Orcein (ROMEIS, 1948)

FIXATION: any general fixative.

SOLUTION:

orcein	1.0 gm.
70% ethyl alcohol	100.0 ml.
hydrochloric acid (assay 37–38%)	1.0 ml.

PROCEDURE:

1. Deparaffinize and hydrate slides to water; remove $HgCl_2$.
2. Stain in orcein: 30–60 minutes.
3. Wash briefly in distilled water.
4. Dehydrate in 95% alcohol: 2 minutes.
5. Differentiate in absolute alcohol until background is almost color-less and elastin fibers are isolated.
6. Rinse in fresh absolute alcohol; clear and mount.

RESULTS:

elastin—red

COMMENTS:

Some disagreement appears in the literature concerning the solution *p*H at which orcein is most effective. *Weiss (1954)* writes that orcein stains only from an acid alcoholic solution between *p*H 3 and 8, that this puts orcein in a category between basic and acidic dyes, which generally operate at the extremes of alkaline and basic *p*H. He there-fore considers there is a formation of hydrogen bond between orcein and elastin. Since this reaction takes place in acid alcohol, it is prob-ably due to a uniquely low positive charge of elastin in such solutions The use of alcoholic solutions is necessary to stabilize the positively charged orcein fractions.

Darrow (1952), experimenting with orcein, found that *p*H 1–2.4 is best for elastin staining, that above *p*H 2.6 collagen stains as well. A dye content of 0.4% is adequate for elastin staining; a higher con-centration adds to collagen staining. For a specific elastin reaction when collagen is present, therefore, it is advisable to check *p*H of acid alcohol used for the solution and to reduce the dye content to 0.4 gm. per 100 ml.

Subcutaneous Tissue Staining

Subcutaneous tissue, areolar tissue, and **omentum** (membranes) can be easily fixed for staining. A simple way is to spread a piece with dissecting needles on a slide, allow to slightly dry and immerse in fixative. The tissue, in most cases, will remain adhering to the slide through staining solutions.

If histologic rings are not available for spreading tissue, cut thick filter paper into circles of a desired diameter and about 6–7 mm. in width. Place the circle of filter paper under the omentum or other tissue to be spread and press against the tissue. Cut out a ring of the tissue, just beyond the outer edge of the paper circle and place in fixative. Carry filter paper and tissue through staining procedures; connective tissue stains can be applied as usual. Finally remove the paper by peeling it off when the tissue is being placed on a slide preparatory to mounting with cover glass.

Bits of loose connective tissue which are difficult to handle may be dehydrated and infiltrated with nitrocellulose. Carefully spread the tissue in a film of nitrocellulose on a slide, allow to slightly dry, and harden in 70% alcohol. It can be stained in place on the slide as this is carried through solutions like a nitrocellulose section. The latter method usually gives more uniform staining.

Bone Staining

Decalcified (ROMEIS, 1948)

FIXATION: formalin, followed by decalcification (see pages 24–26).

SOLUTIONS:
  Thionin:

> thionin, C.I. 52000, saturated in 50% ethyl
>   alcohol .... 10.0 ml.
> distilled water .... 100.0 ml.

If the color does not set correctly, add 1–2 drops of ammonia to staining solution.

Carbol-xylol, see page 410.

PROCEDURE:
1. Deparaffinize and hydrate slides to water. If sections tend to loosen, treat with 0.5–1% nitrocellulose (page 60).
2. Stain in thionin solution: 10 minutes.
3. Wash, distilled water: 20 minutes, change several times.
4. Treat with picric acid, saturated aqueous: 1 minute.
5. Rinse in distilled water.

6. Differentiate in 70% alcohol: 5–10 minutes or more, until no more color comes off.
7. Dehydrate in 95% alcohol, 2 changes: 3 minutes each.
8. Dehydrate and clear in carbol-xylol: 5 minutes.
9. Clear in xylene, and mount.

RESULTS:

lacunae and canaliculi—bordered with bluish black
background—yellow

COMMENTS:

Since occasionally paraffin sections loosen from the slides, some technicians prefer nitrocellulose embedding, but this takes time.

Hand Ground, Undecalcified Sections (ENLOW, 1954)

PROCEDURE:

1. If necessary to remove organic materials and fat, treat in following manner:
    (a) Boil in soap solution: 3–4 hours; and wash in running water: 3–4 hours.
    (b) Suspend over either or chloroform: 36–48 hours.
    (c) Allow to thoroughly dry.
2. Cut slices as thin as possible without cracking them. A jeweler's saw is recommended.
3. Grind on sharpening hones with finely powdered carborundum or household cleansing powder. Keep surface wet with water. Optical or metallurgical grinding and polishing equipment, if available, can be used. The grinding can be done between two stones, or the section can be held on a wet rubber or cork stopper and ground against the hone. If this becomes difficult to manage, glue the section on a slide with Duco cement, and continue to grind. When almost thin enough, loosen from slide with acetone, turn section over, glue it down, and grind opposite side.
4. Polish off both sides with fine leather strop.
5. Place in 95% alcohol: 5 minutes.
6. Air dry.
7. Place in plastic solution, agitate to liberate air bubbles.

    parloidin .... 28.0 gm.
    butyl (or amyl) acetate .... 250.0 ml.

Let stand until parloidin is completely dissolved. Stir thoroughly.

8. Transfer to slide with a drop of solution.
9. Dry thoroughly; do not add more solution.
10. When completely dry, add mounting medium and cover glass.

COMMENTS:

To bring out density and distribution of the mineral in undecalcified bone, see *Frost (1959)*. He describes methods with basic fuchsin, silver nitrate, alizarine red *S* and others.

Dowding (1959) uses methyl methacrylate as a plastic embedding solution, and grinds down the bone as thin as 30 microns.

Hause (1959) describes a block for holding the bone while sawing it and recommends a Razor Saw blade #35-ST (*Lipshaw Manufacturing Company*) as a good cutting instrument.

Kropp (1954) describes a plastic embedded method using heat and pressure.

Yaeger (1958) uses freeze-drying and vacuum infiltration with butyl methacrylate-ethyl methacrylate.

Norris and Jenkins (1960) describe a method using epoxy resin for preparation of bone for radioautography. The resolution is good; there are no chemicals in resin to produce artifacts in nuclear emulsions; the medium does not warp or chip when machined or abraded. (Polyesters and methacrylate do distort when machined.) The design of a metal and lucite mold for the embedding is included. Sections can be made with a microtome (6–10 microns), with a circular saw (50–100 microns) and ground to give sections as thin as 10–50 microns.

Alizarine Red S Method for Embryos (Bone Formation)

FIXATION: a hardening action.

Hollister (1934), 70% alcohol for fish, removal of scales desirable: several days.

Hood and Neill (1948), 95% alcohol, organism preferably free of hair or feathers: 3 days.

Richmond and Bennett (1938), 95% alcohol: 2 weeks.

Some specimens require decolorization. The best method is to lay specimen in 95% alcohol in white tray. Place in direct sunlight for 24 hours each side. An Alpine sunlamp was used by Hollister on sunless days.

SOLUTIONS:

Potassium hydroxide, 2%:

potassium hydroxide, white sticks	20.0 gm.
distilled water	1000.0 ml.

Alizarine stock solution: (*Hollister, 1934*)

alizarine red S, C.I. 58005, saturated solution in 50% acetic acid	5.0 ml.
glycerol	10.0 ml.
chloral hydrate, 1% aqueous	60.0 ml.

Alizarine working solution:

alizarine stock solution	1.0 ml.
1–2% potassium hydroxide in distilled water ..	1000.0 ml.

Make up at least 500 ml.; use at room temperature.

Clearing solution #1: (*Hood and Neill, 1948*)

2% potassium hydroxide	150.0 ml.
0.2% formalin	150.0 ml.
glycerol	150.0 ml.

Clearing solution #2: (*Hood and Neill, 1948*)

2% potassium hydroxide	100.0 ml.
glycerol	400.0 ml.

PROCEDURE:

1. From hardening solution, rinse few minutes in distilled water.
2. Leave in 2% potassium hydroxide until skeleton shows through musculature: 2–4 hours for small embryos, 48 hours or longer for larger forms. (*St. Amand and St. Amand, 1951*, warmed solution to 38°C for quicker action.)
3. When clear, transfer to alizarine working solution: 6–12 hours or longer depending on specimen. Skeleton should be deep red. Large specimens may require fresh changes of dye solution.
4. Transfer directly to 2% potassium hydroxide: 1 day or longer until soft tissues are destained. The KOH may be 1.0–0.5% for small specimens. Sunlight or lamp speeds up process.
5. Clear in solution #1: 2 days, room temperature. Then in solution #2: 1 day.
6. Transfer to pure glycerol with thymol added as preservative.
7. Store in sealed tubes or bottles. Mount on glass rods and seal in museum jars, or embed in plastic.

COMMENTS:

Cumley et al. (*1939*) gradually replaced the glycerol with 95% alcohol, absolute alcohol, and finally toluene. Then the specimens were transferred to toluene saturated with naphthalene, and stored in anise oil saturated with naphthalene. This method is supposed to produce greater clarity than the glycerol storage.

Chapter 14

Silver Impregnation I

RETICULUM TECHNICS

Silver Impregnation

According to *Baker* (*1958*) methods under this heading depend upon the local formation within tissues of a colored substance which is not a dye. **Impregnation** applies to a condition developing when an unreduced metal (silver, etc.) is taken up from a solution of salt or other compound and deposited in a colloidal state on a tissue element. Following impregnation, the tissue is removed to a **reducing** solution of a photographic type and the metal is reduced to the elementary state, probably in the form of a black deposit. Thus the tissue itself does not reduce the metal, but some extraneous reducer is required to perform the reaction.

Silver staining goes back as far as 1843 when Krause tried small pieces of fresh tissue in silver nitrate. The Golgi method appeared in 1873. *Ramón y Cajal* (*1903, 1910*) first experimented with silver nitrate in 1881 and tried reducing it. Also in the early 1900s protargol (Bodian method) and other organic silver compounds were introduced as substitutes for silver nitrate. The albumen fraction in the organic compounds is considered to act as a protective colloid which prevents too rapid reduction by formaldehyde, thereby inducing the formation of finer-grained deposits of silver.) The next step was experimentation with silver on tissue sections, leading to a literature full of modifications of Ramón y Cajal, Bielschowsky, and others.

Ammoniacal silver is the familiar complex, and when reduced by formaldehyde to metallic silver forms a colloidal solution containing negatively charged particles. These may be precipitated out by oppositely charged surfaces which can be changed either to repel or to absorb the silver. Thus, the negatively charged silver (formed by reduction) is deposited on positively charged surfaces and allows selective impregnation of neurofibrils, reticulum, Golgi, etc. The charges of tissue elements may be effected by the fixation and dehydration coagulating the proteins and leaving them positively or negatively charged. The pH of the silver solution is a strong factor in determining charges and depends on whether an ammonium or sodium hydroxide or sodium or lithium carbonate is used (Ramón y Cajal and del Río-Hortega methods).

As already mentioned, protective colloids, such as gum arabic and mastic, and the use of protargol slow down the reduction of the silver to produce a finer grain (Liesegang method). Dilute reducing reagents, combined with the above, can have the same effect (Ramón y Cajal and Bielschowsky methods). Temperature is a factor in this respect, because it increases the kinetic energy of the particles and permits a greater number of collisions of the particles against the tissue surfaces. In some methods, copper is added to the silver solution supposedly to speed up impregnation by initiating the reduction to metallic silver. At the same time too heavy a deposit is prevented by removal of some of the silver from the solution. Thus various applications of the principles can be used to control the impregnation of different kinds of tissue elements (*Silver, 1942*). Chemical properties of tissues and their responses to these conditions all help to determine the place and amount of deposition.

The types of silver impregnation (all ammoniacal) can be classified in the following manner: (1) ammoniacal silver nitrate, (2) ammoniacal silver hydroxide, and (3) ammoniacal silver carbonate. In all of these solutions the silver is present largely in the form of a complex silver ammonia cation $[Ag(NH_3)_2]^+$. In (1) ammonia alone is used to form the precipitate, the chief product in solution being *silver diammino nitrate*. In (2), the *Bielschowsky* method (also modified by *Ramón y Cajal*), sodium hydroxide is used to form the precipitate and ammonia to redissolve it, the chief product being *silver diammino hydroxide*. The difference between the Bielschowsky and the Ramón y Cajal methods lies in the way the silver is applied and the reduction is performed. The

Ramón y Cajal type uses a single ammoniated silver impregnation followed by reduction in pyrogallol, hydroquinone, or one of the amino phenols. The Bielschowsky type uses double impregnation (silver nitrate followed by ammoniated silver) and reduction in formalin. In (3), the *del Río-Hortega* method, sodium carbonate (sometimes lithium carbonate) is used to form the precipitate and is followed by ammonia, the chief product being *silver diammino carbonate*. (Kubie and Davidson, 1928)

The reactions of these solutions to various conditions should be understood:

1. The ammoniacal silver nitrate is most stable, least sensitive to light, least readily reduced, and combines least easily with tissues. During formalin reduction, a cloud of finely divided gray dust slowly develops and the staining is slow. This method is rarely used in preference to other solutions.

2. *Ammoniacal silver hydroxide* lies to the other extremes; it is least stable, most sensitive to light, most readily reduced, and combines most easily with tissues. Almost instantly a heavy black cloud appears. It combines almost at once with the tissue, the solution darkens quickly, and a precipitate begins to form. Since silver nitrate is not reduced in an acid solution, but reduces readily in an alkaline solution, it stands to reason that the ammoniacal silver hydroxide solution is the most sensitive of the three.

3. The *ammoniacal silver carbonate* solution has properties lying between the above two. Its precipitate forms more promptly than that of (1) ammoniacal silver nitrate, but not as fast as that of (2) ammoniacal silver hydroxide. It is darker than that of (1) but not to the degree of (2). Its reaction begins within 5–10 minutes and reaches optimum color before the solution begins to darken. Although solutions number 2 and 3 are used interchangeably, the carbonate solution has the advantage that its hydroxide $(OH)^-$ ion concentration is not high enough to render it as unstable and oversensitive as the hydroxide solution, and the presence of buffer salts makes the reduction proceed steadily and evenly. As the acid, HNO_3, is formed during the reduction the buffer absorbs it and blocks its effect; thus the reduction is not lessened. In addition, the presence of CO_3 ion buffers the formalin and prevents formation of formic acid, also an effective stop to further reduction. *Foot (1929)* buffered his formalin and prolonged the reducing action, making his results darker and more intense. He warned, however, to keep the buffer to a minimum so the reaction will not become too intense. Equimolar silver solutions produce the most uniform results. In most

cases, it is wise not to dissolve completely the precipitate which is first formed; otherwise results can be inferior.

The use of *pyridine,* a fat solvent, precedes some methods, removes lecithin, myelin, mitochondria, galactolipids, etc., and makes subsequent penetration of the silver easier. (This is particularly true for connective tissue.) Toning with gold chloride is optional in many methods, it may yield a more desirable color and may improve contrasts. The timing apparently is variable, actually only long enough to make the desired change in color, usually a few seconds. If the reaction is slow, then the solution has weakened. The final fixing in sodium thiosulfate (*hypo*) is necessary to remove all unreduced silver.

It is readily seen by virtue of the many factors involved to make it specific for certain tissue elements, that silver impregnation can be complex.

Corked bottles should be avoided, since cork extractives may be a disruptive factor resulting in little selective impregnation of tissue elements (Deck and DeSouza, 1959). In all silver methods, take care that metal instruments do not come in contact with the silver solution; a black precipitate may dribble down the surface of slides handled in such a manner. Coat forceps with paraffin, or use horn or wooden instruments. All glassware for metallic stains (silver, gold, etc.) must be acid-clean. Soak in cleaning solution (page 412), wash thoroughly in running water to remove cleaning solution, and rinse 4 or 5 times with distilled water.

Sections loosening from slides is a common problem during silver impregnations. *Davis and Harmon (1949)* use a rinse (0.5 ml. of 2% acetic acid, aqueous, in 50.0 ml. of water) before reduction in sulfite and hydroquinone in the Bodian method (page 203). Many technicians find that the Masson gelatine fixative is superior to Mayer's albumen for affixing sections for silver processes. Transferring unmounted paraffin sections through all solutions and mounting and deparaffinizing at the conclusion of the method is feasible.

Smith (1943) warns that ammoniacal silver hydroxide solutions can become explosive on standing. Several laboratories have experienced explosions when such solutions have been stored for some time; violently explosive silver amide has formed. Prepare ammoniacal silver solutions just before use.

References: Baker (1958); Beech and Davenport (1933); Bensley (1959); Foot (1929); Kubie and Davidson (1928); Long (1948); and Silver (1942).

Silver Impregnation for Reticulum

Bielschowsky-Foot Method (MALLORY, 1938)

FIXATION: 10% formalin or Zenker-formol.

SOLUTIONS:

Ammoniacal silver solution:
In acid-clean glassware place 20 ml. of 10% silver nitrate (10 gm./100 ml. water); add 20 drops of 40% sodium hydroxide (40 gm./100 ml. water). Dissolve precipitate which forms with ammonia, drop by drop, with shaking until the precipitate is almost dissolved. Filter out remaining granules and make up to 80 ml. with distilled water. Make up fresh each time.

Gold chloride:

gold chloride, 1% stock solution (1 gm./100 ml. water)	1.0 ml.
distilled water	99.0 ml.

PROCEDURE:

1. Deparaffinize and hydrate slides to water; remove $HgCl_2$.
2. Rinse in distilled water.
3. Oxidize in potassium permanganate, 0.25% (0.25 gm./100 ml. water): 5 minutes.
4. Wash in running water: 3 minutes.
5. Bleach in oxalic acid, 5% (5 gm./100 ml. water) till clear.
6. Wash in running water: 5 minutes. Rinse in distilled water.
7. Treat in silver nitrate, 2% (2 gm./100 ml. water): 48 hours, in subdued light, not dark.
8. Rinse in distilled water.
9. Impregnate with ammoniacal silver: 30 minutes.
10. Rinse very quickly in distilled water.
11. Reduce in formalin 5% (5 ml./95 ml. water): 30 minutes.
12. Rinse in tap water.
13. Tone in gold chloride until fibers take on blackish grey color.
14. Rinse in distilled water.
15. Fix in sodium thiosulfate, 5% (5 gm./100 ml. water): 3 minutes.
16. Wash in running water: 5–10 minutes.
17. Counterstain if desired.
18. Dehydrate, clear, and mount.

RESULTS:

Reticulum—dark violet to black

del Río-Hortega Method (MALLORY, 1938)

FIXATION: any good general fixative.

SOLUTIONS:

Ammoniacal silver carbonate:

To 10 ml. of 10% silver nitrate add 10 ml. of saturated lithium carbonate, aqueous. Shake, allow precipitate to settle. Decant and wash precipitate with distilled water 5 times. Add 25 ml. of distilled water. Almost dissolve precipitate with ammonia (28% reagent), drop by drop, with shaking. Allow a few grains of precipitate to remain. Add 95% alcohol up to 100 ml. Filter. Warm uncovered at 50°C for 20 minutes. Ready for use. Can be reused, but heat to 50°C and filter before doing so. Keep in brown bottle.

Formalin solution:

formalin	10.0 ml.
distilled water	50.0 ml.

Gold chloride:

gold chloride 1% stock solution (1 gm./100 ml. water)	12.5 ml.
distilled water	50.0 ml.

PROCEDURE:

1. Deparaffinize and hydrate slides to water; remove $HgCl_2$.
2. Treat with potassium permanganate, 0.2% (0.2 gm./100 ml. water): 3 minutes.
3. Wash in distilled water: 2 minutes.
4. Bleach in oxalic acid, 5% (5 gm./100 ml. water): 3 minutes.
5. Wash thoroughly in distilled water, several changes: 10 minutes.
6. Impregnate with silver solution in 37°C oven: 15–30 minutes. Do not expose to bright light. Keep metal instruments out of solution.
7. Rinse quickly in distilled water.
8. Reduce in formalin solution: 3 minutes.
9. Wash in distilled water: 3 minutes.
10. Gold tone until yellow color turns to purplish grey.
11. Rinse briefly in distilled water.
12. Fix in sodium thiosulfate, 5% (5 gm./100 ml. water): 3 minutes.
13. Wash in running water: 5 minutes.

14. Counterstain (if desired) in hematoxylin and picro-ponceau (van Gieson), page 165.
15. Dehydrate, clear, and mount.

RESULTS:

reticulum—black
collagen—red to rose
nuclei—black, blue or brownish
cytoplasm—greyish yellow
muscle fibers, elastin—light yellow

COMMENTS:

To prevent loosening of sections, *Mallory (1938)* substituted an alcoholic for the aqueous silver solution of the original method. See also *German (1939)*.

Gridley's Method (1951)

FIXATION: any good general fixative.

SOLUTION:

Ammoniacal silver hydroxide:

To 20.0 ml. of 5% silver nitrate add 20 drops of 10% sodium hydroxide. Add fresh 28% (reagent) ammonia drop by drop until precipitate which forms is almost redissolved. Add distilled water up to 60.0 ml.

PROCEDURE:

1. Deparaffinize and hydrate slides to water. Remove $HgCl_2$ if present.
2. Treat with 0.5% periodic acid (0.5 gm./100 ml. water): 15 minutes.
3. Rinse in distilled water.
4. Treat with 2% silver nitrate (2 gm./100 ml. water): 30 minutes, room temperature.
5. Rinse in 2 changes of distilled water.
6. Impregnate in ammoniacal silver solution: 15 minutes, room temperature.
7. Rinse rapidly in distilled water.
8. Reduce in 30% formalin (30 ml./70 ml. water): 3 minutes. Agitate gently.
9. Rinse in 3 or 4 changes of distilled water.
10. Tone in gold chloride (10 ml. 1% stock solution/40 ml. water) until yellow brown color has changed to lavender-grey.

11. Rinse in distilled water.
12. Fix in 5% sodium thiosulfate (5 gm./100 ml. water): 3 minutes.
13. Wash in running water: 5 minutes.
14. Counterstain if desired.
15. Dehydrate, clear, and mount.

RESULTS:

reticulum fibers—black
other tissue elements—depends on counterstain

COMMENTS:

Gridley uses periodic acid for oxidation in preference to potassium permanganate and oxalic acid because the latter combination frequently causes the sections to detach from the slides.

Laidlow's Method (1929)

FIXATION: Bouin's recommended. Formalin-fixed can be Bouinized 3 days to produce almost Bouin's results.

SOLUTIONS:

Ammoniacal silver carbonate solution:

In a clean 125 or 250 ml. glass-toppered graduate, dissolve 6 gm. of silver nitrate in 10 ml. distilled water. Add 115 ml. saturated solution of lithium carbonate in distilled water. Shake well. Settle precipitate and pour off solution to leave about 35 ml. of precipitate. Wash well with distilled water 4 or 5 times. Allow to settle, pour off wash water and gradually add ammonia, shaking occasionally until fluid is almost clear. A few grains of precipitate should remain. Add distilled water to a total of 60 ml. Shake and filter into brown stock bottle. Keeps for several months.

Gold chloride:

gold chloride stock solution, 1% (1 gm./100 ml. water)	10.0 ml.
distilled water	40.0 ml.

PROCEDURE:

1. Deparaffinize and hydrate slides to water; remove $HgCl_2$ if present.
2. Oxidize in potassium permanganate, 0.25% (0.25 gm./100 ml. water): 3 minutes.
3. Wash in running water: 3 minutes.

4. Bleach in oxalic acid, 5% (5 gm./100 ml. water); 3 minutes or until clear.
5. Wash in running water: 10 minutes.
6. Wash in distilled water, 3 changes: 5–10 minutes total.
7. Impregnate in ammoniacal silver carbonate, 50°C: 5 minutes.
8. Rinse in distilled water, several dips.
9. Reduce in formalin, 1% (1 ml./99 ml. water), 2 changes: 3 minutes total.
10. Rinse in distilled water, few dips.
11. Tone in gold chloride until sections turn purplish grey.
12. Rinse in distilled water, few dips.
13. Fix in sodium thiosulfate, 5% (5 gm./100 ml. water); 3 minutes.
14. Wash in running water: 5–10 minutes.
15. Dehydrate, clear, and mount.

RESULTS:
reticulum—black
collagen—reddish purple
formalin-fixed nuclei—black; cytoplasm—colorless
Bouin-fixed nuclei—colorless; cytoplasm—blackish

Lillie's Method (1946)

FIXATION: any good general fixative.

SOLUTIONS:
Ferric chloride:

ferric chloride, official solution (29.1%)	1.0 ml.
distilled water	49.0 ml.

Ammoniacal silver hydroxide:

Use acid-clean glassware. Place 1 ml. ammonia (28% reagent) in small flask; add 7–8 ml. silver nitrate 10% (10 gm./100 ml. water) rapidly. Continue to add silver nitrate drop by drop, shaking between each addition until a faint turbidity remains (approximately 9–10 ml. silver nitrate). Dilute resultant solution with equal amount of distilled water.

PROCEDURE:
1. Deparaffinize and transfer slides to absolute alcohol.
2. Coat with celloidin; drain; harden in 80% alcohol.
3. Hydrate slides to water; remove $HgCl_2$.
4. Oxidize in potassium permanganate, 0.5% (0.5 gm./100 ml. water): 2 minutes.

5. Wash in running water: 5 minutes.
6. Bleach in oxalic acid 5% (5 gm./100 ml. water): 2 minutes or until sections are clear.
7. Wash in running water: 5–10 minutes.
8. Treat with ferric chloride solution: 2 minutes.
9. Wash in running water: 3 minutes.
10. Wash in distilled water, 2 changes.
11. Impregnate in ammoniacal silver hydroxide solution: 3 minutes.
12. Rinse briefly in distilled water.
13. Reduce in formalin, 10%: 2 minutes.
14. Wash in running water: 3 minutes.
15. Tone in gold chloride: few seconds or until color has turned to purplish grey.
16. Rinse briefly in distilled water.
17. Fix in sodium thiosulfate, 5% (5 gm./100 ml. water): 3 minutes.
18. Wash in running water: 5 minutes.
19. Counterstain if desired.
20. Dehydrate, clear, and mount.

RESULTS:

reticulum—black

other tissue elements—depends on counterstain

COMMENTS:

Lillie warns that hematoxylin counterstaining may not offer enough contrast with reticulum, because presence of ferric chloride makes the hematoxylin take black.

Wilder's Method (1935)

FIXATION: any good general fixative.

SOLUTIONS:

Phosphomolybdic acid, 10%:

phosphomolybdic acid	10.0 gm.
distilled water	100.0 ml.

Uranium nitrate:

uranium nitrate	1.0 gm.
distilled water	100.0 ml.

Ammoniacal silver nitrate:

Add ammonia (28% reagent), drop by drop to 5 ml. of 10% silver nitrate (10 gm./100 ml. water) until precipitate which forms is almost dissolved. Add 5 ml. of 3.1% sodium hydroxide (3.1 gm./100 ml. water). Barely dissolve the resulting precipitate with a few drops of ammonia. Make the solution up to 500 ml. with distilled water. Use immediately. Glassware must be acid-clean.

Reducing solution:

distilled water	50.0 ml.
formalin	0.5 ml.
uranium nitrate, 1% (above)	1.5 ml.

Make up fresh each time.

Gold chloride:

gold chloride stock solution (1 gm./100 ml. water)	10.0 ml.
distilled water	40.0–80.0 ml.

PROCEDURE:

1. Deparaffinize and hydrate slides to water; remove $HgCl_2$.
2. Wash thoroughly in distilled water.
3. Treat with phosphomolybdic acid: 1 minute.
4. Wash in running water: 5 minutes.
5. Treat with uranium nitrate: 5 seconds or less.
6. Rinse in distilled water.
7. Impregnate with ammoniacal silver nitrate solution: 1 minute.
8. Dip quickly in 95% alcohol and immediately into reducing solution: 1 minute.
9. Wash in distilled water: 2–3 minutes.
10. Tone in gold chloride until yellow colors turn purplish grey.
11. Brief rinse in distilled water.
12. Fix in sodium thiosulfate, 5% (5 gm./100 ml. water): 3–5 minutes.
13. Wash in running water: 5 minutes.
14. Counterstain if desired.
15. Dehydrate, clear, and mount.

RESULTS:

reticulum fibers—black
other tissue elements—depends on counterstain

COMMENTS:

Phosphomolybdic acid replaces potassium permanganate as an oxidizer; the former shows less tendency to loosen sections. Sensitization with uranium nitrate reduces the time and eliminates the heat required by some reticulum methods. *Lillie* (*1946*) disagrees that uranium nitrate is a sensitizer; claims it is an oxidizer.

Reticulum, Collagen, and Elastin. (HUMASON AND LUSHBAUGH 1960)

FIXATION: any good general fixative.

SOLUTIONS:
   Ammoniacal silver carbonate:

To 10 ml. of 10.2% silver nitrate (1.2 gm./100 ml. water) add ammonia (28% reagent) drop by drop until the precipitate, which forms, is almost dissolved. Add 10 ml. of 3.1% sodium carbonate (3.1 gm./100 ml. water) and distilled water to make 100 ml. Filter.

Buffered formalin:

formalin, 5%	50.0 ml.
sodium carbonate, 1% (1 gm./100 ml. water)	1.0 ml.

Orcein solution:

orcein	0.5 gm.
70% ethyl alcohol	100.0 ml.
hydrochloric acid, concentrated	0.6–1.0 ml.

Aniline blue solution:

aniline blue *WS*, C.I. 42780	0.1 gm.
oxalic acid	2.0 gm.
phosphomolybdic acid	15.0 gm.
distilled water	300.0 ml.

PROCEDURE:
1. Deparaffinize and rinse off xylene in absolute alcohol.
2. Pyridine-glycerol (2:1), room temperature: overnight, *or* 15% aqueous pyridine: 15 minutes.
3. Treat with 95% alcohol: 3 minutes.
4. Wash in running water: 5 minutes. Remove $HgCl_2$ if present.
5. Treat with periodic acid, 0.5% (0.5 gm./100 ml. water): 15 minutes.
6. Wash in running water: 5 minutes; rinse in distilled water.
7. Impregnate with ammoniacal silver carbonate solution, 37°C: 1.5–2.0 hours.
8. Rinse in ammoniated distilled water (1 drop ammonia/100 ml. water) a few seconds to remove excess silver precipitates. Rinse in distilled water.
9. Reduce in buffered formalin: 5 minutes. Use fresh solution.

10. Wash in distilled water: 2–3 minutes.
11. Tone in gold chloride (10 ml. 1% stock/80 ml. water) until yellow color turns purplish grey.
12. Rinse briefly in distilled water.
13. Fix in sodium thiosulfate, 5% (5 gm./100 ml. water): 3 minutes.
14. Wash in running water: 5 minutes; rinse in 70% alcohol.
15. Stain in orcein solution, 37°C: 15 minutes, or at room temperature: 1 hour.
16. Rinse in 70% alcohol, followed by distilled water.
17. Treat with phosphomolybdic acid, 5% (5 gm./100 ml. water): 10–15 minutes.
18. Briefly rinse in distilled water.
19. Stain in aniline blue solution: 2–3 minutes.
20. Rinse off some of blue in distilled water, and transfer to acidulated water (1 ml. glacial acetic acid/100 ml. water): 5 minutes or longer.
21. Dehydrate, clear, and mount.

To modify with the addition of orange G, proceed after step **19** *with a rinse in distilled water and continue as follows:*

20. Stain in orange G (C.I. 16230) 2% (2 gm./100 ml. water): 1–2 minutes. Extended time dulls aniline blue.
21. Rinse in distilled water and treat with acidulated water.
22. Dehydrate, clear, and mount.

RESULTS:

reticulum—black
elastin—red
collagen—blue
colloid—brown or grey
nuclei—brown-black
erythrocytes—orange
smooth muscle—beige
striated muscle—grey-blue or mauve
epithelium—light grey-brown

COMMENTS:

The orange G can be added to the aniline blue solution but separate solutions offer better individual control of each color intensity. If sections tend to loosen, follow step 14 by dehydrating slides to absolute alcohol, apply a coat of celloidin, harden it in 70% alcohol and proceed to step 15.

The method was developed for use in pathological problems concerning vascular invasion and capsular infiltration by carcinoma and degenerative diseases of the connective tissue and blood vessels.

Any of the other silver impregnation solutions and methods for reticulum may be substituted for the above step 7.

Chapter 15

Silver Impregnation II

NEUROLOGICAL TECHNICS

Briefly, the neurological elements may be grouped as follows:

1. SUPPORTING ELEMENTS; the neuroglial fibers and cells, also some connective tissue
   a. **Astrocytes**—support the neurons
   b. **Oligodendroglia**—help to form and maintain the myelin
   c. **Microglia**—part of the defense system of the nervous system
2. NERVE CELL BODIES (*neurons*), including various cytoplasmic structures
   a. **Nissl's granules**
   b. **Neurofibrils,** fine cytoplasmic fibers
   c. Mitochondria and Golgi (sometimes present; see p. 259)
   d. Melanin and lipofuchsins (see p. 241)
3. NERVE FIBERS (**axons** and **dendrites**)
   a. **Myelin**—a glistening fatty material that coats the axons in the outer layer of the developing spinal cord
4. NERVE ENDINGS
   a. **Pericellular end bulbs,** sensory
   b. **Motor end plates**

When impregnating tissues from the central nervous system certain facts should be kept in mind. If the hydroxide method is used, astrocytes and microglia are not specially impregnated. If the carbonate method is used, the opposite effect takes place. Use body temperature for impregnation, not hot solutions. For nervous tissue, frozen sections actually are best; the alcohol and xylene embedding processes may remove lipids, which can be an essential part of the tissue. Lipid extraction may result in no impregnation of oligodendroglia and weakened microglia, since their impregnation depends on lipid complexes. Also, periodic and chromic acid oxidation weaken the reaction of oligodendroglia and microglia. (The reverse is true for connective tissue, when pyridine, periodic, or chromic acid treatment is desirable to suppress nervous tissue elements from confusing the picture.)

Neurological technics, as perhaps has become evident, so often necessitate highly specialized methods that many technicians prefer to avoid them. Precise attention to all details, however, can produce beautiful and exciting slides. Carefully follow directions for fixation—the solution composition and the duration of fixation, and whether fixation is or is not followed by washing. Always wash in distilled water unless tap water is specified. For making silver and other special solutions use double (glass) distilled water if possible and clean glassware—cleaned in cleaning solution (page 412), washed well in running water, and rinsed 4 or 5 times in distilled water. All chemicals should be at least reagent grade. Use no corks in containers and no metal instruments in silver solutions. If in doubt about the age of solutions, make fresh ones. If, during toning with gold chloride, the tissue retains a yellow or brownish hue, the gold chloride is weakened. Prepare a new solution.

Sometimes artifact precipitates are difficult to avoid, but strict adherence to procedure details will reduce them to a minimum.

Embedding and sectioning will depend on the impregnating or staining technic to follow. Paraffin and nitrocellulose methods are used at times, but as mentioned above frozen sections usually are more satisfactory. Section thickness frequently is thicker than for other tissues — 7 to 20 microns, or even more.

When fixing an entire *brain,* do not allow it to rest on the bottom of the container. Carefully insert a cord under the circle of Willis on the underside of the brain and support the two ends of the cord on the sides of the container. The brain, hanging upside down, should be free of the bottom of the vessel but remain completely submerged in fixative. The *spinal cord* can be supported in a graduated cylinder filled with fixative. Run a thread through one end of the spinal cord and tie the thread around an applicator stick supported on the edges of the cylinder. For a perfusion method for the brain, see pages 22.

Note: In neurological technics the methods sometimes employ section-staining and sometimes employ block-staining. The letters **S** and **B** will be used in the headings of this chapter to indicate which type of staining is being described.

Neurological Staining

Heidelberger's Victoria Blue (MODIFIED BY PROESCHER, 1934) S

FIXATION: 10% formalin.

PROCEDURE:
1. Cut frozen sections, 10–15 microns.
2. Place sections in distilled water. If not stained at once they may be stored in 10% formalin for 24 hours, but no longer.
3. Stain in Victoria blue *B*, C.I. 44045, saturated aqueous solution: 12–24 hours.
4. Wash rapidly in distilled water and mount on albumen-coated slides. Blot with filter paper and dry in air.
5. Expose to ultraviolet light: 30 minutes.
6. Immerse in N/20 iodine solution (aqueous): few seconds.
7. Remove from iodine, blot, air dry for 10 minutes.
8. Differentiate in xylene-aniline (1:1), clear in 2 or 3 changes of xylene, and mount.

RESULTS:
glia cell bodies and fibrils—light to deep blue
nerve cell bodies, dendrites, and axis cylinders—faintly stained

COMMENTS:
1. Staining time can be shortened to 30–35 minutes at 56°C.
2. Proescher experimented with oxidizing agents—potassium chromate and dichromate and hydrogen peroxide—and found they could be substituted for ultraviolet. Potassium dichromate was most successful and can be used as a 0.5% aqueous solution for 30 minutes.
3. Victoria blue may be replaced by methyl violet *2B*, ethyl violet, or crystal violet.

Nassar and Shanklin's Silver Impregnation (1951) S

FIXATION: 4 days in:

formalin	70.0 ml.
ammonium bromide	14.0 gm.
distilled water	680.0 ml.

WASHING, EMBEDDING, and SECTIONING:

1. After fixation, wash tissue blocks in distilled water plus strong ammonia (50 drops ammonia to 100 ml. water): 10 hours. Keep container covered to prevent escape of ammonia.
2. Wash in 2 changes of distilled water: 1–2 hours each.
3. Dehydrate, clear, and embed in paraffin. Cut sections at 10–15 microns and prepare slides.

SOLUTION:

Ammoniated Silver (Lillie, 1946):

To 1 ml. of concentrated ammonia rapidly add 7–8 ml. of 10% silver nitrate, aqueous. Continue to add 10% silver nitrate drop by drop, shaking each time, until only a faint turbidity remains (9–10 ml.). Dilute with an equal amount of distilled water.

PROCEDURE:

1. Deparaffinize and hydrate to 3 changes of distilled water: 1–2 minutes each.
2. Sensitize in 5% sodium sulfite (5 gm./100 ml. water): 2 hours.
3. Transfer quickly through 3 changes of distilled water.
4. Impregnate in ammoniated silver solution: 2–5 minutes, room temperature.
5. Dip in distilled water: 1–2 seconds.
6. Reduce in 2% formalin (2 ml./98 ml. water): 1 minute. Agitate gently, and change formalin solution 3–4 times.
7. Wash in distilled water: 1 minute.
8. Tone in gold chloride (1 gm./500 ml. water): few seconds to 1 minute, or until section turns grey.
9. Fix in 5% sodium thiosulfate (5 gm./100 ml. water): 1–2 minutes.
10. Wash in running water: 5 minutes.
11. Counterstain if desired. Dehydrate, clear, and mount.

RESULTS:

neuroglia—dark grey to black

COMMENT:

del Río-Hortega's silver carbonate solution also can be used in this method.

Astrocytes

Ramón y Cajal's Gold Chloride Sublimate Method (MALLORY, 1938) S

FIXATION: Fix thin slices of tissue in:

formalin	15.0 ml.
ammonium bromide	2.0 gm.
distilled water	85.0 ml.

37°C: 1 day

SECTIONING: frozen sections, 15 microns thick.

SOLUTIONS:

Gold chloride sublimate solution:

mercuric chloride crystals (*not powder*)	0.5 gm.
gold chloride, 1% aqueous	6.0 ml.
distilled water	35.0 ml.

Prepare fresh, using acid-clean glassware. Pulverize mercuric chloride; add to distilled water. Heat gently. When dissolved, add gold chloride, and filter.

del Río-Hortega's carbol-xylol-creosote mixture:

creosote	10.0 ml.
phenol (carbolic acid), melted	10.0 ml.
xylene	80.0 ml.

PROCEDURE:

1. Place sections in 1% formalin.
2. Wash quickly in distilled water, 2 changes.
3. Place in freshly prepared gold chloride (in acid-clean glassware). Flatten sections, keep in dark at room temperature: 4–6 hours. When sections appear purplish, examine for astrocytes.
4. Wash in distilled water: 5–10 minutes.
5. Fix in 5% sodium thiosulfate (5 gm./100 ml. water): 5–10 minutes.
6. Wash in distilled water, several changes.
7. Float on slide, dehydrate with 95% alcohol.

8. Clear with del Río-Hortega's solution.
9. Blot and mount.

RESULTS:

astrocytes and processes—black
background—unstained or light brownish purple
nerve cells—pale red
nerve fibers—unstained

COMMENTS:

Extra sections after being fixed in hypo can be preserved in 1% formalin for long periods.

Oligodendroglia and Microglia

Penfield's Modification of del Río-Hortega's Silver Carbonate Method (MCCLUNG, 1950) S

FIXATION: 10% formalin at least one week; longer fixation also will give excellent results, or fix in:

formalin	14.0 ml.
ammonium bromide	2.0 gm.
distilled water	86.0 ml.

SECTIONING: frozen sections, 20 microns.

SOLUTIONS:

Globus' hydrobromic acid:

40% hydrobromic acid	5.0 ml.
distilled water	95.0 ml.

Silver carbonate solution:

Combine 5.0 ml. of 10% silver nitrate and 20.0 ml. of sodium carbonate. Add ammonium hydroxide, drop by drop, until precipitate is just dissolved. Add distilled water up to 75 ml. Filter. The solution keeps for long periods if stored in a dark bottle.

PROCEDURE:

1. Place sections in 1% formalin or distilled water.
2. Transfer to distilled water plus 1% of ammonia. Cover to prevent escape of ammonia, and leave overnight.
3. Transfer to hydrobromic acid, 38°C: 1 hour.
4. Wash in 3 changes of distilled water.

5. Mordant in 5% sodium carbonate (5 gm./100 ml. water): 1 hour. Tissue may remain in this solution 5–6 hours with no ill effect.
6. Impregnate in silver solution: 3–5 minutes or until sections turn a smooth grey when transferred to reducer. Try single sections at 3 minutes, 5 minutes, or longer.
7. Reduce in 1% formalin. Agitate during reduction.
8. Wash in distilled water.
9. Tone in gold chloride (1 gm./500 ml. water) until bluish grey.
10. Fix in 5% sodium thiosulfate, 3 minutes.
11. Wash in running water: 5 minutes. Dehydrate, clear, and mount.

RESULTS:

oligodendroglia and microglia—dark grey to black

COMMENTS:

If only the oligodendroglia are to be shown, cut fixation time down to 2 days. Long fixation tends to increase the staining of the microglia and astrocytes.

Procedure for oligodendroglia:
1. Follow fixation by treatment with 95% alcohol: 36 & 48 hours.
2. Wash, freeze, and cut sections.
3. Stain in a stronger silver solution by diluting the above solution to only 45 ml.: 15 minutes or more, until the sections begin to turn brown.
4. Wash for a few seconds in distilled water.
5. Reduce with agitation, wash, and tone as above.
6. Dehydrate, clear, and mount.

RESULTS:

oligodendroglia—black

Nissl Substance

Cresyl Violet (KELLER, 1945) S

Nissl substance is characteristic of fixed nerve cells. It is found in a granular form distributed through the cytoplasm and stains brilliantly with basic aniline dyes.

FIXATION: Bouin's recommended; others are satisfactory; Zenker's not recommended.

SECTIONING: Paraffin method, 10 microns; thinner sections of no advantage.

SOLUTIONS:

Cresyl violet:

cresyl violet-acetate	0.5 gm.
distilled water	100.0 ml.

Resin-xylene:

mounting resin	50.0 ml.
xylene	50.0 ml.

PROCEDURE:

1. Deparaffinize and hydrate to water; remove $HgCl_2$.
2. Stain in cresyl violet: 3–5 minutes.
3. Rinse in distilled water, 2 changes: few seconds each.
4. Dehydrate in 95% alcohol: 30 seconds.
5. Dehydrate in absolute alcohol: 30 seconds.
6. Transfer to xylene: 1 minute.
7. Treat with resin-xylene: 2 minutes.
8. Differentiate in absolute alcohol: 10–30 seconds. Check under microscope.
9. Clear and mount.

RESULTS:

nissl substance—purple.

COMMENTS:

Steps 7, 8, and 9 may be repeated several times until desired differentiation is reached.

Banny and Clark (1950) recommend *Coleman and Bell* for the best cresyl violet for Nissl staining.

Thionin (CLARK AND SPERRY, 1945) S

FIXATION: Bouin's recommended; other's are satisfactory; Zenker's not recommended.

SECTIONING: 10 microns; thinner sections of no advantage.

SOLUTIONS:

Lithium carbonate, 0.55%:

lithium carbonate	5.5 gm.
distilled water	1000.0 ml.

Thionin:

thionin, C.I. 52000	0.25 gm.
0.05% lithium carbonate	100.00 ml.

PROCEDURE:

1. Deparaffinize and hydrate slides to water; remove $HgCl_2$.
2. Treat with lithium carbonate solution: 5 minutes.
3. Overstain in thionin: 5–10 minutes.
4. Rinse in distilled water.
5. Dip in 70% alcohol: few seconds.
6. Dehydrate in butyl alcohol, 2 changes: 2–3 minutes in each.
7. Clear and mount.

RESULTS:

nissl substance—bright blue

COMMENTS:

If differentiation is necessary, briefly rinse slides in 95% ethyl alcohol (following step 5) and place in aniline, then in lithium carbonate saturated in 95% alcohol. Proceed to step 6.

Gallocyanin (EINARSON, 1951) S

FIXATION: any general fixative.

SECTIONING: 10 microns.

SOLUTION:

gallocyanin	0.15 gm.
chrome alum (chromium potassium sulfate) ...	5.0 gm.
distilled water	100.0 ml.

Dissolve chrome alum in warm water, add gallocyanin and boil gently for 10 minutes. Keeps well for about 1 week.

PROCEDURE:

1. Deparaffinize and hydrate slides to water; remove $HgCl_2$.
2. Stain in gallocyanin: overnight.
3. Wash in running water: 5 minutes.
4. Dehydrate, clear, and mount.

RESULTS:

nissl substance—blue

Neurofibrils

Ramón y Cajal's Method (MODIFIED FROM FAVORSKY, 1930) B

FIXATION: cut slices perpendicular to organ surface, about 5 cm. thick. Place in 70% alcohol, plus .5% glacial acetic acid: 6 hours.

PROCEDURE:

1. Transfer to 80% alcohol: 6 hours.
2. Treat with ammoniacal alcohol: 24–36 hours.
   (*a*) For cerebrum, cerebellum, spinal cord, or ganglia add 4 drops of ammonia to 50 ml. of 95% alcohol.
   (*b*) For medulla, add 9 drops of ammonia to 50 ml. of 95% alcohol.
3. Wash in distilled water, several changes, until pieces sink.
4. Treat with pyridine: 1–2 days.
5. Wash in running water: overnight, followed by distilled water, several changes.
6. Blot on filter paper and place in relatively large volume of 1.5% silver nitrate, aqueous (1.5 gm./100 ml. water): 5 days in dark, 38°C.
7. Rinse in distilled water and place in following fluid: 24 hours. Ramón y Cajal's reducing fluid:

pyrogallic acid or hydroquinone	1.0 gm.
distilled water	100.0 ml.
neutral formalin	15.0 ml.

8. Rinse in distilled water, several changes over a period of at least 1 hour.
9. Dehydrate and embed in paraffin, celloidin, or double embed.
10. Make sections perpendicular to surface of organ and about 15 or more microns thick.
11. Affix to slides, dry, remove paraffin with xylene and mount. Lay celloidin sections on slides and mount in resin.

RESULTS:

neurofibrils—black
background—brownish yellow

Nerve Cells and Fibers

Golgi's Rapid Method (MALLORY, 1938) B

FIXATION: fix small pieces in:

potassium dichromate, 2.5% aqueous	40.0 ml.
osmic acid, 1% aqueous	10.0 ml.

Place cotton in bottom of container so fixing fluid has access to all sides: 1–7 days. Renew fixative if it becomes turbid.

STAINING:

1. Dry pieces of tissue with filter paper, place in 0.75% aqueous silver nitrate (0.75 gm./100 ml. water): 24–48 hours. If solution turns yellow, renew it.
2. Transfer to 40% ethyl alcohol, several changes: 1–2 hours.
3. Transfer to 80% and 90% alcohol: 1 hour each.

EMBEDDING and SECTIONING:

1. Dehydrate in absolute ethyl alcohol: 12 hours.
2. Transfer to absolute alcohol-ether (1:1): 2–4 hours.
3. Infiltrate with 4% celloidin or nitrocellulose: 1–2 days.
4. Embed and cut thick sections, 20–25 microns, or more if desirable.

MOUNTING:

1. Wash sections carefully in 80% alcohol to remove excess silver.
2. Dehydrate in absolute alcohol: few minutes. (Add few ml. chloroform to absolute alcohol to prevent loss of nitrocellulose.)
3. Clear in clove oil, terpinol, or the like.
4. Mount on slides, press with filter paper. Add a drop of thick mounting medium. Warm to drive off solvent and just before resin cools, add cover glass.

RESULTS:

nerve cells and processes—deep black
background—light yellow

COMMENTS:

If tissue has been fixed in 10% formalin, blot off excess formalin and chromate for 1–2 days, room temperature, in one of the following fluids (Davenport and Combs, 1954).

1. potassium dichromate, 5% aqueuos	100.0 ml.
glacial acetic acid	6.9 ml.
2. zinc or cadmium chromate	1.5 gm.
distilled water	25.0 ml.
glacial acetic acid	6.0 ml.
when chromate has dissolved, add:	
potassium dichromate, 5% aqueous	65.0 ml.
3. potassium dichromate,	3.0 gm.
potassium acetate, anhydrous	1.8 gm.
distilled water	100.0 ml.
4. *A.* cadmium nitrate ($4H_2O$) or zinc nitrate ($6H_2O$)	3.0 gm.
distilled water	25.0 ml.

      B. potassium dichromate, 5% aqueous .....   65.0 ml.
           glacial acetic acid ....   6.0 ml.
Mix *A* and *B*.

Remove tissues from any of above fluids, blot and place immediately in silver solution: 18–24 hours. Proceed into step number 2 above (under Staining).

Moliner's Modification (1957)

FIXATION: fix 3–5 mm. pieces, 3 days, change daily.

      potassium dichromate, 6% aqueous ....   40.0 ml.
      potassium chlorate, 5% aqueous ....   20.0 ml.
      chloral hydrate, 20% aqueous ....   30.0 ml.
      formalin ....   10.0 ml.

STAINING:
1. Transfer tissue blocks to 3% aqueous potassium dichromate: 3 days, change twice a day.
2. Transfer to 1% aqueous silver nitrate (1gm./100 ml. water): 3 days, room temperature.

SECTIONING AND MOUNTING:
1. Cut frozen sections, 50–100 microns. Sections can be kept in absolute alcohol until mounted.
2. Mount on slides and clear. Synthetic mountants can be used with a cover glass. (Before synthetic mountants were developed, *Golgi* preparations had to be mounted in balsam without a cover glass.)

Ramón y Cajal's Pyridine-Silver Method (MODIFIED BY DAVENPORT *et al.,* 1934) **B**

FIXATION: as soon as possible in:

      absolute ethyl alcohol ....   98.0 ml.
      ammonia, concentrated ....   2.0 ml.

Fix for 1–6 days, preferably no longer.

PROCEDURE:
1. Treat tissue blocks in 5% aqueous pyridine: 24 hours. This is recommended; but Davenport *et al.* say it can be optional.
2. Wash in distilled water: 2–6 hours; change every half hour.
3. Impregnate in 1.5–2.0% aqueous silver nitrate (1.5–2.0 gm./100 ml. water), 37°C: 2 to 3 days, or longer depending on size of tissue blocks. A minimum time yields the best differentiated tissue. The

longer the tissue is left in silver nitrate, the greater the tendency for everything to stain. This time will have to be determined by trial and error.

4. Wash in distilled water: 20 minutes to 1 hour. This is a critical step. The amount of silver washed from the tissue depends on whether the water is changed often or whether the tissue is shaken in the water. Change every 10 minutes or use a large volume of water and shake every 10 minutes. Equal staining of the periphery as well as central parts of the tissue determines correct washing. A light periphery indicates too much washing.
5. Reduce in 4% aqueous pyrogallol solution: 4 hours.
6. Dehydrate, clear, embed, and section.
7. Mount on slides, deparaffinize, and clear. Add mountant and cover glass.

RESULTS:

nerve cells—yellow to brown
neurofibrils—brown to black
axis cylinders of myelineated fibers—yellow to brown
axis cylinders of nonmyelinated fibers—black

COMMENTS:

If the preparation tends to be too light, reduce the time in pyridine and washing.

If the preparation is too dark, omit the pyridine and wash 48 hours after fixation, or reduce the concentration of the silver nitrate solution and wash longer between impregnation and reduction.

Bielschowsky Method (MODIFIED BY DAVENPORT *et al.*, 1934) **B**

FIXATION: 10% formalin: 2 days. For embryos add 0.5% of trichloracetic acid to 10% formalin.

SOLUTION:

Ammoniated silver:

Add 5.0 ml. of concentrated ammonia to 40.0 ml. of 2% sodium hydroxide (aqueous). Mix well. Add slowly from a burette or pipette with shaking 8.5% aqueous silver nitrate until an opalescence remains in the solution (about 40.0 ml.). Add 0.5–1.0 ml. of ammonia. Dilute with about 5 parts of distilled water. (Dilution is not critical.)

PROCEDURE:

1. After fixation, wash for 1 hour.
2. Transfer to 50% aqueous pyridine: 1–2 days.

3. Wash in distilled water: 2–6 hours depending on size of block. Change every half hour.
4. Impregnate with 1–1.5% aqueous silver nitrate (1.0–1.5 gm./100 ml. water): 3 days, 37°C.
5. Wash in distilled water: 20 minutes to 1 hour, depending on size. Change every 10 minutes or use a large volume of water and shake every 10 minutes. Periphery and central portions must be equally stained.
6. Impregnate in ammoniated silver solution: 6–24 hours.
7. Wash in distilled water: 15 minutes to 1 or 2 hours, depending on size.
8. Reduce in 1% formalin: 6–12 hours.
9. Wash in running water: 10–15 minutes.
10. Dehydrate, clear and embed. Section and mount.
11. Deparaffinize, clear, and cover.

Alternate method, for gold toning:
  (*a*) Hydrate sections to water.
  (*b*) Gold tone and fix.
  (*c*) Dehydrate, clear, and mount.

RESULTS:
nerve fibers, neurofibrils—brown to black (no gold toning)
—grey to black (with gold toning)

Fluorescent Method (ZEIGER *et al.,* 1951) **S**

FIXATION: 95% ethyl alcohol.

SECTIONING: paraffin method.

PROCEDURE:
1. Deparaffinize and hydrate slides to water.
2. Stain in 0.1% acridine orange (C.I. 46005): 6 minutes.
3. Differentiate in 95% ethyl alcohol: 2 seconds.
4. Blot with filter paper and mount in fluorescent mountant.

RESULTS:
unmyelinated fibers—bluish gray
myelinated fibers—brownish orange

COMMENTS:
Fresh tissue can be cut frozen and stained in acridine orange made up in physiological saline (page 410) or in Ringer's solution (page 411).

Nerve Fibers and Endings

Bodian Method (1936, 1937) S

FIXATION: Bodian recommends:

formalin	5.0 ml.
glacial acetic acid	5.0 ml.
80% ethyl alcohol	90.0 ml.

Not suitable are chromates, chromic and osmic acid, or mercuric chloride. 10% formalin causes excessive staining of connective tissue.

SECTIONING: paraffin method.

SOLUTIONS:

Protargol solution:

Protargol [1]	1.0 gm.
distilled water	100.0 ml.

Sprinkle Protargol on surface of water in a wide dish or beaker. Do not stir, this is critical. Keep on hot plate at 37°C until Protargol is dissolved.

Reducing solution:

hydroquinone	1.0 gm.
sodium sulfite	5.0 gm.
distilled water	100.0 ml.

Gold chloride:

gold chloride	1.0 gm.
distilled water	100.0 ml.

Acidified water:

glacial acetic acid	0.5 gm.
distilled water	100.0 ml.

PROCEDURE:

1. Deparaffinize and hydrate slides to water.
2. Impregnate in Protargol solution plus 5 gm. clean copper (wire, shot or sheet, cleaned with 1 part HNO_3/3 parts HCl) to 100 ml. of solution, 37°C: 12–24 hours.
3. Wash in distilled water, several changes.
4. Reduce: 5–10 minutes.

[1] Roboz Surgical Instrument Co., Washington, D.C.

5. Rinse in distilled water, 3 changes: 1 minute total.
6. Tone in gold chloride: 4 minutes.
7. Rinse in distilled water, 3 changes: 1 minute total.
8. Develop in 2% oxalic acid (2 gm./100 ml. water). Check under microscope until background is grey and fibers are sharply defined: approximately 3 minutes.
9. Wash in distilled water, 3 changes: 1 minute each.
10. Fix in 5% sodium thiosulfate (5 gm./100 ml. water): 5 minutes.
11. Wash in running water: 5–10 minutes.
12. Rinse in distilled water.
13. Counterstain if desired.
14. Treat with acidified water: 5 minutes.
15. Dehydrate, clear, and mount.

RESULTS:

nerve fibers—black
background colors—depending on counterstain

COMMENTS:

Foley (1943) considers counterstaining essential, claiming that it serves as contrast for nervous and non-nervous tissue and adds to transparency of the sections. Follow step 11 with:

12. Stain in gallocyanin (page 138): overnight.
13. Wash thoroughly running water: 5–10 minutes.
14. Mordant in 5% phosphotungstic acid (5 gm./100 ml. water): 30 minutes.
15. Transfer directly to dilution (20 ml./30 ml. water) of following stock solution: 1 hour.

aniline blue *WS*, C.I. 42780	0.1 gm.
fast green *FCF*, C.I. 42053	0.5 gm.
orange *G*, C.I. 16230	2.0 gm.
distilled water	92.0 ml.
glacial acetic acid	8.0 ml.

16. Differentiate through 70% and 95% alcohols.
17. Dehydrate, clear, and mount.

Ungewitter's Modification (1943)

PROCEDURE:

1. Deparaffinize and hydrate sections to water.
2. Treat with Protargol solution (plus copper), 37°C: 12–24 hours.

3. Rinse in distilled water, 2 changes.
4. Reduce: 5–10 minutes, agitating for first minute:

Elon	0.2 gm.
sodium sulfate, anhydrous	10.0 gm.
hydroquinone	0.5 gm.
sodium borate	0.1 gm.
distilled water	100.0 ml.

5. Wash in distilled water, 4–5 changes.
6. Treat with silver nitrate, 1% aqueous (1 gm./100 ml. water): 10–20 minutes, room temperature or 37°C.
7. Wash in distilled water, 2–3 changes.
8. Reduce (step 4 above).
9. Wash in distilled water, 4 changes. Examine. If nerve fibers show distinct differentiation, dehydrate, clear, and mount. If not well differentiated, repeat steps 6, 7, 8, and 9 until desired results are reached.
10. Toning may be done in 0.2% gold chloride (0.2 gm./100 ml. water) until greyish in color. Fix, dehydrate, clear, and mount.

Chloral Hydrate-Silver Method (NONIDEZ, 1939) B

FIXATION: 24 hours or longer (up to 3 days):

chloral hydrate	25.0 gm.
50% ethyl alcohol	100.0 ml.

PROCEDURE:

1. Wipe off excess fixative and put blocks in:

95% ethyl alcohol	60.0 ml.
ammonia, concentrated	4 drops

Leave for 24 hours, but change at least once, particularly if blocks are large or contain a large amount of fat.
2. Rinse in distilled water: 5 minutes.
3. Place in 2% aqueous silver nitrate (2 gm./100 ml. water) in dark, 37–40°C: 5–6 days. Replace silver solution after 2 days, or as soon as it becomes brownish in color.
4. Rinse in distilled water: 2–3 minutes.
5. Reduce for 24 hours in:

pyrogallol	2.5–3.0 gm.
formalin	8.0 ml.
distilled water	100.0 ml.

6. Wash in several changes of distilled water: 2–3 hours.
7. Transfer to 50% alcohol, change twice over a period of 24 hours.
8. Dehydrate, clear, and embed.
9. Section, mount on slides, deparaffinize, clear, and cover.

RESULTS:

nerve fibers and endings—brown to black

COMMENT:

Gold toning does not improve impregnation.

Pericellular End-Bulbs (or Boutons)

Chloral Hydrate-Silver Method (DAVENPORT, 1933) B

FIXATION: Perfusion (page 22) with 10% chloral hydrate is a desirable procedure, followed by fixation in 10% chloral hydrate: 1–2 hours. (After perfusion cut whole organ into tissue blocks, 5–8 mm. thick.)

PROCEDURE:

1. Treat tissue blocks with 20–40% pyridine (aqueous): 2 days.
2. Wash in distilled water: 1–2 hours, no more. Change water every half hour.
3. Impregnate with 1.5% aqueous silver nitrate (1.5 gm./100 ml. water): 3–7 days. (Time is not critical within these limits.)
4. Wash in distilled water: 20–30 minutes, change water once.
5. Reduce in 2% aqueous pyrogallol (2 gm./100 ml. water): 5 hours.
6. Dehydrate, clear, and embed.
7. Section (15–20 microns) and mount on slides.
8. Deparaffinize and gold tone if desired, or clear and cover.

RESULTS:

nerve fibers and endings—black
cells—pale yellowish brown

COMMENTS:

Davenport suggests that the chloral hydrate is perfused into the aorta and can be pumped through the system for about 1–3 minutes before the heart stops.

The washing after the silver impregnation is critical. If not sufficiently washed the periphery will be overstained. One-half hour leaves the superficial as well as the central zones well stained. Five hours of washing produces pale staining and leaves the end bulbs unstained. Cat tissue gave excellent results.

Nauta and Gygax Method (1951) B

FIXATION: 10% formalin: 2 weeks to 6 months.

SECTIONING: frozen sections, 15–20 microns.

SOLUTIONS:

Silver solution *A:*

silver nitrate	1.5 gm.
distilled water	100.0 ml.
pyridine	5.0 ml.

Silver solution *B* (ammoniated silver):

Dissolve 0.45 gm. silver nitrate in 20.0 ml. distilled water. Add 10.0 ml. of 95% ethyl alcohol. From calibrated pipettes add 2.0 ml. ammonia (concentrated) and 2.2 ml. of 2.5% sodium hydroxide. Mix thoroughly and keep the container covered to prevent escape of ammonia.

Reducing solution:

10% ethyl alcohol	45.0 ml.
10% formalin	2.0 ml.
1% citric acid	1.5 ml.

PROCEDURE:

1. Demyelinate sections in 50% ethyl alcohol plus 1.0 ml. ammonia per 100 ml.: 6–12 hours. A longer time has no ill effect.
2. Wash in distilled water, 3 changes: few seconds each.
3. Impregnate in silver solution *A:* 12–24 hours.
4. With no washing, transfer into silver solution *B:* 2–5 minutes.
5. Transfer directly into reducing solution until the sections turn gold in color.
6. Transfer to 2.5% sodium thiosulfate (2.5 gm./100 ml. water): 1–2 minutes.
7. Wash in distilled water, at least 3 changes.
8. Dehydrate rapidly, clear, and mount.

RESULTS:

nerve fibers and endings—black
cells—pale yellowish brown

COMMENTS:

This method is nonselective and stains normal as well as degenerating axons. For degenerating axons see following methods.

Degenerating Axons

Nauta and Gygax (1954) S

FIXATION: perfusion method seems to be preferred.

Anderson (1959):

1. Perfuse with 0.9% sodium chloride (intracardiac and intra-aortic canulation) until fluid escaping is clear.
2. Perfuse with 500 ml. of 5% potassium dichromate and 2.5% potassium chlorate. This is peculiar to *Anderson;* others perfuse with the fixing solution.
3. Remove tissue and fix in 10% formalin neutralized with carbonate: 1 week or longer. *Nauta and Gygax* recommend 1–3 months as best.

EMBEDDING AND SECTIONING:

1. If embedding is necessary use gelatine. Wash slices (5–10 mm. thick) in running water: 24 hours. Incubate in 25% gelatine, 37°C (cover tightly): 12–18 hours. Wipe off excess gelatine and immerse in cool formalin: 6 hours or longer.
2. *Frozen sections.* Cut sections 15–25 microns and place in 10% formalin, room temperature or cooler. Can be stored in formalin, preferably in refrigerator. Process only a few sections (6–10) at one time.

   Adey et al. (1958) prefer a dual-freezing block method, using dry ice evaporated in 70% alcohol, over CO_2 freezing. This produces more even freezing. Rapid freezing and thawing with CO_2 may rupture some of the fibers (Freon equipment eliminates some of this problem).

SOLUTIONS:

Ammoniacal silver nitrate:

silver nitrate	0.9 gm.
distilled water	20.0 ml.

When dissolved add:

absolute ethyl alcohol	10.0 ml.
ammonia, concentrated	1.8 ml.
sodium hydroxide, 2.5% aqueous	1.5 ml.

Reducing fluid:

distilled water	400.0 ml.
absolute ethyl alcohol	45.0 ml.

| formalin, 10% | 13.5 ml. |
| citric acid, 1% aqueous | 13.5 ml. |

PROCEDURE:

1. Soak sections in 15% alcohol: 30 minutes.
2. Wash briefly in distilled water and soak in 0.5% phosphomolybdic acid (0.5 gm./100 ml. water): 15–20 minutes.
3. No wash; transfer to 0.5% potassium permanganate (0.5 gm./100 ml. water): 4–10 minutes. Can be critical; make trial runs at 5, 7, and 9 minutes. Turn sections over occasionally.
4. Rinse in distilled water.
5. Decolorize in equal parts of 1% hydroquinone (1 gm./100 ml. water) and 1% oxalic acid (1 gm./100 ml. water): 1–2 minutes.
6. Wash thoroughly in distilled water, 3 changes.
7. Treat with 1% silver nitrate (1 gm./100 ml. water): 20–30 minutes.
8. Transfer sections individually; a brief wash in distilled water and then into freshly prepared ammoniacal silver: 1 minute.
9. Transfer to reducing solution, allowing sections to float on surface of solution. Brown color within 1 minute. If too light, add a little sodium hydroxide to ammoniacal silver solution; if too dark add some ammonia.
10. Wash briefly, fix in 1% sodium thiosulfate (1 gm./100 ml. water; 2 minutes.
11. Wash in distilled water, 3 changes.
12. Mount, *Albrecht's (1954)* method:
    (*a*) Transfer into equal parts of 1.5% gelatine (1.5 gm./100 ml. water) and 80% alcohol: 5 minutes or longer.
    (*b*) Tease section onto slide, withdraw from fluid with slide tilted allowing rapid drainage of excess fluid. Wipe around section, but do not allow it to completely dry.
    (*c*) Blot gently with smooth filter paper. If section sticks to paper, first moisten paper with 95% alcohol.
    (*d*) Immerse rapidly in 95% alcohol to congeal gelatine.
13. Dehydrate, clear, and mount.

RESULTS:

disintegrating axons—black
normal axons—various shades of brown

COMMENTS:

See also Nauta and Gygax (1951); Nauta and Ryan (1952); Wall (1950); White (1960); and additional references included therein.

Hamlyn (1957) and Guillery *et al.* (1961) describe methods for paraffin-embedded sections that are stained after mounting.

Marchi Method B

FIXATION: 10% formalin plus 1% of potassium chlorate: 24–48 hours, no longer. (Swank and Davenport, 1934)

SOLUTION:

Marchi fluid (Poirier *et al.*, 1954):

osmic acid, 0.5% aqueous	11.0 ml.
potassium chlorate 1% aqueous	16.0 ml.
formalin	3.0 ml.
acetic acid, 10% aqueous	3.0 ml.
distilled water to make	100.0 ml.

PROCEDURE:

1. Cut tissue into thin slices—about 3 mm. for easier impregnation.
2. Chromate, 2.5% potassium dichromate, aqueous, in dark: 7–14 days, change twice.
3. Transfer directly to Marchi fluid, a volume 15–20 times that of tissue: 1–2 weeks depending on size of tissue. Turn tissue over every day to improve penetration.
4. Wash in running water: 24 hours.
5. Dehydrate and embed. If using celloidin, keep embedding steps to a minimum. If using paraffin, avoid xylene and its solvent action on osmic acid. Chloroform is safer; also keeps steps to minimum.
6. Deparaffinize slides with chloroform and mount in chloroform-resin.

RESULTS:

degenerating myelin—black
background—brownish yellow
neutral fats—black

COMMENTS:

The principle behind the Marchi method is based on the fact that myelin of medullated nerves oxidizes more easily than degenerated myelin. Normal myelin is oxidized by chromating and will not react with osmic acid. Degenerate myelin contains oleic acid which does not oxidize during chromating and therefore reduces the osmic acid and stains black.

References: Culling (1957); Lillie (1954); Mettler (1932); Mettler and Hanada (1942); Poirier *et al.* (1954); and Swank and Davenport (1934 A,B and 1935 A,B).

Motor End Plates

Cole Method (1946) (Whole Mounts)

FIXATION: none, carry fresh tissue directly into step 1.

PROCEDURE:

1. Remove striated costal muscle and place in 10% citric acid in physiological saline (page 410): minimum time 10 minutes, maximum 30 minutes.
2. Transfer directly to 1% aqueous gold chloride (1 gm./100 ml. water). Make up day before used. Keep in dark: 60 minutes or until tissue turns dark yellow. (If pieces are larger than 4 mm. in width a longer time is required.)
3. Transfer directly to 20% aqueous formic acid (20 ml./80 ml. water): 10–20 hours in dark. Do not use metal forceps, coat them with paraffin or use glass rods.
4. Rinse in tap water.
5. Transfer to 95% methyl alcohol-glycerol (1:1): several hours. Then remove top of container and allow alcohol to evaporate.
6. Transfer to pure glycerol.
7. *To mount:* with a sharp razor cut muscle strips into small pieces. Place a piece in a very small drop of glycerol (usually, amount carried over by the piece is sufficient) on a round cover glass. Lay a smaller size cover glass over it. Spread the muscle fiber to single fiber thickness by using gentle pressure and strokes at right angles to the fibers. Turn cover glasses over and mount in *Permount* (or the like) on a glass slide. (Double cover glass mounting, page 123.)

RESULTS:

muscle fibers—red-blue
motor end plates and medullated axons—black
muscle fiber nuclei—unstained

Carey's (1941) modification:

Carey used undiluted fresh filtered lemon juice in place of the citric acid. He claimed that if longer than 12 hours was required in the formic acid (step 3), the gold chloride technic was faulty. The color of the tissue should be gold, not brown.

Warren's (1944) modification:

Warren writes that large pieces of muscle give better results than small ones because in the latter the muscle fibers may become too dark. He removed 5 or 6 ribs from a rabbit with the muscle and tendons intact. In this case the timing in solutions will have to be extended.

PROCEDURE:
1. Treat with citric acid: 2 hours.
2. Wash in 2 changes of distilled water: 5 minutes each.
3. Transfer to gold chloride: 2 hours.
4. Transfer to formic acid: 24 hours; change solution at end of first 12 hours.
5. Wash in 3 changes of distilled water: 5 minutes each.
6. Treat with pure glycerine: 24 hours, then change to a fresh solution.
7. *To mount:* cut the muscle from between the ribs, cutting close to the bone. Cut the muscle in small strips 5 mm. long. Keep strips stored in the glycerine while preparing them for mounting. Prepare thin mounts as in technic above.

COMMENTS:

The author has not used this method, but makes the following suggestion: to prevent swelling of the tissue, do not go directly from water (step 5) into glycerine (step 6). First treat with 50% alcohol-glycerine (1:1) several hours or overnight, then proceed with step 6.

Myelin

Luxol Fast Blue (MARGOLIS AND PICKETT, 1956) S

FIXATION: any good general fixative.

EMBEDDING: paraffin method.

SOLUTIONS:

Luxol fast blue:

Luxol fast blue *MBSN* [2]	0.1 gm.
95% alcohol	100.0 ml.
acetic acid, 10% aqueous	0.5 ml.

Keeps indefinitely.

[2] E. I. DuPont de Nemours and Company.

Periodic acid, 0.5%:

    periodic acid .... 0.5 gm.

    distilled water .... 100.0 ml.

Lithium carbonate, 0.05%:

    lithium carbonate .... 0.5 gm.

    distilled water .... 1000.0 ml.

Schiff's reagent, see page 294.

Sulfurous acid:

    sodium metabisulfite, 10% aqueous .... 6.0 ml.

    distilled water .... 100.0 ml.

    1N HCl (see page 408) .... 5.0 ml.

Mayer's hematoxylin, see page 125.

PROCEDURE:

1. Deparaffinize and run slides down to 95% alcohol, but remove $HgCl_2$ if present.
2. Stain in Luxol fast blue, 60°C: overnight.
3. Rinse off excess stain in 95% alcohol.
4. Rinse in distilled water.
5. Dip in lithium carbonate: 15 seconds.
6. Differentiate in 70% alcohol: 20–30 seconds.
7. Rinse in distilled water.
8. Place in lithium carbonate, second solution: 20–30 seconds.
9. Differentiate in 70% alcohol: 20–30 seconds.
10. Rinse in distilled water. If differentiation is not complete, repeat steps 8 and 9.
11. Oxidize with periodic acid: 5 minutes.
12. Wash in distilled water, 2 changes: 5 minutes.
13. Treat with Schiff's reagent: 15–30 minutes.
14. Treat with sulfurous acid, 3 changes: 2 minutes each.
15. Running water: 5 minutes.
16. Stain in Mayer's hematoxylin (or the like): 3 minutes.
17. Wash in running water: 5 minutes.
18. Dehydrate, clear, and mount.

RESULTS:

myelin—blue-green

PAS positive elements—rose to red

nuclei—blue

COMMENTS:

Margolis and Pickett include methods for following luxol fast blue with phosphotungstic acid-hematoxylin to differentiate neuroglia from myelin, and oil red *O* to distinguish degenerating myelin from normal myelin.

Dziabis (1958) describes a method for gross brain sections.

Luxol Fast Blue–Holmes Silver Nitrate (MARGOLIS AND PICKETT, 1956) S

FIXATION: 10% formalin preferred.

EMBEDDING: paraffin method.

SOLUTIONS:

Silver nitrate, 20%:

silver nitrate	20.0 gm.
distilled water	100.0 ml.

Boric acid:

boric acid	12.4 gm.
distilled water	1000.0 ml.

Borax:

borax	19.0 gm.
distilled water	1000.0 ml.

Impregnating fluid:

In 500 ml. cylinder mix 55 ml. boric acid solution and 45 ml. borax solution. Dilute to 494 ml. with distilled water. With pipette, add 1 ml. of 1% aqueous silver nitrate (1 gm./100 ml. water). With another pipette add 5 ml. of 10% aqueous pyridine (10 ml./100 ml. water). Mix thoroughly.

Reducer:

hydroquinone	1.0 gm.
sodium sulfite (crystals)	10.0 gm.
distilled water	100.0 ml.

Can be used repeatedly, but only for a few days.

Luxol fast blue—see page 212.

PROCEDURE:

1. Deparaffinize and hydrate sections to water.
2. Treat with 20% silver nitrate in dark, room temperature: 1 hour. Prepare impregnating fluid.

3. Wash in distilled water, 3 changes: 10 minutes.
4. Impregnate, 37°C: overnight.
5. Shake off superfluous fluid and place in reducer: 2 minutes.
6. Wash in running water: 3 minutes; rinse in distilled water.
7. Tone in gold chloride, 0.2% (0.2 gm./100 ml. water): 3 minutes.
8. Rinse in distilled water.
9. Treat with oxalic acid, 2% (2 gm./100 ml.): 3–10 minutes; when axons are thoroughly black, remove.
10. Rinse in distilled water.
11. Fix in sodium thiosulfate, 5% (5 gm./100 ml.): 3 minutes.
12. Wash in running water: 10 minutes.
13. Rinse briefly in 95% alcohol.
14. Stain in Luxol fast blue: overnight.
15. Rinse in 95% alcohol; rinse in distilled water.
16. Treat with lithium carbonate, 0.05% (.5 gm./1000 ml. water): 15 seconds.
17. Differentiate in 70% alcohol: 20–30 seconds.
18. Rinse in distilled water.
19. Repeat steps 16 and 17 if necessary. (The author finds that usually 3 repeats is necessary for sharp differentiation.)
20. Dehydrate, clear, and mount.

RESULTS:

axis cylinders—black
myelin sheaths—green blue

COMMENTS:

Margolis and Pickett write that slides may be left in step 6 until time to prepare them for Luxol fast blue staining. This tends to encourage loose sections. The author has lost no sections by carrying the slides through to step 13. Transfer them into absolute alcohol and coat them with nitrocellulose. Harden the nitrocellulose and store the slides in 70–80% alcohol until ready to stain in luxol fast blue. Slides have been left in this condition for over the weekend with completely satisfactory results. The nitrocellulose protection also permits freer agitation of slides in the differentiating fluids than without this coating.

Ora's Method (1958) S

FIXATION: 10% formalin.

SECTION: at 17 microns, paraffin method.

SOLUTIONS:
   Mordant, modified Marchi fluid:

potassium dichromate	25.0 gm.
sodium sulfate	1.0 gm.
distilled water	100.0 ml.
Add 1 ml. of above to:	
ferric alum, 5% aqueous (3 gm./60 ml. water)	60.0 ml.

Hematoxylin:

hematoxylin	1.0 gm.
absolute ethyl alcohol	10.0 ml.
Dissolve hematoxylin in alchohol and add:	
distilled water	90.0 ml.
lithium carbonate, saturated aqueous	4.0 ml.

Mix thoroughly. Prepare fresh each time.

Differentiating solution:

potassium permanganate	0.5 gm.
distilled water	100.0 ml.

Thin celloidin:

gum mastic, saturated in absolute alcohol	2.0 ml.
celloidin or nitrocellulose, 10%	7.0 ml.
ether, anhydrous	45.0 ml.
absolute ethyl alcohol	45.0 ml.
acetone	10.0 ml.

PROCEDURE:
   1. Deparaffinize and run slides into absolute alcohol: 2 minutes.
   2. Dip twice in thin celloidin, blot lightly with filter paper and harden in 95% and 80% alcohol: 2 minutes each.
   3. Hydrate down to water.
   4. Mordant, 60°C: 30 minutes.
   5. Preheat hematoxylin, 60°C, add slides, stain: 30 minutes.
   6. Wash in running water until sections blue: 2 minutes.
   7. Differentiate with potassium permanganate until myelin fibers are jet black and background is light yellow: maximum 30 seconds.
   8. Wash in running water: 2 minutes.
   9. Dehydrate, clear, and mount.

RESULTS:
  myelin sheaths—black
  background—light yellow

Mahon Method (1937) S

FIXATION: 10% formalin. Cut paraffin sections 15–20 microns. Not good for frozen sections.

EMBEDDING: paraffin method.

SOLUTIONS:
  Mordant:

ferric ammonium sulfate (ferric alum)	4.0 gm.
distilled water	100.0 ml.

  Hematoxylin:

lithium carbonate solution (to 93 ml. distilled water add 7 ml. of saturated aqueous lithium carbonate	90.0 ml.
hematoxylin solution (1 gm./10 ml. absolute alcohol	10.0 ml.

  Mix immediately before use.

PROCEDURE:
1. Deparaffinize and hydrate slides to water.
2. Mordant: 15–30 minutes.
3. Rinse in 2 changes distilled water: 1 minute.
4. Stain in hematoxylin: 30–60 minutes.
5. Wash in running water: 2 minutes.
6. Treat with lithium carbonate, 7% (7 gm./100 ml. water) until myelin is dark blue and background is colorless: 15–30 minutes. Watch carefully that too much dye is not extracted; also, prolonged exposure to lithium carbonate may loosen sections.
7. Wash thoroughly in running water: at least 5 minutes.
8. Dehydrate, clear, and mount.

RESULTS:
  myelin—dark blue
  background—colorless

Chapter 16

Hematologic Elements and Related Tissues

Blood is a fluid (*plasma*) that contains suspended in it cells and fragments of cytoplasm. The fragments are **platelets** and the cells are either **red cells (erythrocytes)** or **white cells (leukocytes)**. The erythrocytes are nonnucleated, but 90% of their solid content is made up of *hemoglobin,* a protein. Leukocytes are all nucleated and are classified as five different kinds. The *granular* leukocytes have a granular cytoplasm and include the **neutrophils, eosinophils** and **basophils.** The nongranular leukocytes have nongranular cytoplasm and are the **lymphocytes** and **monocytes.** The granular leukocytes are named according to the affinity of their granules for certain types of stains—neutral, acid (eosin), and basic. The term **polymorphs** is often applied to neutrophils because of their many-formed or many-lobed nuclei.

Bone marrow is a **hemopoietic** (blood forming) tissue and is described as either red or yellow. The red marrow is red due to great numbers of red blood cells in various stages of formation; it is actively producing blood cells. Yellow marrow contains large quantities of fat; it is not actively manufacturing blood cells but is storing fat. Yellow marrow nonetheless retains the potential to resume production of blood cells. (*Reference: Ham, 1957*)

Blood cells and fluid may become parasitized in various ways, as with malaria, trypanosomes, inclusion bodies of various diseases, such as rickettsia and psittacosis. These foreign elements, in most cases, are best demonstrated with a Romanowsky type of stain.

Blood Smears

Preparation for Thin Smears

Slides must be clean for a uniform smear. Handle slides at the edges, keeping fingers off the clean surface. Prick the finger and when a small drop of blood appears, wipe it away. Touch the next drop of blood to the clean surface of the right end of the slide. Place the narrow edge of another slide at about a 20° angle on the first slide and to the left of the drop blood. Pull to the right until the slide touches the blood. As soon as the blood has spread along the line of contact, push the right hand toward the left. Push steadily until all the blood disappears or the other end of the slide is reached. This method drags the blood but does not run over it and crush some of the cells. The hand can be kept from shaking by resting it on the table. Also do not use a slide with a rough edge to leave streaks in the smear. If the blood seems thick, reduce the 20° angle to feed it out at a slower rate. With thin blood increase the angle. (See *Pequeno, 1960,* for a clever method using a pen to make thin smears.)

Dry the slides rapidly in the air; waving them facilitates drying, and prevents **crenation** (notching or scalloping of edges) of the red cells.

Preferably blood smears are stained immediately or within 24 hours. If they must be stored, place them in a tight box away from dust and flies.

Blood smears are commonly stained with a Romanowsky type of stain, or neutral stain (page 110). Neutrality is essential, and therefore dilution usually is made with a buffer solution of a known *p*H. Distilled water often is too acid, and tap water too alkaline. The smears require no fixation in the usual sense, since *Wright's stain (1902)* includes both fixing agent (methyl alcohol) and stain.

Thin Smear Method

SOLUTIONS:

Wright's stain:

The stain may be purchased in three forms: (1) by the bottle, 10, 25 or 100 gms.; (2) in capsule form, 0.1 gm. per capsule; or (3) in solution, 4, 8 or 16 ounces.

The powder (bulk or capsule) is ground up with methyl alcohol (0.1 gm. to 60.0 ml.). The alcohol must be labeled "neutral" and "acetone free." Grind thoroughly in a glass mortar, and pour off **supernatant** (surface-floating) liquid. If undissolved powder remains, pour back the liquid and grind again.

Buffer solution, *p*H 6.4:

monobasic potassium phosphate	6.63 gm.
anhydrous dibasic sodium phosphate	2.56 gm.
distilled water	1000.0 ml.

PROCEDURE:

1. With wax pencil draw 2 marks across slide delineating region to be stained (length of 40 mm. cover glass).
2. Cover with 10–12 drops of Wright's stain: 1–2 minutes.
3. Add an equal amount of buffer: 2–4 minutes.
4. Rinse in distilled water, 1 or 2 dips. Precipitate deposit on the slide can be avoided by flushing the slide with a pipette, or carry the stain with the slide into the wash water; do not drain it off first.
5. Blot with 2 sheets of filter paper; press but do not rub.
6. Allow slide to thoroughly dry before applying cover glass.

RESULTS:

erythrocytes—pink
nuclei—deep blue or purple
basophilic granules—deep purple
eosinophilic granules—red to red-orange, bluish cytoplasm
neutrophilic granules—reddish brown to lilac, pale pink cytoplasm
granules of monocytes—azure
lymphocyte granules—larger and more reddish than monocyte granules, sky blue cytoplasm
platelets—violet to purple

COMMENTS:

Precipitate formation can be troublesome; the dark granules obscure the blood cells and are confusing in malarial smears. In addition to poor washing in step 4, another case of precipitate may be evaporation during exposure to undiluted stain. Methyl alcohol is highly volatile and readily lost by evaporation. In dry warm weather use more Wright's, or shorten the time a bit, or cover the slides with a petri dish. Rapid evaporation is easily detected, and more stain can always be added.

The longer the washing with water, the more stain is removed from the white cells. Usually only a dip or two is sufficient, but if the white cells are overstained, differentiate them by longer washing.

If the slides are overstained, the erythrocytes are too red, the white cells too pale, or the stain has precipitated, the slides can be recovered: (1) Cover the entire slide almost to excess with additional Wright's stain: 15–30 minutes; (2) rinse with distilled water; (3) dry. (*Morrison and Samwick, 1940*)

Preparation of Thick Blood Films

This type of film concentrates a relatively large quantity of blood in a small area, thereby increasing the possibilities of finding parasites. The concentration and timing of staining are adjusted so the action is stopped at the point when the leukocytes have stained, some hemoglobin has been dissolved and the red cell membranes have not yet begun to stain. At this point the leukocytes, platelets and protozoa only are stained and lie on an unstained or very lightly stained background, yellowish from remaining hemoglobin. Freshly prepared films stain better than films one or more days old.

Puncture the skin deep enough to form a large drop of blood. On a slide cover a space the size of a dime with enough blood (about 3–4 average drops) to spread easily. Too much blood will crack and peel off when dry. Smear it by circling the slide under the finger without making actual contact. Some find it easier to swirl the blood with a dissecting needle or the corner of a slide. Practice will determine the best method and how much blood to use. Too thin a film has no advantage over a thin smear. An ideal film is several cell layers thick in the center, tapering off to one cell thickness at the periphery.

Allow the slide to dry in a horizontal position; if tilted the blood will ooze to one edge of the film. Protect from dust and flies, and do not use excessive heat for drying.

Thick Film Method

SOLUTIONS: *Field (1941)*
   Solution *A*:

methylene blue, C.I. 52015	0.8 gm.
azure *A*, C.I. 52005	0.5 gm.
dibasic sodium phosphate, anhydrous	5.0 gm.
monobasic potassium phosphate	6.25 gm.
distilled water	500.0 ml.

Solution *B:*

eosin *Y*, C.I. 45380	1.0 gm.
dibasic sodium phosphate, anhydrous	5.0 gm.
monobasic potassium phosphate	6.25 gm.
distilled water	500.0 ml.

Dissolve phosphate salts first, then add stains. (The azure will go into solution by grinding in glass mortar with a small amount of phosphate solvent.) Set aside for 24 hours. Filter.

PROCEDURE:

1. Dip slides in solution *A:* 1 second.
2. Rinse gently in clean distilled water: few seconds, or until stain ceases to flow from film.
3. Dip in solution *B:* 1 second. Use this solution with care; it tends to decolorize the leukocytes stained with methylene blue-azure, and accelerates the dissolving of hemaglobin.
4. Rinse gently in distilled water: 2–3 dips.
5. Dry, do not blot. Stand slides on end and allow to air dry.
6. When completely dry, add mounting medium and cover glass.

RESULTS:

There will be a thicker central area of partially laked blood. This may not be well-suited for examination. But the surrounding area and especially at the edge toward which the hemaglobin drained will be creamy, sometimes mottled with pale blue. This is the best area for study.

leukocytes:
cytoplasm—pale blue, poorly defined
nuclei—dark blue, well defined
eosinophilic granules—bright red, large, well defined
neutrophilic granules—pale purple pink, small indistinct
basophilic granules—deep blue with reddish cast
platelets—pale purple or lavender

parasites:
cytoplasm—blue
chromatin—purplish red or deep ruby red
pigment—unstained yellow granules of varying intensity

SOLUTIONS: *Wilcox (1943)*

Wright-Giemsa:

Giemsa powder	2.0 gm.
glycerol	100.0 ml.

Heat in water bath, 55–60°C: 2 hours, stirring at intervals. Avoid absorption of moisture by covering mouth of flask with double thickness of paper secured with rubber band.

Add: aged Wright's staining solution (2.0 gm. per 1000.0 ml. methyl alcohol)	100.0 ml.
Let stand overnight: add additional Wright's staining solution	800.0 ml.

Filter; ready for use.

Working solution:

Wright-Giemsa stock solution	1 part
Neutral distilled water (buffer)	9 parts

Buffer, pH 7.0:

Solution *A:*

dibasic sodium phosphate, anhydrous	9.5 gm.
distilled water	1000.0 ml.

Solution *B:*

monobasic potassium phosphate	9.7 gm.
distilled water	1000.0 ml.

Working Solution:

Solution *A*	61.1 ml.
Solution *B*	38.9 ml.
distilled water	900.0 ml.

PROCEDURE:

Short Method:

1. Stain film: 10 minutes.
2. Flush scum from top of solution with natural water to avoid picking up precipitate on slides.
3. Remove slides to neutral distilled water: 1 minute.
4. Dry slides standing on end. Do not blot. Mount.

Long Method (a more brilliant stain):

1. Stain: 45 minutes in dilution of 1 to 50 of neutral water.

2. Flush off scum and transfer slides to neutral distilled water: 3–5 minutes.
3. Dry as above.

Note: Thin smear and thick film can be stained on same slide. Fix thin portion in methyl alcohol for 1–2 minutes, taking care that thick film does not come in contact with alcohol. Stain as above (short method), but shorten washing time to 2 or 3 dips so thin smear is not too light; this shorter washing time will leave a deeper background in the thick film.

MODIFICATIONS:

Fenton and Innes (1945).
Manwell (1945).
Modified Wright's stain, Steil (1936).

STAINING OLD BLOOD SMEARS:

Old smears will stain more brilliantly if treated 5–10 minutes in alcohol-acetic solution—10 drops glacial acetic acid to 60 ml. absolute alcohol.

Blood Tissue Elements and Inclusion Bodies [1]

Giemsa Stain, Wolbach's Modification (MALLORY, 1944)

FIXATION: any good general fixative.

SOLUTIONS:

Acid alcohol:

70% ethyl alcohol	100.0 ml.
glacial acetic acid	0.5–1.0 ml.

Giemsa stock solution:

Giemsa powder	1.0 gm.
methyl alcohol, neutral, acetone-free	66.0 ml.
glycerol	66.0 ml.

Work Giemsa powder into glycerol and place in 60°C oven for 2 hours. Add methyl alcohol and stopper tightly.

Working solution:

Stock Giemsa solution	2.5 ml.
methyl alcohol	100.0 ml.
distilled water	3.0 ml.

[1] See p. 306.

Rosin stock solution: (Colophonium)

    white wood rosin .... 10.0 gm.

    absolute alcohol .... 100.0 ml.

Working solution:

    rosin stock solution .... 5.0 ml.

    95% ethyl alcohol .... 40.0 ml.

PROCEDURE:

1. Deparaffinize and hydrate slides to water. Remove $HgCl_2$.
2. Treat in acid alcohol: 5 minutes (not necessary if tissue has been subjected to acid decalcification).
3. Wash, running water: 5 minutes.
4. Rinse in distilled water.
5. Place in freshly mixed Giemsa working solution: 1 hour.
6. Transfer to second jar of Giemsa working solution: overnight.
7. Rinse in distilled water.
8. Differentiate in rosin alcohol.
9. Rinse in 95% alcohol.
10. Dehydrate in absolute alcohol, 2 changes; clear and mount.

RESULTS:

nuclei—reddish purple

other tissue elements—similar to Wright's stain

inclusion bodies—blue to purplish blue

COMMENTS:

For other stains for inclusion bodies, see pages 326–328.

Staining for Malaria

Jenner-Giemsa (MCCLUNG, 1939, MODIFIED MAY-GRÜNWALD)

FIXATION: Smears may be fixed during staining process. Tissue sections in any good general fixative, preferably containing mercuric chloride and alcohol.

SOLUTIONS:

Jenner's solution:

    Jenner's stain .... 0.2 gm.

    methyl alcohol, neutral, acetone free .... 100.0 ml.

Giemsa stock solution:

    Giemsa powder .... 3.8 gm.

    methyl alcohol, neutral, acetone free .... 75.0 ml.

    glycerol .... 25.0 ml.

Work stain into glycerol, warm for 2 hours, 60°C oven. Add methyl alcohol.

Working solution:

Giemsa stock solution	10.0 ml.
distilled water	100.0 ml.

or 1.0 ml. to 10.0 ml. water for flooding a slide.

PROCEDURE:

1. Deparaffinize sections and run down to 50% alcohol. (Remove $HgCl_2$, if present.)

2. (*a*) Sections—flood with ample amount of Jenner's solution and add an equal amount of distilled water, or mix equal amounts of Jenner's solution and water and flood slide or stain slide in coplin jar: 4 minutes.

   (*b*) Smears—flood with Jenner's solution: 3 minutes. Add equal amount of distilled water: 1 minute.

3. Pour off Jenner's; no rinse.

4. Flood with diluted Giemsa solution or place in coplin jar of solution: 15–20 minutes.

5. Rinse off stain with distilled water and continue to differentiate with distilled water. If too blue, eosin color can be brought out by rinsing in 1% acetic acid in water.

6. Dehydrate in following sequence of acetone and xylene. Do not use alcohol; it extracts the stain.

   acetone 95 parts: xylene 5 parts
   acetone 70 parts: xylene 30 parts
   acetone 50 parts: xylene 50 parts
   acetone 30 parts: xylene 70 parts
   acetone 5 parts: xylene 95 parts

7. Clear in xylene and mount.

RESULTS:

malaria:
chromatin—red or purplish red
cytoplasm—blue (other elements' color similar to Wright's stain)
pigment—yellow brown to black
Schüffner's stippling—red

COMMENTS:

A beautiful clear stain for any blood picture, particularly blood parasites.

Brooke and Donaldson (*1950*) recommend the use of Triton X-30, a nonionic liquid detergent to prevent the transfer of malarial parasites between films when mass staining.

Bone Marrow Staining

Maximow's Eosin-Azure Stain (BLOCK *et al.*, 1953)

FIXATION: Zenker-neutral formalin: 2 hours. Neutralize formalin by adding 2 gm. lithium or magnesium carbonate to 500 ml. of formalin. Excess of carbonate should be present. Wash in running water 1–24 hours before preparation for embedding. (See Comment 4)

SOLUTIONS:

Solution *A:*

eosin Y, C.I. 45380	0.1 gm.
distilled water	100.0 ml.

Solution *B:*

azure II	0.1 gm.
distilled water	100.0 ml.

Working solution:

distilled water	85.0 ml.
Solution *A*	15.0 ml.

Stirring vigorously, add gradually

Solution *B*	10.0 ml.

Fresh solutions are best; their action deteriorates after 3 or 4 weeks. Working solution should appear deep violet in color, and a precipitate should not form in it for an hour or more. If a precipitate forms on the slides, the stain mixture was improperly made; solution *B* was added to solution *A* too rapidly or without stirring. If the eosin loses its brilliance, solutions are old.

PROCEDURE:

1. Deparaffinize and hydrate slides to water; remove $HgCl_2$. If tissue was fixed in a fixative without potassium dichromate, chromate slides overnight in 2.5–3% aqueous potassium dichromate. Wash thoroughly in running water: 15 minutes. Proceed to step 2.
2. Stain in Mayer's hematoxylin: 30–45 seconds, no more. (See Comment 3.)

3. Wash in running water: 5–10 minutes.
4. Wash in distilled water: 5 or more minutes.
5. Stain in eosin-azure overnight.
6. Differentiate in 95% alcohol: may require 2–3 hours. In stubborn cases of differentiation (old solution) a brief immersion in colophonium alcohol (page 225) may help to sharpen the colors, but not as well as a new solution. The over-all appearance of the slide should be blue with a slightly greenish tinge, but differentiation must be done under the microscope.
7. Dehydrate, absolute alcohol; clear and mount.

RESULTS:

nuclei—dark purple blue
erythrocytes—light pink
eosinophilic granules—brilliant red
cytoplasm—pale blue

COMMENTS:

1. After 2 hours fixation, cells in center are not as well fixed as those at periphery, but fixation longer than 2 hours produces granular cytoplasm in eosinophilic erythrocytes and erythroblasts.
2. Block embeds in celloidin and mounts with clove oil, page 77 and stains with a weak solution of Delaefield's hematoxylin, 2 drops/100 ml. distilled water, overnight, or in a mixture of 10–15 drops/100 ml. for approximately 5 minutes, or till nuclei are faint blue; check under microscope. The author has had good results with the above-scheduled method (step 2), but take care not to stain too long, never over 60 seconds.
3. Bone marrow when collected should have an anticoagulant added to it. *Gardner (1958)* and many other workers mix the bone marrow in a tube containing 0.5 mg. heparin powder. *Kniseley*[2] wets his syringe with d-potassium EDTA as an anticoagulant. Smears can be made with some of the **aspirated** (drawn out by suction) marrow. The remaining material is poured into a small funnel lined with "Filtrator Coffee Paper" (*Zbar and Winter, 1959*). Rinse marrow, while in funnel, several times with saline, or until the marrow has lost most of its color. This also helps to wash the material into one mass at the apex of the funnel. Partially clotted marrow will be broken up and washed free of blood, leaving excellent clear particles of marrow. Fold in the filter paper, place in

[2] Ralph M. Kniseley, Chief of Clinical Research and Training, Oak Ridge Institute of Nuclear Studies. Personal communication.

tissue receptacle and carry through fixation, washing, dehydration and infiltration without removing. No marrow will be lost.

Minute amounts of marrow may prove difficult to recover from the filter paper without loss of material. The author has avoided loss by allowing the paraffin around the marrow (on the filter paper) to congeal slightly. Then carefully scrape paraffin and marrow together and remove to melted paraffin in mold. The congealed paraffin containing the marrow will sink to the bottom of the mold or can be pressed down into desired position. This method keeps the marrow concentrated reasonably well.

4. *Gude and Odell (1955)* recommend for dilution VINISIL (*Abbott Laboratories*), a 3.5% solution of polyvinylpyrrolidone (PVP) in normal saline.

Endicott (1945) used plasma serum as a diluting fluid to thin smears. The serum can be kept on hand for several months if stored in refrigerator.

5. For a fluorescent method, see *Werth (1953)*.

Phloxine-Methylene Blue (THOMAS, 1953)

FIXATION: any general fixative.

SOLUTIONS:

Phloxine solution:

phloxine *B*, C.I. 45410	0.5 gm.
distilled water	100.0 ml.
glacial acetic acid	0.2 ml.

A slight precipitate will form. Filter before use. (The author has found this of no importance; the precipitate settles at bottom of bottle and does not collect on the tissue.)

Methylene blue-azure solution:

methylene blue, C.I. 52015	0.25 gm.
azure *B*, C.I. 52010	0.25 gm.
borax	0.25 gm.
distilled water	100.0 ml.

PROCEDURE:

1. Deparaffinize and hydrate slides to water; remove $HgCl_2$.
2. Stain in phloxine: 1–2 minutes.
3. Rinse well in distilled water.

4. Stain methylene blue-azure: 0.5–1 minute.
5. Partially destain in 0.2% aqueous acetic acid.
6. Complete differentiation in 95% alcohol, 3 changes.
7. Dehydrate, absolute alcohol; clear and mount.

RESULTS:
nuclei—blue
plasma cell cytoplasm—blue
other tissue elements—shades of rose and red

COMMENTS:
Thomas substitutes azure *B* for azure II of other methods because of the uncertain composition of the latter. It is unnecessary to use colophonium alcohol as in other methods. The author recommends Thomas' method over all others she has tried. It is practically fool-proof.

Delez and Davis (1950) make up their phloxine with oxalic acid; 1% phloxine in 0.05% aqueous oxalic acid.

This staining method frequently is used for general staining in place of a hematoxylin-eosin method.

Staining for Fibrin

Ledrum's Acid Picro-Mallory Method (CULLING, 1957)

FIXATION: any good general fixative.

SOLUTIONS:
Celestin blue:

celestin blue *B*, C.I. 51050	0.25 gm.
ferric alum, 5% (5 gm./100 ml. water)	50.0 ml.
Boil 3 minutes. Cool and filter. Add:	
glycerol	7.0 ml.

Keeps for several months.

Mayer's hematoxylin, see page 125.

Picro-orange:

picric acid saturated in 80% alcohol	100.0 ml.
orange *G*, C.I. 16230	0.2 gm.

Acid fuchsin:

acid fuchsin, C.I. 42685	1.0 gm.
distilled water	100.0 ml.
trichloracetic acid	3.0 gm.

Phosphotungstic acid:

phosphotungstic acid	1.0 gm.
distilled water	100.0 ml.

Aniline blue:

aniline blue, *WS*, C.I. 42780	2.0 gm.
distilled water	100.0 ml.
glacial acetic acid	2.0 ml.

PROCEDURE:

1. Deparaffinize and hydrate slides to water; remove $HgCl_2$.
2. Stain in celestin blue: 3–5 minutes.
3. Rinse in tap water.
4. Stain in Mayer's hematoxylin: 5 minutes.
5. Wash in running water: 5 minutes.
6. Rinse in 95% alcohol.
7. Stain in picro-orange: 2 minutes.
8. Stain in acid fuchsin: 5 minutes.
9. Rinse in distilled water.
10. Dip in equal parts of picro-orange and 80% alcohol: few seconds.
11. Differentiate in phosphotungstic acid: 5–10 minutes, until colors are clear.
12. Rinse in distilled water.
13. Stain in aniline blue: 2–10 minutes.
14. Rinse in distilled water: 2–3 minutes.
15. Dehydrate; clear and mount.

RESULTS:

fibrin—clear red
erythrocytes—orange
collagen—blue
nuclei—blue-black

COMMENTS:

This method is specific for fibrin, setting it off sharply from other tissue elements. See also Phosphotungstic acid-Hematoxylin (page 136), and Gram-Weigert (page 307).

Chapter **17**

Pigments and Minerals

Pigments are a heterogeneous group of substances containing enough natural color to be visible without staining. Sometimes, however, color is added to give them more intense differential staining. Some pigments are artifacts, such as formalin pigment (page 7). Others, **exogenous** pigments, are foreign pigments that have been taken into the tissue in some manner. Carbon is a common pigment found in the lungs of city dwellers, particularly of people from coal-burning cities. **Endogenous** pigments are found within the organism and arise from nonpigmented materials. Iron-containing hemoglobin can become broken down into iron-containing pigment, **hemosiderin,** and a noniron-containing pigment, **hematoidin,** or **bilirubin** (brown) which can be oxidized to **biliverdin** (green). Normal hemoglobin, when not broken down into hemosiderin, will not show a positive Prussian blue reaction (page 233). The iron is **masked** or **occult,** and the organic part of the hemoglobin molecule must be destroyed, the iron must be unmasked. Hydrogen peroxide has become the reliable reagent for this purpose, producing ferric oxide, and finally a fairly good Prussian blue reaction.

Melanin (brown or black pigment) is found normally in the skin, hair, and eye, but may occur pathologically anywhere in the body. **Lipofuchsin,** sometimes known as the "wear and tear" pigment, can be found in the heart muscle, adrenals, ganglion cells, and liver. Melanin and lipofuchsin are brownish pigments stainable by fat dyes and some basic aniline dyes such as fuchsin. They are metachromatic (page 110) with methyl green and give a positive Schiff reaction after periodic acid treatment (page 298). *Reference:* Ham (1957).

Testing for Iron

According to *Baker (1958)* the iron reaction is an example of local formation of a colored substance which is not a dye. It is a type of histochemical test wherein a tissue is soaked in a colorless substance. Certain tissue elements react with the substance and become colored. The well-known test is the *Berlin blue, Prussian blue* or *Perl's reaction,* in which the iron is dissolved from hemosiderin by hydrochloric acid, and then reacts with potassium ferrocyanide to form the Berlin blue precipitate, *ferric ferrocyanide.*

Sometimes fading occurs in slides due to the reduction of the Berlin blue to colorless *ferro ferrocyanide.* The mounting resin probably takes up oxygen while drying and deprives the sections of oxygen, thereby reducing them to the colorless condition. If this takes place and it is essential to recover the slides, treat them with hydrogen peroxide. The newer synthetics are not as prone to reduce Berlin blue as former resins; also Lustron 2020 is recommended (page 118).

Iron Reaction (GOMORI, 1936)

FIXATION: 10% buffered formalin; other general fixatives are satisfactory but acid content may dissolve some of the hemosiderin (iron bearing pigment, *Lillie, 1954B*).

SOLUTIONS:

Hydrochloric acid, 20%:

hydrochloric acid (sp.gr. 1.188–1.192, 37–38% HCl)	20.0 ml.
distilled water	80.0 ml.

Potassium ferrocyanide, 10%:

potassium ferrocyanide, $K_4Fe(CN)_6 \cdot 3H_2O$	10.0 gm.
distilled water	100.0 ml.

Safranin:

safranin O, C.I. 50240	0.2 gm.
distilled water	100.0 ml.
glacial acetic acid	1.0 ml.

PROCEDURE:

1. Deparaffinize and hydrate slides to water; remove $HgCl_2$.
2. Wash in distilled water: 1–2 minutes.
3. Place slides in equal parts of hydrochloric acid and potassium ferrocyanide mixed immediately before use: 20 minutes. Do not handle slides with metal forceps.
4. Wash thoroughly in distilled water (*not* tap water).
5. Counterstain with safranin (or other red nuclear stain): 2–3 minutes.
6. Rinse in 70% alcohol.
7. Dehydrate, clear, and mount.

RESULTS:

iron pigment—brilliant greenish blue
nuclei and other tissue elements—shades of rose and red

COMMENTS:

For masked or occult iron (*Glick, 1949*), pre-treat slides with 30% hydrogen peroxide alkalized with dilute ammonia (1 drop/100 ml. peroxide): 10–15 minutes. Wash well and proceed to step 3. If the hydrogen peroxide tends to form bubbles under the sections and loosen them, keep the solution and slides cool in the refrigerator during the treatment.

Iron Reaction (HUTCHISON, 1953)

FIXATION: Hutchison recommends:

sodium sulfate	12.0 gm.
glacial acetic acid	33.0 ml.
formalin	40.0 ml.
distilled water to make	200.0 ml.

Go directly into 70% alcohol from fixative.

SOLUTIONS:

Ferrocyanide-hydrochloric acid solution:

(*a*)	potassium ferrocyanide	2.0 gm.
	distilled water	50.0 ml.
(*b*)	hydrochloric acid	2.0 ml.
	distilled water	50.0 ml.

Freshly mix above solutions, warm slightly and filter. Place in paraffin oven, 56°C a short time before using.

Safranin, see page 233.

PROCEDURE:

1. Deparaffinize and hydrate slides to water.
2. Wash in distilled water: 3 minutes.
3. Treat with ferrocyanide-hydrochloric acid, 56°C: 10 minutes.
4. Rinse, several changes distilled water: 5 minutes.
5. Counterstain with safranin (or other red nuclear stain): 2–3 minutes.
6. Rinse in 70% alcohol.
7. Dehydrate, clear, and mount.

RESULTS:

iron pigment—brilliant greenish-blue
nuclei—red
other tissue elements—shades of red and rose

COMMENTS:

Hutchison claims that the warm solution is the most important step in this method. Do not leave the slides in the solution longer than 10 minutes, and if they have been well washed in distilled water, precipitate seldom forms on the sections. In the author's experience, this method produces deeper, more brilliant colors than Gomori's method.

Turnbull Blue Method for Ferrous Iron (PEARSE, 1953)

FIXATION: 10% buffered formalin; other general fixatives satisfactory if acid is absent.

SOLUTIONS:

Ammonium sulfide: a saturated solution $(NH_4)_2S$, 20–30% content, analytical reagent.

Potassium ferricyanide:

potassium ferricyanide, $K_3Fe(CN)_6$	20.0 gm.
distilled water	100.0 ml.

Hydrochloric acid:

hydrochloric acid (sp.gr. 1.188–1.192, 37–38% HCl)	1.0 ml.
distilled water	100.0 ml.

Safranin, see page 233.

PROCEDURE:

1. Deparaffinize and hydrate slides to water; remove $HgCl_2$.
2. Wash in distilled water.

3. Treat with yellow ammonium sulfide: 1–3 hours.
4. Rinse in distilled water.
5. Treat with equal parts of potassium ferricyanide and hydrochloric acid, freshly mixed: 10–20 minutes.
6. Rinse in distilled water.
7. Counterstain with safranin (or other red nuclear stain): 2–3 minutes.
8. Rinse in 70% alcohol.
9. Dehydrate, clear, and mount.

RESULTS:

ferrous iron and ferric iron converted to ferrous iron—deep blue
other tissue elements—shades of rose and red

Iron Reaction: Di-nitrosoresorcinol (HUMPHREY, 1935)
FIXATION: 10% buffered formalin, general fixative without acid.

SOLUTIONS:

Ammonium sulfide, 30% analytical reagent.
Di-nitrosoresorcinol (resorcin green), saturated aqueous solution, or a 3% solution in 50% alcohol.

PROCEDURE:

1. Deparaffinize and hydrate slides down to water.
2. Treat with ammonium sulfide: 1 minute.
3. Rinse in water.
4. Transfer to di-nitrosoresorcinol: 6–24 hours.
5. Wash in water (or 50% alcohol).
6. Dehydrate, clear, and mount.

RESULTS:

iron—dark green
background—brown

COMMENTS:

Reagent is more effective if solution has aged for a few days. Undissolved chemical should be present in the saturated aqueous solution. Author's reaction—a disappointingly dull slide.

Testing for Calcium

Von Kossa, modified from Mallory (1944)

FIXATION: 10% formalin or alcohol, although other fixatives give reasonably good results.

SOLUTIONS:

Silver nitrate:

silver nitrate, $AgNO_3$ .... 5.0 gm.

distilled water .... 100.0 ml.

Fresh solution always best; never use one more than 1 week old. Safranin, see page 233.

PROCEDURE:

1. Deparaffinize and hydrate slides to distilled water; remove $HgCl_2$.
2. Treat with silver nitrate in dark: 30 minutes.
3. Rinse thoroughly in distilled water.
4. Expose slides (in distilled water) to bright light (75–100W bulb satisfactory): 1 hour. Lay them over a white background to expediate reaction.
5. Wash thoroughly in distilled water.
6. Counterstain in safranin (or other red nuclear stain): 2–3 minutes.
7. Rinse in 70% alcohol.
8. Dehydrate, clear and mount.

RESULTS:

calcium deposits—dark brown to black

nuclei and other tissue elements—shades of red and rose

COMMENTS:

If iron blocks out the calcium, treat 10–15 minutes with .005M sodium EDTA (ethylenediaminetetraacetic acid) in normal saline. Wash in distilled water and proceed to step 2. (*McGee-Russell, 1958*)

This reaction actually demonstrates phosphates and carbonates rather than calcium itself, but since soluble phosphates and carbonates are washed out, the calcium phosphates and calcium carbonates remain to react with the silver (*Lillie, 1954B*) and the test can be regarded as sufficiently specific (*Pearse, 1953*).

Renaud (*1959*) demonstrates that a high percentage of alcohol (at least 80% content) in the fixing fluid is necessary in order to detect calcium in some tissues (i.e., heart and coronary vessels). Water and even buffered formalin can dissolve out some small deposits of calcium salts.

Alizarine Red S, PEARSE (1953)

FIXATION: preferably one containing 80% alcohol, for maximum preservation of calcium.

SOLUTIONS:

Alizarine red *S:*

alizarine red *S*, C.I. 58005	1.0 gm.
distilled water	100.0 ml.

Toluidine blue:

toluidine blue *O*, C.I. 52040	0.1 gm.
distilled water	100.0 ml.

PROCEDURE:

1. Deparaffinize and hydrate slides to water.
2. Stain in alizarine red: 3–5 minutes.
3. Rinse in distilled water.
4. Stain in toluidine blue: 1 minute.
5. Rinse in distilled water.
6. Dehydrate, clear and mount.

RESULTS:

calcium—orange-red
nuclei—blue
inorganic iron (not hemosiderin)—purple

COMMENTS:

Any counterstain should be kept light to provide contrast for the alizarine red color.

Hemoglobin Staining

Benzidine Method (RALPH'S, 1941; GLICK, 1949)

FIXATION: alcohol or formalin.

SOLUTIONS:

Benzidine reagent:

benzidine	1.0 gm.
absolute methyl alcohol	100.0 ml.

Peroxide reagent:

peroxide (reagent 3%)	25.0 ml.
70% ethyl alcohol	75.0 ml.

PROCEDURE:

1. Deparaffinize sections and hydrate to water. Not necessary for smears, which will be fixed by benzidine reagent.
2. Flood with benzidine reagent: 1–2 minutes.

3. Drain, and flood with peroxide reagent: 1.5 minutes.
4. Wash in distilled water: 15 seconds.
5. Counterstain if desired with a red nuclear stain.
6. Dehydrate, clear, and mount.

RESULTS:

hemoglobin—dark brown
For hemosiderin, see iron reactions, page 233.

Cyanol Reaction (DUNN, 1946)

FIXATION: formalin, preferably buffered to pH 7; fix no longer than 48 hours. Dried smears may be methyl alcohol fixed and then proceed to step 2 below.

SOLUTIONS:

Cyanol reagent:
Stock solution:

cyanol	1.0 gm.
distilled water	100.0 ml.
zinc powder, C.P.	10.0 gm.
glacial acetic acid	2.0 ml.

Bring to boiling point. In short time the solution is decolorized. Stable for several weeks.

Working reagent:
Filter 10 ml. of stock reagent, and add:

glacial acetic acid	2.0 ml.
hydrogen peroxide, commercial 3%	1.0 ml.

PROCEDURE:

1. Deparaffinize and hydrate slides down to water.
2. Treat with working reagent: 3–5 minutes.
3. Rinse in distilled water.
4. Counterstain in red nuclear stain.
5. Dehydrate, clear, and mount.

RESULTS:

hemoglobin—dark blue to bluish grey

COMMENTS:

Gomori (1952) uses 1 gram acid fuchsin instead of cyanol and produces a red hemoglobin. Counterstain with hematoxylin or other blue nuclear stain.

Bile Pigment Staining

Glick (1949)

FIXATION: formalin or alcohol: approximately 6 hours.

SOLUTIONS:

Tincture of iodine:

iodine	10.0 gm.
potassium iodide	6.0 gm.
distilled water	5.0 ml.
95% ethyl alcohol	95.0 ml.

Lugol's solution:

iodine	1.0 gm.
potassium iodide	2.0 gm.
distilled water	100.0 ml.

Dissolve potassium iodide in water first, then add iodine.

Stein's working solution:

tincture of iodine	10.0 ml.
Lugol's solution	30.0 ml.

Sodium thiosulfate, 5%:

sodium thiosulfate	5.0 gm.
distilled water	100.0 ml.

Safranin, see page 233.

PROCEDURE:
1. Deparaffinize and hydrate slides to water.
2. Treat with Stein's iodine solution: 6–12 hours.
3. Wash in distilled water: 5–10 minutes.
4. Bleach in sodium thiosulfate: 5–10 minutes.
5. Wash in distilled water: 2–3 minutes.
6. Counterstain in safranin (or other red nuclear stain): 2–3 minutes.
7. Rinse in 70% alcohol.
8. Dehydrate, clear, and mount.

RESULTS:

bile pigment—emerald green
nuclei—red

COMMENTS:

This reaction can not be considered reliable at all times because the reactants are diffusible; also the final color can spread from the original site. The test is based on oxidation of the bile pigment (bilirubin) to green biliverdin by the iodine solution.

Melanin and Lipofuchsin Staining

Lillie (1956 A, B), **Nile Blue Method**

FIXATION: any good general fixative.

SOLUTION:

Nile blue *A*:

Nile blue *A*, C.I. 51180	0.05 gm.
sulfuric acid, 1% (1 ml. conc. H_2SO_4/99 ml. distilled water)	100.0 ml.

PROCEDURE:

1. Deparaffinize and hydrate slides to water; remove $HgCl_2$.
2. Stain in Nile blue *A* solution: 20 minutes.
3. Wash in running water: 10–20 minutes.
4. Mount in glycerol jelly.

RESULTS:

lipofuchsins—dark blue or blue green
melanin—pale green
erythrocytes—greenish yellow to greenish blue
myelin—green to deep blue
nuclei—poorly stained

Alternate Method:

PROCEDURE:

Steps 1 and 2 as above.

3. Do not wash in water. Rinse quickly in 1% sulfuric acid to remove excess dye.
4. Dehydrate at once, acetone, 4 changes: 15 seconds each.
5. Clear in xylene and mount.

RESULTS:

cutaneous, ocular, meningeal melanins—dark green
mast cells—purple red
lipofuchsins—unstained but appear yellow to brownish

muscle, myelin, erythrocytes—unstained
nuclei—greenish to unstained

COMMENTS:

Lipofuchsins stain with Nile blue by two mechanisms: a fat solubility
method operating at pH below 1.0; and an acid-base mechanism operating at levels above pH 3.0. When stained by the second method,
they retain a green stain after acetone or brief alcoholic extraction,
but when the first mechanism is used, they are promptly decolorized
by acetone or alcohol. (*Lillie, 1956 B*)

Melanins stain with basic dyes at pH levels below 1.0 and retain
the stain when dehydrated and mounted. (*Lillie, 1955*)

Ferric-Ferricyanide Method (LILLIE, 1957)

FIXATION: avoid chromate fixatives, others are satisfactory.

SOLUTIONS:

Ferrous sulfate:

ferrous sulfate ($FeSO_4 \cdot 7H_2O$)	2.5 gm.
distilled water	100.0 ml.

Potassium ferricyanide:

potassium ferricyanide ($K_3Fe(CN)_6$)	1.0 gm.
distilled water	99.0 ml.
glacial acetic acid	1.0 ml.

PROCEDURE:

1. Deparaffinize and hydrate slides to water.
2. Treat with ferrous sulfate: 1 hour.
3. Wash in distilled water, 4 changes: total 20 minutes.
4. Treat with potassium ferricyanide: 30 minutes.
5. Wash in 1% acetic acid (1 ml./99 ml. water): 1–2 minutes.
6. Counterstain if desired, picro-ponceau satisfactory, do not use
   hematoxylin.
7. Dehydrate, clear, and mount.

RESULTS:

melanin—dark green
background—faint greenish or unstained; with picro-ponceau, collagen stains red and muscle and cytoplasm will be yellow and brown

COMMENTS:

Lillie says this method is highly selective. No other pigments react
in this procedure, except occasionally hemosiderin.

Morton *et al.* (1960)

FIXATION: any general fixative, or fresh frozen sections.

SOLUTION:

sodium-2,6-dichlorobenzenone-indophenol	0.1 gm.
50% ethyl alcohol	100.0 ml.

Prepare just before use. Filter and add:

1% hydrochloric acid (1 ml./99 ml. water) until color of solution is red (approximately 1:5) or until *p*H is 2.

PROCEDURE:
1. Deparaffinize and hydrate slides to water.
2. Treat with HCl-indophenol: 5 minutes.
3. Dip in tap water several times until background loses color.
4. Mount in glycerol jelly or *Apathy*.

RESULTS:
lipofuchsins—red
erythrocytes—blue
other tissue elements—colorless to blue or slight pink

COMMENTS:
Avoid alcohol; it removes color immediately. Stain fades in about 1 day.

Removal of Pigments

Melanin pigment (PEARSE, 1953)

This will appear as brown, greyish, or almost black granules.

Permanganate Method of Removal
1. Hydrate slides to water.
2. 0.1% potassium permanganate, aqueous: 12–24 hours.
3. Wash in running water: 5 minutes.
4. 1% oxalic acid, aqueous: 1 minute.
5. Wash in running water: 10 minutes, and proceed to stain.

Performic or Paracetic Acid Methods of Removal

Lillie (1954 B) claims that the above method can be unpredictable and that the best bleaching is done with performic and paracetic acid: 1–2 hours:

PERFORMIC ACID: to 8 ml. of 90% formic acid, aqueous, add 31 ml. of 30% H_2O_2 (undiluted reagent) and 0.22 ml. of concentrated

H_2SO_4. Keep at or below 25°C. About 4.7% performic acid is formed within 2 hours, but it deteriorates after a few more hours.

PERACETIC ACID: to 95.6 ml./glacial acetic acid add 259 ml. of 30% H_2O_2 (undiluted reagent) and 2.2 ml. concentrated H_2SO_4. Let stand 1–3 days. Add 40 mg./disodium phosphate as stabilizer. Store at 0.5°C. Keeps for months in refrigerator.

Chlorate Method of Removal

Treat sections 24 hours in 50% alcohol plus small mount of potassium chlorate and a few drops of HCl (concentrated). Wash 10 minutes before staining.

Bromine Method of Removal

1% bromine in water: 12–24 hours. Wash well before staining.

Chromic Acid Method of Removal

Mixture of equal parts of 1% chromic acid and 5% calcium chloride, aqueous: 8–12 hours. Wash well.

Peroxide Method of Removal

10% H_2O_2: 24–48 hours. Wash well before staining.

The peroxide method is considered by some to be the best; it is specific for melanin; other pigments resist longer than 48 hours. The permanganate and chromic acid methods bleach all pigments, which allows for no differentiation among them.

Formalin pigment

Brown and black crystalline granules and artifacts, produced by formalin, are found in and around blood.

Baker (1958) Method of Removal

1% potassium hydroxide in 80% alcohol, or picric acid dissolved in alcohol, until precipitate is removed.

Murdock (1945) Method of Removal

3% H_2O_2, 25 ml.; acetone, 25 ml.; and 1 drop ammonia, until precipitate is gone: 1–2 hours.

Barrett (1944) Method of Removal

Saturated solution of picric acid in alcohol: 10 minutes to 2 hours.

Malarial pigment

This appears as amorphous brown-black granules.

Gridley (1957) Method of Removal

Method 1:

1. Slides down to water.
2. Bleach for 5 minutes in:

   acetone .... 50.0 ml.

   3% H_2O_2 .... 50.0 ml.

   28–29% ammonia (conc.) .... 1.0 ml.

   or overnight in 5% aqueous ammonium sulfide (diluting 20% analytical reagent 4:1).
3. Wash thoroughly, running water: 15 minutes or longer.

Method 2: 3% H_2O_2: 2 hours.

Carbon

Carbon (opaque black) usually appears in the lungs and adjacent lymph nodes, sometimes in the spleen and liver. If it is necessary to distinguish it from malarial pigment, iron, or some other pigment or precipitate, carbon is black and is insoluble in concentrated sulfuric acid, in which other pigments will dissolve.

Hemosiderin

This yellowish, brownish, or greenish brown pigment resists bleaching and does not dissolve in alkalis or acids. It can be identified by Perl's test, page 233.

Bile pigments

These are yellowish green and resist bleaching, but can be converted by H_2O_2, Lugol's solution, nitrous acid, or dichromates into greenish biliverdin-emerald green. Use Lugol's solution (page 410): 6–12 hours. Decolorize with sodium thiosulfate.

Glick (1949) does not consider this reliable, because of diffusibility of the reactants.

For extensive consideration of pigments and other organic substances, see: *Glick (1949); Gomori (1952); Gurr (1958).*

Chapter 18

Cytoplasmic Elements

Protein Staining

Protein demonstration is of minor importance, but sometimes it becomes necessary to determine the protein or nonprotein nature of granulation in cells. The Millon reaction is one of the oldest and most reliable methods but actually is specific for *phenols* and for the one amino acid, *tyrosine*.

Millon Reaction (GOMORI, 1952)

FIXATION: any good general fixative.

SOLUTIONS:

A. mercuric acetate	5.0 gm.
distilled water	100.0 ml.
trichloracetic acid	15.0 gm.
B. sodium nitrite, 1% aqueous	10.0 ml.

PROCEDURE:
1. Run sections down to water. (Cut sections at least 10 microns thick.)
2. Incubate sections in solution *A*, 30–37°C; 5–10 minutes.
3. Add solution *B*: incubate another 25 minutes.
4. Rinse in 70% alcohol.
5. Dehydrate, clear and mount.

RESULTS:

tyrosine proteins—pink to brick red

Ninhydrin Reaction (SERRA, 1946)

FIXATION: 10% formalin.

SOLUTION:

Ninhydrin:

phosphate buffer, *p*H 6.98, page 418.
ninhydrin, 0.4% aqueous (triketo-hydrindene-hydrate)
Mix equal amounts for staining.

PROCEDURE:

1. Deparaffinize and hydrate slides to water, or use frozen sections.
2. Place slides on a rack over boiling water, cover with stain, and steam for 1–2 minutes.
3. Drain stain off the slide and mount in glycerol jelly.

RESULTS and COMMENT:

Blue or violet color indicates the presence of amino acids, peptides, and proteins. The slide should be examined at once because the color diffuses readily and begins to fade within a day or two.

The Argentaffin Reaction

The argentaffin reaction should not be confused with *silver impregnation* (page 175). In argentaffin reactions some substances (ascorbic acid, aldehydes, uric acid, polyphenols, and others) reduce silver solutions under specific conditions. This reaction with the tissue itself, therefore, can be used histochemically to identify these substances.

The only source of error in the method can be found in calcification areas, but only if these are in large masses. Most silver phosphates and carbonates will be dissolved out during the the process. If not, the slides can be treated with 0.2 to 0.5% nitric acid or hydrochloric acid in absolute alcohol, 2–3 minutes before step 3 below. Wash off the acid in absolute and 95% alcohol and then proceed with step 3.

Uric Acid Staining

Argentaffin Method (GOMORI, 1952)

FIXATION: 95% or absolute alcohol.

SOLUTIONS:

Methenamine silver solution:

silver nitrate, 5% aqueous (5 gm./100 ml. water) ....   5.0 ml.

methenamine, 3% aqueous (3 gm./100 ml. water) .... 100.0 ml.

Mix and shake. Precipitate which forms redissolves. Keep in cool dark place. Good for several months.

Buffer solution, $pH \pm 9.0$:

M/5 boric acid (12.368 gm./1000 ml. water) ...   20.0 ml.

M/20 borax (19.071 gm./1000 ml. water) .....   80.0 ml.

Working solution:

methenamine silver solution ....   30.0 ml.

buffer solution ....   8.0 ml.

PROCEDURE:

1. When mounting sections on slides, float on water only a few seconds or try 95% alcohol.
2. Deparaffinize and run slides down to 95% alcohol.
3. Treat in methenamine silver working solution, prewarmed to 37°C: 30 minutes.
4. Rinse in distilled water.
5. Fix in sodium thiosulfate, 5% aqueous: 3 minutes.
6. Wash in running water: 5 minutes. (Gold toning optional)
7. Counterstain if desired.
8. Dehydrate, clear, and mount.

RESULTS:

uric acid crystals—black crystalline fine granules

Enterochromaffin (EC) Cell Stain

Fontana Method (CULLING, 1958), and **Methenamine Silver** (GOMORI, 1952; 1954B)

FIXATION: Zenker formol preferred; do not use alcohol—it dissolves argentaffin granules.

During embedding, do not expose to paraffin longer than 30 minutes.

SOLUTIONS:

Silver solution *A*: (Fontana Method)

To 25 ml. of 10% silver nitrate (10 gm./100 ml. water) add ammonia

(28%), drop by drop until the precipitate which forms is almost dissolved. Add 25 ml. distilled water. Store for 24 hours in brown bottle. Filter before use. Good for 2 weeks.

Methenamine silver solution *B:* (Gomori's Method)

Solution I:

methenamine, 3% (3 gm./100 ml. water)	100.0 ml.
silver nitrate, 5% (5 gm./100 ml. water)	5.0 ml.

Shake until white precipitate disappears. Keeps for several months if stored in a cool dark place.

Solution II:

M/5 boric acid (12.368 gm./1000 ml. water) ...	80.0 ml.
M/5 borax (19.071/1000 ml. water)	20.0 ml.

pH should be 7.8 to 8.0

Working solution:

Stock solution I	30.0 ml.
Stock solution II	8.0 ml.

Gold chloride:

gold chloride stock solution, 1%	10.0 ml.
distilled water	100.0 ml.

Safranin:

safranin *O*, C.I. 50240	1.0 gm.
distilled water	100.0 ml.

Add a few drops of glacial acetic acid.

PROCEDURE:

1. Deparaffinize and hydrate slides to water.
2. Treat with Lugol's solution (page 410): 30 minutes to 1 hour.
3. Wash in running water: 3 minutes.
4. Bleach in sodium thiosulfate, 5% (5 gm./100 ml. water): 3 minutes.
5. Wash in running water: 5 minutes. The above treatment suppresses background staining.
6. Treat with silver solution *A* in dark, room temperature: 18–48 hours.

Alternate Method. Use Methenamine silver solution *B*, 60°C: 3.5 hours; or at 37°C: 12–24 hours—until EC cells stand out black. Then continue:

7. Rinse in several changes of distilled water.
8. Tone in gold chloride: 10 minutes.
9. Rinse in distilled water.
10. Fix in sodium thiosulfate, 5% (5 gm./100 ml. water): 3 minutes.
11. Wash in running water: 5 minutes.
12. Counterstain in safranin (or other red nuclear stain).
13. Rinse in 70% alcohol: few seconds.
14. Dehydrate, clear, and mount.

RESULTS:

argentaffin granules—black
melanin—black
other tissue elements—reds and pinks
grayish to blackish background—slide is overstained

COMMENTS:

Chromaffin material is found only in the adrenal medulla and the gastrointestinal tract, and received its name because of its reaction with chromium salts and certain other metals to produce a yellowish to brown color, a brownish chromium oxide. A dichromate fixative should be used to preserve this material, or post-chromating with potassium dichromate, page 23. Chromaffin is also argentaffin and is blackened in the above method. **Melanin,** also brownish, is not a chromaffin substance.

Diazo-safranin Method (LILLIE *et al.*, 1953)

FIXATION: 10% formalin buffered with 2% of calcium acetate: 1–3 days.

SOLUTION:

Diazotized safranin:

Stock solutions:

Acid safranin:

safranin *O*, C.I. 50240	3.6 gm.
distilled water	60.0 ml.
N HCl	30.0 ml.

Stable for several weeks.

N sodium nitrite:

sodium nitrite, $NaNO_2$	6.9 gm.
distilled water	100.0 ml.

Keep in refrigerator, stable for 3 months.

Disodium phosphate, M/10:

  disodium phosphate, Na_2HPO_4 anhydrous .... 14.2 gm.

  distilled water .... 1000.0 ml.

Working solution: (*do not prepare until immediately before use, see step 2 below*)

To 4.5 ml. of ice-cold safranin solution add 0.5 ml. of sodium nitrite solution. The resulting mixture turns deep blue and foams. Keep at 0 to 5°C for 15 minutes for diazotization. Dilute 1 ml. of the solution with 40 ml. of ice-cold disodium phosphate solution and use immediately. (*p*H should *be about 7.7*)

PROCEDURE:

1. Deparaffinize and hydrate slides to distilled water.
2. Place slides in a previously chilled coplin jar and pour over them the freshly prepared diazo-safranin solution: 5 minutes.
3. Decant stain and wash slides in 3 changes of N/10 aqueous hydrochloric acid or acid-alcohol (1 ml. conc. HCl/99 ml. 70% alcohol): 10–30 seconds total, to remove most of adherent stain. Longer extraction lightens the colors but does not improve contrast.
4. Wash off acid with water (if N/10 HCl is used) or 95% alcohol (if acid-alcohol is used).
5. Dehydrate, clear, and mount.

RESULTS:

  enterochromaffin granules—black
  gastric gland, chief cell granules—dark red
  Paneth cell granules—red
  mucin—unstained
  nuclei and cytoplasm—pink to red

Ferric-Ferricyanide Method (Modified Schmorl Technic)

(LASKY AND GRECO, 1948; LILLIE AND BURTNER, 1953)

FIXATION: 10% formalin buffered with 2% of calcium acetate: 1–3 days.

SOLUTION:

  Ferric-ferricyanide:

    potassium ferricyanide, 1% aqueous .... 10.0 ml.

    ferric chloride, 1% aqueous .... 75.0 ml.

    distilled water .... 15.0 ml.

PROCEDURE:

1. Deparaffinize and hydrate slides to water.
2. Stain in freshly prepared ferric-ferricyanide: 5 minutes.

3. Rinse in 3 changes of distilled water.
4. Counterstain in safranin, or like.
5. Dehydrate, clear, and mount.

RESULTS:

enterochromaffin granules—dark blue
nuclei—red

COMMENTS:

Lillie and his co-workers have been devoting several years to research on the enterochromaffin granules along with melanins, etc. A few of these references are: Glenner and Lillie (1957); Lillie (1955, 1956A, B, and C, 1957A, B, and C, 1960, 1961); Lillie *et al.* (1953); Lillie *et al.* (1957); Lillie *et al.* (1961).

Azo-Coupling Method (GURR, 1958)

FIXATION: formalin or Bouin's.

SOLUTION:

Garnet reagent:

Garnet GBC salt[1]	0.5 gm.
distilled water	100.0 ml.
borax, saturated aqueous	2.5 ml.

If it is necessary to purify the garnet GBC, see page 346.

PROCEDURE:

1. Deparaffinize and hydrate to water.
2. Transfer to garnet solution: 30–60 seconds.
3. Wash in running water: 30 seconds.
4. Stain in Mayer's (or other) hematoxylin: 3 minutes.
5. Wash in running water: 5 minutes.
6. Dehydrate, clear and mount.

RESULTS:

argentaffin granules—red
nuclei—blue
background—light yellow

---

[1] Imperial Chemical Industries, Manchester, England, is best source. Other sources: Dajac Laboratories or American Cyanamid Company.

Fat Staining

Lipids (*synonyms:* lipoids, fatty substances) include a large number of substances grouped together because of their solubility properties. They are insoluble in water and soluble in fat solvents: alcohol, ether, chloroform pyridine, benzene, and acetone, to name a few. Classifying the lipids is not to be undertaken here, but a few familiar groups can be mentioned: carotenoids (*vitamin A*), fatty acids, triglycerids (*neutral fats*), phosphatids, and lipid pigments (*lipofuchsins*—page 232).

For the fixation of fats, formalin is best, particularly if 1% of calcium chloride is added to make the phospholipids insoluble (*Gomori, 1952*). Because of the use of fat solvents, the tissue cannot be embedded in paraffin or nitrocellulose, but it can be embedded in carbowax. Frozen sections are simpler and most frequently used. During any processing alcohol higher than 70% must be avoided. (Concerning the fixation of lipoids, see *Elftman, 1958*.)

The dying of fats is one of the simplest forms of staining; the coloring agent merely dissolves in a fluid contained within the tissues. In addition, it should be emphasized that a dye solvent should be used which does not dissolve the lipid itself. The dye, therefore, must meet certain requirements:

1. The dye must be strongly colored.
2. It must be soluble in the substance which it is intended to show, but must not be soluble in water, the major constituent of cells.
3. It must not attach itself to any tissue constituents except by solution.
4. It must be applied to tissues in a solvent which will not dissolve the substance to be dyed, and must be less soluble in the solvent than in the substance.

Baker (*1958*) suggests the name "Lysochromes" for these dyes that dissolve in the tissue elements to be colored. The name is derived from the Greek *lúsis* meaning solution. The Sudans were the first synthetic dyes of this sort, followed by the Nile blues and reds.

These dyes are used in saturated solutions and often introduce a problem of dye precipitate on the tissue. *Vlachos* (*1959*) makes a sensible proposal that the precipitate probably is formed by the solution becoming oversaturated and that perhaps a saturated solution is unnecessary. He suggests two alternatives:

1. Make up the concentration below the saturation point; for example, 0.25 gm. Sudan IV per 100 ml. 60% alcohol.

2. Desaturate the solution by: (*a*) dilution of a saturated solution with equal volumes of 60% alcohol, or (*b*) by refrigeration. When the solution has been refrigerated long enough to have acquired the refrigerator temperature, filter. Either method does not alter the staining quality of the solution and produces negligible amounts of precipitate.

Oil Red *O* for Fat

FIXATION: 10% formalin or other aqueous general fixatives.

SOLUTIONS:

Oil red *O* stock solution:

oil red *O*, C.I. 26125, saturated in 99% alcohol (250–500 mg. dye/100 ml. alcohol)

Working solution:

stock solution	6.0 ml.
distilled water	4.0 ml.

Let stand 5–10 minutes (no longer). Filter. Use immediately.

Hematoxylin, see page 125.

PROCEDURE:
1. Frozen sections, 15 microns.
2. Place in distilled water.
3. If $HgCl_2$ is present, treat with Lugol's and thiosulfate; wash.
4. Stain in oil red *O*: 10 minutes, in closed container to reduce evaporation. If dye begins to settle out before 10 minutes have elapsed, remove sections to water, or precipitate may settle on sections.
5. Wash in water. Make transfers with glass rod and wipe it clean after each section.
6. Stain in Mayer's hematoxylin (or like): 2–3 minutes.
7. Wash in tap water: 3 minutes.
8. Blue in Scott's solution (page 412): 3 minutes.
9. Wash in tap water: 5 minutes. Mount in gum syrup or glycerol jelly. For permanency, ring cover glass.

RESULTS:

fat—orange-red or brilliant red
nuclei—blue

Oil Red *O* with Tween 40 (BELL, 1959)

FIXATION: Baker's formalin recommended (page 14), or other general aqueous fixative, no alcohol.

SOLUTIONS:

Alcohol-Tween solution:

Tween 40 [2]	1.0 ml.
distilled water	70.0 ml.
absolute alcohol to make	100.0 ml. total

Oil red *O* solution:

Add to above, 250 mg. Oil red *O*, C.I. 26125. Incubate at 60°C for not less than 24 hours well sealed to prevent evaporation. Agitate occasionally. Cool, filter under vacuum.

Hematoxylin, see page 125.

PROCEDURE:
1. Frozen sections, 15 microns; place in water.
2. Transfer to alcohol-Tween without dye: 10 minutes, agitate.
3. Stain at least 4 hours: may be overnight.
4. Differentiate in alcohol-Tween: 10–15 minutes.
5. Wash in distilled water.
6. Stain in Mayer's hematoxylin (or like): 2–3 minutes.
7. Wash in water, and blue in Scott's solution.
8. Wash in tap water: 5 minutes. Mount in gum syrup, glycerol jelly, or Farrant's medium. Ring cover glass for permanency.

RESULTS:
fat—brilliant red
nuclei—blue

COMMENTS:

This method rarely deposits precipitate on the sections. The author always uses it in preference to the former method.

Sudan IV or Sudan Black B (CHIFFELLE AND PUTT, 1951)

FIXATION: 10% formalin, no alcohol.

SOLUTION:

Dissolve 0.7 gm. Sudan IV, C.I. 26105, or Sudan black *B*, C.I. 26150, in 100 ml. propylene or ethylene glycol. Add small amounts at a time, and heat to 100–110°C, stirring, for a few minutes. Do not exceed 110°C or a gelatinous suspension is formed. Filter hot through Whatman #2 paper, and cool. Filter again through fritted glass filter with aid of suction, or glass wool with vacuum.

[2] Atlas Powder Co., Wilmington, Delaware.

PROCEDURE:

1. Frozen sections, 15 microns, into water.
2. Place in pure propylene or ethylene glycol: 3–5 minutes, 2 changes. Agitate.
3. Stain, 2 changes: 5–7 minutes each, agitate occasionally.
4. Differentiate in glycol and water (85:15): 3–5 minutes, agitate.
5. Wash in distilled water: 3–5 minutes.
6. Counterstain in hematoxylin if desired.
7. Mount in glycerol jelly.

RESULTS:

fat—Sudan IV, orange to red; Sudan black *B,* blue-black to black

COMMENTS:

Chiffelle and Putt recommend glycols as a perfect solvent for a fat stain because it does not extract lipids.

Zugibe et al. (1958, 1959) suggest Carbowax 400 as a solvent for Oil red *O* and Sudan IV.

Gomori (1952) questions the use of glycols because they are solvents for so many water-insoluble substances, and he prefers triethyl phosphate. It has a low volatility and is harmless to lipids. His method follows.

PROCEDURE:

1. Frozen sections are rinsed in water and transferred into 50% alcohol: few minutes.
2. Stain in a saturated, filtered solution of any of the fat dyes in 60% triethylphosphate, 5–20 minutes.
3. Differentiate in 50% alcohol: 1 minute.
4. Counterstain in hematoxylin or any preferred stain.
5. Mount in glycerol jelly.

Osmic Acid (MALLORY, 1944)

FIXATION: 10% formalin, no alcohol.

SOLUTION:

Osmic acid:

osmic acid (osmium tetraoxide) ....   1.0 gm. ampule
distilled water ....   100.0 ml.

With file, score a circle around ampule and drop it into bottle with the distilled water. Several sharp shakes will break the ampule and allow the water to dissolve the crystals. This method eliminates possibility of breathing the fumes.

PROCEDURE:
1. Frozen sections, 15 microns, into water.
2. Transfer to osmic acid solution: 24 hours.
3. Wash in several changes distilled water: 6–12 hours.
4. Treat in absolute alcohol: 4–5 hours, for secondary staining of fat.
5. Wash well in distilled water: 5 minutes or more.
6. Mount in glycerol jelly.

RESULTS:
fat—black
background—yellowish brown

Naphthalene Yellow (SILLS AND MARSH, 1959)

Naphthalene yellow in 60% acetic acid was used to restore the yellow color to the fat of gross formalin-fixed specimens. This cannot be used for sections; the color is too pale.

Fluorescent Method (METCALF AND PATTON, 1944; PELTIER, 1954)

FIXATION: 10% formalin (salts of heavy metals—$HgCl_2$—have a quenching effect on fluorescence), or use fresh tissue.

SOLUTION:
Phosphine 3R:

phosphine 3R[3]	0.1–1.0 gm.
distilled water	100.0 ml.

PROCEDURE:
1. Cut frozen sections, 10 microns.
2. Wash in distilled water.
3. Stain in phosphine solution: 5 minutes.
4. Rinse quickly in distilled water.
5. Mount in glycerol, or examine as a water mount.

RESULTS:
lipids (except fatty acids, cholesterol and soaps) will fluoresce brilliant white

COMMENT:
For details concerning fluorescent microscope and equipment, see page 102.

---

[3] George T. Gurr, London, England; or Pfatz and Bauer, Inc., Empire State Bldg., N.Y.

Nile Blue A (Sulfate) (MALLORY, 1938)

This is a useful method for separating neutral fats from other fats.

FIXATION: 10% formalin, no alcohol.

SOLUTION:

Nile blue *A*:

Nile blue *A*, C.I. 51180	1.5 gm.
distilled water	100.0 ml.

PROCEDURE:

1. Frozen sections, 15 microns, into distilled water.
2. Stain in Nile blue sulfate: 20 minutes.
3. Rinse in tap water.
4. Differentiate in 1% acetic acid (1 ml./99 ml. water), 10–20 minutes, or until colors are clear; can happen in 1–2 minutes.
5. Wash thoroughly, distilled water, several changes.
6. Mount in glycerol jelly or *Abopon*.

RESULTS:

neutral fats—pink to red
fatty acids—blue to violet
nuclei and elastic tissue—dark blue

COMMENTS:

There appears to be some doubt about the specificity of this reaction —whether it actually differentiates between neutral fats and fatty acids. *Gomori (1952)* says that not all structures staining pinks, reds, or blue are lipid. Use the method with tongue in cheek.

Staining for Phospholipids (ELFTMAN, 1957B)

FIXATION:

mercuric chloride, 5% aqueous	100.0 ml.
potassium dichromate	2.5 gm.

Mix fresh. Fix for 3 days; oxidizes phospholipids and makes them insoluble in fat solvents such as are used in paraffin embedding.

SOLUTIONS:

Sudan black *B*:

Dissolve 0.7 gm. Sudan black *B*, C.I. 26150, in 100.0 ml. ethylene glycol with heat, 100–110°C (not above). Stir. Filter while hot through Whatman #2 filter paper. Cool and filter through fritted glass filter of medium porosity with suction.

Ethylene glycol solution (or propylene glycol), 85%:

ethylene glycol .... 85.0 ml.
distilled water .... 100.0 ml.

PROCEDURE:

1. Deparaffinize and transfer slides into absolute alcohol: 2 minutes.
2. Transfer to absolute ethylene glycol.
3. Stain in Sudan black solution: 30 minutes.
4. Differentiate in 85% ethylene glycol: 2–3 minutes.
5. Wash in distilled water.
6. Counterstain, if desired.
7. Wash well, mount in *Apathy*, or in glycerol jelly.

RESULTS:

phospholipids—black

COMMENT:

Phospholipids are finding increasing popularity in the study of mitochondria and Golgi apparatus, and are an important constituent of myelin.

Golgi Apparatus and Mitochondria

The **Golgi apparatus** (Golgi bodies, Golgi substance, Golgi complex) usually is lost in routine fixation and requires special treatment. Since the methods are not always predictable under all conditions, it may be necessary to modify the fixing and/or staining time before attaining precise results. In osmium and silver methods the Golgi appears either as a dark net, a granular mass, a cord, or even a more diffuse condition. These methods seem to indicate it is fatty in nature.

Mitochondria are tiny bodies, granular, rod-like or filamentous in shape and scattered through the cytoplasm. They are lipo-protein in composition and are easily lost in routine preparation. It is therefore imperative that small pieces of tissue be fixed rapidly in order to preserve any mitochondria.

Golgi Apparatus Staining

Osmium Tetroxide: Ludford's Method (LILLIE, 1954B; COWDRY, 1952)

FIXATION: Mann's osmic sublimate: 18 hours.

> osmic acid, 1% (1 gm./100 ml. water) ....   50.0 ml.
> mercuric chloride, saturated aqueous, plus 0.37
> gm. sodium chloride ....   50.0 ml.

PROCEDURE:

1. Wash blocks of tissue in distilled water: 30 minutes.
2. Impregnate, 2% osmic acid: 3 days, 30°C
      2% osmic acid: 1 day, 35°C
      1% osmic acid: 1 day, 35°C
      0.5% osmic acid: 1 day, 35°C
3. Wash in distilled water: 1 day.
4. Dehydrate, clear, and embed.
5. Section 6–7 microns, mount and dry.
6. Deparaffinize, clear, and mount.

RESULTS:

golgi apparatus—black
yolk and fat—black (these may be bleached out with turpentine)

COMMENTS:

If it is advantageous to have mitochondria stained on the same slide, follow deparaffinization (step 6) by hydrating to water (include cautious treatment with 0.125% potassium permanganate), and stain by Altmann Method (page 263). Mitochondria will be crimson.

DaFano's Method (CULLING, 1957; COWDRY, 1952)

FIXATION: 3–18 hours in:

> cobalt nitrate ....   1.0 gm.
> distilled water ....   100.0 ml.
> formalin ....   15.0 ml.

SOLUTIONS:

Ramón y Cajal's developer:

> hydroquinone ....   2.0 gm.
> formalin ....   6.0 ml.
> distilled water ....   100.0 ml.
> sodium sulfite, anhydrous ....   0.15 gm.

Gold chloride:

> gold chloride stock solution (page 410) ......   1.0 ml.
> distilled water ....   80–90.0 ml.

PROCEDURE:

1. Rinse blocks of tissue in distilled water.
2. Impregnate in 1.5% silver nitrate (1.5 gm./100 ml. water): 1–2 days. (Can use 1% for very small pieces or embryonic tissues, 2% for fatty tissues and spinal cord).
3. Rinse briefly in distilled water.
4. Cut blocks into slices thinner than 2 mm. Reduce in developer: 5 hours.
5. Wash thoroughly in distilled water.
6. Dehydrate, infiltrate, and embed.
7. Section, 6–7 microns, mount and dry.
8. Deparaffinize and hydrate to water.
9. Tone in gold chloride: 2 hours.
10. Rinse in distilled water and fix in 5% sodium thiosulfate: 3 minutes.
11. Wash in running water: 5 minutes.
12. Counterstain, if desired, in hematoxylin, thionin, carmalum, etc.
13. Dehydrate, clear, and mount.

RESULTS:

golgi—black
cytoplasm—grey
mitochondria—medium to dark grey or black

COMMENTS:

The silver preparations depend on fixation with salts of a heavy metal —cobalt in DaFano's method. *Aoyama* (*Baker, 1945*) varies the method using

cadmium chloride	1.0 gm.
formalin	15.0 ml.
distilled water	85.0 ml.

The rest of the procedure is the same as DaFano's.

Direct Silver Method (ELFTMAN, 1952)

PROCEDURE:

1. Immerse small blocks of fresh tissue in silver nitrate, 2% (2 gm./ 100 ml. water): 2 hours.
2. Rinse briefly in distilled water.
3. Develop: 2 hours, in:

hydorquinone	2.0 gm.
formalin 15% (15 ml./85 ml. water)	100.0 ml.

4. Return to 10% formalin to complete fixation: at least overnight.
5. Wash, dehydrate, and embed.
6. Section, 6–7 microns, mount and dry.
7. Deparaffinize, clear and mount.

RESULTS:

Golgi—black

COMMENTS:

Do not use buffered formalin; it may limit the solubility of the silver salts.

If the silver is too dense, Elftman suggests bleaching it with 0.1% iron alum. Check under the microscope and stop the reaction by washing thoroughly in running water.

The silver is readily oxidized, so gold toning is usually preferable for a more permanent slide. This can follow deparaffinization; see other Golgi methods. Also counterstaining may be included before dehydrating and clearing slides.

Elftman warns that all the black is not necessarily Golgi.

Mitochondria Staining

Fast Green (HARMON, 1950)

FIXATION: Regaud solution (page 20).

SOLUTIONS:

Fast green:

fast green *FCF*, C.I. 42054	4.0 gm.
aniline	10.0 ml.
distilled water	90.0 ml.

Phosphomolybdic acid:

phosphomolybdic acid	1.0 gm.
distilled water	100.0 ml.

Safranin:

safranin *O*, C.I. 50240	1.0 gm.
50% ethyl alcohol	100.0 ml.

PROCEDURE:

1. Deparaffinize and hydrate slides to water.
2. Warm fast green solution to 62°C just before use. Add slides, remove from heat and allow to slowly cool: 6 minutes.
3. Rinse rapidly in distilled water.

4. Treat with saturated picric acid, aqueous: 10 minutes.
5. Rinse in distilled water.
6. Treat with phosphomolybdic acid: 1 minute.
7. Rinse in distilled water: 1 minute.
8. Stain in safranin: 3–6 minutes.
9. Dehydrate, clear and mount.

RESULTS:

mitochondria—dark bluish green
erythrocytes, nucleoli, plasmosomes—grass green (only other elements staining green)

Altmann's Method: (MODIFIED BY COWDRY, MCCLUNG, 1939).

FIXATION: Regaud solution (page 20): change every day for 4 days, in refrigerator.

Mordant in 3% potassium dichromate: 8 days, change every second day.

Wash in running water: overnight; dehydrate and embed.

SOLUTIONS:

Altmann's aniline fuchsin:

Make a saturated solution of aniline in distilled water by shaking the two together. Filter. Add 10 gm. acid fuchsin, C.I. 42685, to 100 ml. of filtrate. Let stand for 24 hours. Good for only 1 month.

Methyl green:

methyl green, C.I. 42590	1.0 gm.
distilled water	100.0 ml.

PROCEDURE:

1. Deparaffinize and hydrate slides to water.
2. Treat with potassium permanganate, 1% (1 gm./100 ml. water): 30 seconds (see comments below).
3. Rinse briefly in distilled water and bleach in oxalic acid, 5% (5 gm./100 ml. water): 30 seconds.
4. Rinse in several changes distilled water: 1–2 minutes.
5. Dry slide around sections with filter paper, cover with Altmann's fuchsin. Heat gently until fumes smelling of aniline come off. Cool. Allow stain to remain 6 minutes.
6. Dry off most of stain. Rinse in distilled water until sections only hold stain. If a large amount is left in sections it will form a trou-

blesome precipitate with the methyl green. If too much is removed, mitochondria will be lightly colored.

7. Pipette methyl green on slide, watching colors by holding it over white paper: about 5 seconds.
8. Drain off stain, rinse briefly in 95% alcohol.
9. Dehydrate in absolute alcohol, clear, and mount.

RESULTS:

mitochondria—bright red

COMMENTS:

If the methyl green removes all fuchsin, mordanting by dichromate was incomplete. Omit steps 2 and 3, or treat sections for a few seconds with 2% potassium dichromate before staining.

If fuchsin is so intense that the methyl green removes it imperfectly, the mordanting was too great. Correct this in steps 2 and 4. If the methyl green washes out, omit rinsing in 95% alcohol; go directly to absolute.

A solution of aurantia,[4] saturated in 70% ethyl alcohol (30 seconds) may be used in place of methyl green. Go directly to absolute alcohol.

Altmann-Benda's Method: (CHAMPY-KULL MODIFICATION, MCCLUNG, 1939)

FIXATION: Champy fluid: 24 hours (page 17).

Wash in distilled water: 1 hour.

Treat 24 hours in:

pyroligneous acid	50.0 ml.
chromic acid, 1% aqueous	50.0 ml.

Mordant in potassium dichromate, 2% aqueous: 3 days. Wash in running water: 24 hours, dehydrate and embed. Cut thin sections, 3–4 microns.

PROCEDURE:

1. Deparaffinize and hydrate slides to water.
2. Cover slides with Altmann's fluid (page 263). Heat gently but do not boil. Cool and allow to stain 6 minutes.
3. Pour off stain, and rinse rapidly in distilled water.

[4] Michrome stains: Edward Gurr, Ltd., London, England, *or* Grübler stains: Roboz Surgical Instrument Co., Washington, D.C.

4. Flood with toluidine blue *O*, 0.5% (0.5 gm./100 ml. water): 1–2 minutes (see comments below).
5. Rinse in distilled water.
6. Cover with aurantia, 0.5% (0.5 gm./100 ml. 70% alcohol): 20–40 seconds.
7. Differentiate in 95% alcohol.
8. Dehydrate, absolute alcohol, clear, and mount.

RESULTS:

mitochondria—red
nuclei—blue
cytoplasm—greenish yellow

COMMENTS:

If sections are too red, increase the time in toluidine blue. If they remain too blue, increase the time in aurantia.

Benda's staining solution is sometimes used in place of Altmann's fuchsin.

SOLUTION:

crystal violet saturated in 70% alcohol .... 1 part.
absolute alcohol .... 1 part.
aniline saturated in water .... 2 parts.

Dilute with equal parts of distilled water.

Use like Altmann's fuchsin.

PROCEDURE:

(*a*) Blot and immerse in dilute acetic acid (30 ml./70 ml. water): 1 minute.
(*b*) Blot, immerse in absolute alcohol until only a little stain comes out.
(*c*) Clear and mount.

RESULTS:

mitochondria—deep violet
background—rose

Iron Hematoxylin also can be used for mitochondria. Best fixative is *Regaud,* and mordant in 3% potassium dichromate: 7 days. Use the long method of staining: overnight in iron alum and overnight in hematoxylin. The method is not as specific as Altmann or Benda; other granules also stain.

Osmic Method (NEWCOMER, 1940)

FIXATION: Zirkle's solution: 48 hours.

potassium dichromate	1.25 gm.
ammonium dichromate	1.25 gm.
copper sulfate	1.0 gm.
distilled water	100.0 ml.

PROCEDURE:

1. Wash tissue blocks 8 hours to overnight.
2. Impregnate in 2% osmic acid (2 gm./100 ml. water): 4–6 days. Change solution on alternate days.
3. Wash for 8 hours or overnight.
4. Dehydrate, clear, and embed. Use benzene, not xylene, for clearing.
5. Cut 5-micron sections, mount on slides.
6. Deparaffinize and hydrate slides to water.
7. Bleach in 1% potassium permanganate (1 gm./100 ml. water): 5 minutes.
8. Rinse in distilled water.
9. Treat with 3% oxalic acid (3 gm./100 ml. water): 2–3 minutes.
10. Wash in running water: 15 minutes.
11. Dehydrate, clear, and mount.

RESULTS:

mitochondria—black

COMMENTS:

Newcomer used his method on plant cells. A counterstain such as acid fuchsin may be added.

Saccharides (Carbohydrates)

Carbohydrates appear as four types of substances: (1) simple **polysaccharides** (includes **glycogen**); (2) **mucoid substances (mucopolysaccharides, mucoproteids, glycoproteins**); (3) **glycolipids;** and (4) **nucleic acids.** In addition to the use of certain specific stains, **aldehyde** reactions are a common means of demonstrating carbohydrates. The aldehyde groups must first be liberated by some chemical agent, either oxidized (periodic or chromic acid), or hydrolyzed (dilute hydrochloric acid). Then the specific reagent for aldehydes can be applied. See the *Feulgen* and *periodic acid-Schiff* reactions, page 292.

Alcohol or alcoholic mixtures are usually recommended as fixatives for saccharides (*exception:* nucleic acids). *Gomori (1952)* writes that theoretically, when glycogen is enclosed in a complex mixture of proteins and lipids, it can be true that a good protein precipitant will coat the glycogen with a protein membrane. This will be impermeable to the large glycogen molecules and keep them *in situ*. He considers Bouin's good but mercuric chloride is poor as a glycogen fixative. The fixative should act and harden rapidly. Alcohol or acid fixatives form glycogen in coarse droplets, while formalin-containing fixatives distribute the glycogen in fine granules. In some tissues (liver), unless the tissue and fixative are chilled, enzymes can cause a loss of glycogen. Although in most tissues glycogen is more stable, *Gomori (1952)* recommends placing the tissue in fixative in the refrigerator.

After proper fixation paraffin embedding is satisfactory, but after deparaffinizing the mounted slides, rinse them in absolute ethyl alcohol and protect the sections with a coat of 1% nitrocellulose to prevent diffusion of the glycogen during staining. (*Gomori, 1952*)

Glycogen Staining

Best's Carmine

FIXATION: avoid aqueous media (McManus and Mowry, 1958)

absolute alcohol	9 parts.
formalin	1 part.

Start dehydration for embedding with 95% alcohol.

MOUNTING SLIDES: The author has preserved better localization of glycogen by mounting paraffin sections with 95% alcohol in place of water. As soon as sections are spread, drain off excess fluid and continue to dry.

SOLUTIONS:

Best's carmine, stock solution:

carmine, C.I. 75470	2.0 gm.
potassium carbonate	1.0 gm.
potassium chloride	5.0 gm.
distilled water	60.0 ml.
Boil gently: 5 minutes. Cool. Filter. Add:	
ammonium hydroxide	20.0 ml.

Lasts 3 months at 0–4°C.

Working solution:

carmine stock solution	30.0 ml.
ammonium hydroxide	25.0 ml.
methyl alcohol	25.0 ml.

Lasts 2–3 weeks.

Differentiating fluid.

absolute ethyl alcohol	16.0 ml.
methyl alcohol	8.0 ml.
distilled water	20.0 ml.

PROCEDURE:

1. Deparaffinize and transfer into absolute alcohol: 3 minutes.
2. Coat with 1% celloidin; dry slightly in air.
3. Dip 2 or 3 times in 70% alcohol and then into water.
4. Stain in Mayer's hematoxylin: 5 minutes.
5. Wash, blue in Scott's, and wash.
6. Stain, Best's carmine working solution: 15–30 minutes.
7. Treat with differentiating fluid: 5–15 minutes.
8. Rinse quickly in 80% alcohol.
9. Dehydrate, clear, and mount.

RESULTS:

glycogen—red
nuclei—blue

COMMENTS:

Pearse (1953) proposes the following method of fixation, claiming that it shows a localization of glycogen comparing favorably with that preserved by freeze-drying.

Lison's "Gendre fluid."

picric acid, saturated in 96% alcohol	85 parts.
formalin	10 parts.
glacial acetic acid	5 parts.

Cool to $-73°C$ before use in an acetone-CO_2 snow mixture.

Use small pieces; fix for 18 hours.

See also the *Bauer-Feulgen reaction* for glycogen, page 301.

Acid Mucopolysaccharides

Alcian Blue Method (STEDMAN, 1950; MODIFIED BY MOWRY, 1956)[5]

FIXATION: 10% formalin or any general fixative.

SOLUTION:

alcian blue *8GX*, C.I. 74240	....	0.5–1.0 gm.
distilled water	....	100.0 ml.
glacial acetic acid	....	3.0 ml.

Filter; add thymol crystal to prevent mold.

PROCEDURE:

1. Deparaffinize and hydrate slides to water.
2. Stain in alcian blue: 30 minutes.
3. Rinse in distilled water.
4. Counterstain with hematoxylin, safranin, or other nuclear stain.
5. Dehydrate, clear, and mount.

RESULTS:

acid mucopolysaccharides—blue green
nuclei—depending on stain used

COMMENTS:

1. Can be followed by PAS (page 298) for demonstration of both acidic groups and 1,2 glycols, or the Feulgen Reaction (page 293).
2. *Lison (1954)* counterstains with chlorantine fast red for efficient differentiation of mucin from collagen (mucin—bluish green; collagen—cherry red): Follow steps 1, 2, and 3 above: Then
a. Treat with phosphomolybdic acid, 1% aqueous: 10 minutes.
b. Rinse in distilled water.
c. Stain in chlorantine fast red: 10–15 minutes.

chlorantine fast red *5B*[6]	....	0.5 gm.
distilled water	....	100.0 ml.

d. Rinse in distilled water, dehydrate, clear, and mount.
3. *Williams and Jackson (1956)* observed possible diffusion of acid mucopolysaccharides under aqueous conditions. The fixative should form complexes insoluble in water and alcohol. They suggest two possible solutions containing organic chemicals which form such insoluble complexes with acid mucopolysaccharides:

[5] Also see Metachromatic Method, p. 280.
[6] Edward Gurr, 42 Upper Richmond Road West, London SW 14, or Ciba, Ltd., Montreal, Canada.

(*a*) 0.5% cetylpyridium chloride (CPC) in 4% aqueous formalin.

(*b*) 0.4% 5-aminoacridine hypochloride in 50% ethyl alcohol.

4. *Spicer and Meyer* (*1960*) precede staining with alcian blue by 5 minutes in aldehyde-fuchsin (page 287); to 70% alcohol, running water, and then into alcian blue.

5. *Mowry* (*1960*) reports that lots of alcian blue have differed in staining efficiency and fastness. Current stocks of alcian blue *8GX* are more soluble, less fast and more stable. He has changed his staining method: 0.5–2.0% acetic acid or in 0.1 M, *p*H 2.2–2.4, hydrochloric acid-sodium citrate buffer: 1–2 hours.

Colloidal Iron Method (RITTER AND OLESON, 1950)

FIXATION: 10% formalin in 90% alcohol; do not use dichromate—it oxidizes polysaccharides.

SOLUTIONS:

Colloidal iron solution:

dialyzed iron, Merck's	50.0 ml.
2M acetic acid (11.5 ml./88.5 ml. water)	50.0 ml.

Potassium ferrocyanide in HCl:

potassium ferrocyanide, 1% aqueous	86.0 ml.
N HCl (page 408)	14.0 ml.

Periodic acid:

periodic acid	0.4 gm.
distilled water	100.0 ml.
M/5 sodium acetate (135 mg. hydrated salt/35 ml. ethyl alcohol)	5.0 ml.

Reducing rinse:

potassium iodide	1.0 gm.
sodium thiosulfate	1.0 gm.
distilled water	20.0 ml.

Add with stirring:

absolute ethyl alcohol	30.0 ml.
2N HCl (page 408)	0.5 ml.

Sulfite rinse:

water	50.0 ml.
concentrated HCl	0.5 ml.
potassium metabisulfite	0.2 gm.

Schiff reagent (page 294)

PROCEDURE:

1. Deparaffinize and hydrate slides to water.
2. Treat with colloidal iron: 10 minutes.
3. Wash well in distilled water.
4. Treat with potassium ferrocyanide: 10 minutes.
5. Wash well in distilled water.
6. Flood with 70% alcohol.
7. Treat with periodic acid: 5 minutes.
8. Rinse with 70% alcohol.
9. Transfer to reducing rinse: 5 minutes.
10. Rinse with 70% alcohol.
11. Transfer to Schiff reagent: 1 hour.
12. Use 3 sulfite rinses: 1.5 minutes in each.
13. Wash well in running water: 5 minutes.
14. Stain with hematoxylin if desired.
15. Dehydrate, clear, and mount.

RESULTS:

acid polysaccharides—blue
glycogen—magenta

COMMENTS:

Nito and Stokes (*1960*) prepare a dialyzed iron as follows: Dissolve 100 gm. ferric chloride in 230 ml. distilled water. Add 130 ml. glycerol and mix well. Divide into 2 portions of $\frac{1}{4}$ and $\frac{3}{4}$. To the large volume add concentrated ammonia in small quantities with vigorous stirring. A precipitate forms and dissolves more and more slowly until the mixture becomes pasty (approximately 110 ml. ammonia). Add drop by drop and with constant stirring the smaller portion until the solution becomes clear dark reddish brown. It now contains a slight excess of ferric chloride.

Dialyze against distilled water using a cellophane bag—capacity about 4 times that of the solution. Change the distilled water every day until the solution in the bag has reverted to its original volume (about 2 weeks). Store at room temperature. For use dilute with equal amount of water.

Acid mucopolysaccharides combine with dialyzed iron and then become blue in potassium ferrocyanide (Prussian blue). *Mowry* (*1958*) considers this method more specific than others, and it stains more strongly than alcian blue.

Colloidal Iron Method (MOWRY, 1958)

SOLUTIONS:

Colloidal iron solution:

Stock solution:

Bring 250 ml. distilled water to boil. While boiling pour in 4.4 ml. of 29% ferric chloride (USP XI) solution. Stir. When solution is dark red, remove from heat and allow to cool. The color must be dark red and clear. It is stable for months.

Working solution:

glacial acetic acid	5.0 ml.
distilled water	15.0 ml.
stock colloidal iron solution	20.0 ml.

*p*H should be 1.1–1.3. Nonspecific staining takes place at *p*H 1.4 or higher. Effective for 1 day.

Hydrochloric acid-ferrocyanide.

2% HCl (2 ml./98 ml. water)	50.0 ml.
2% potassium ferrocyanide (2 gm./100 ml. water)	50.0 ml.

Mix immediately before use.

PROCEDURE:

1. Deparaffinize and hydrate slides to water: remove $HgCl_2$.
2. Rinse in 12% acetic acid (12 ml./88 ml. water): 30 seconds (prevents dilution of reagent).
3. Transfer to freshly prepared colloidal iron (working solution): 60 minutes.
4. Rinse in 12% acetic acid, 4 changes: 3 minutes each.
5. Treat with hydrochloric acid-ferrocyanide, room temperature: 20 minutes. (Include a control slide, one not treated with colloidal iron.)
6. Wash in running water: 5 minutes.
7. Counterstain if desired: Feulgen, PAS, or hematoxylin.
8. Optional: dip in aqueous picric acid to color cytoplasm and erythrocytes; rinse for few seconds in tap water. (*Author's comment:* acetic-orange G also may be used.)
9. Dehydrate, clear, and mount.

RESULTS:

acid mucopolysaccharides—bright blue; uncolored in control slide. mucins of connective tissue, epithelium, mast cell granules, capsules of some microbial agents, pneumococci—bright blue

COMMENT:

For staining of weakly acidic polysaccharides, see Wolman (1961).

Mucin Staining

Mayer's Mucicarmine

FIXATION: any general fixative, but alcoholic preferred.

SOLUTION:

Stock solution: (*Southgate's solution, 1927*)

carmine, C.I. 75470	1.0 gm.
aluminum hydroxide, powder	1.0 gm.
aluminum chloride, anhydrous	0.5 gm.
50% ethyl alcohol	100.0 ml.

Heat in boiling water bath with frequent shaking: 2.5 minutes. Cool under tap and filter.

Working solution:

stock solution	1.0 ml.
distilled water	9.0 ml.

Mix 1–2 days before using.

PROCEDURE:
1. Deparaffinize and hydrate to water; remove $HgCl_2$.
2. Stain in diluted mucicarmine: 15–20 minutes; check under microscope. (Flood the slides with the working solution.)
3. Rinse quickly in distilled water.
4. Dehydrate, clear and mount.

RESULTS:

mucin—red

COMMENTS:

If desirable to stain nuclei, precede staining with mucicarmine by Weigert's or Groat's iron hematoxylin (page 126).

This method has lost its popularity and is not used extensively, but has been included for technicians who might want to refer to it. For more popular methods, see the metachromatic procedures (page 279).

Fluorescent Method (HICKS AND MATTHAEL, 1958)

FIXATION: 10% formalin preferred.

SOLUTIONS:

Iron alum:

ferric ammonium sulfate	4.0 gm.
distilled water	100.0 ml.

Acridine orange:

acridine orange, C.I. 46005	0.1 gm.
distilled water	100.0 ml.

PROCEDURE:

1. Deparaffinize and hydrate paraffin sections to water, or cut frozen sections and place in distilled water.
2. Treat with iron alum solution, 5–10 minutes.
3. Wash briefly in distilled water.
4. Stain in acridine orange, $1\frac{1}{2}$ minutes.
5. Rinse briefly in distilled water, blot and mount in *Harleco Fluorescence Oil Mountant.*[7]

RESULTS:

mucin—brilliant reddish orange fluorescence

COMMENTS:

This is not a permanent slide. The iron inhibits the production of fluorescence with acridine orange in nearly all tissue components except mucin. *Hicks and Matthaei* also suggest that the mucins of acid polysaccharides rather than mucoproteins fluoresce.

For details concerning fluorescent microscope and equipment, see page 102.

Amyloid Staining

Higman's Congo Red: (MODIFIED BY LILLIE, 1954)

FIXATION: 10% formalin or an alcoholic fixative.

SOLUTIONS:

Congo red:

Congo red, C.I. 22120	0.5 gm.
50% ethyl alcohol	100.0 ml.

Potassium hydroxide:

potassium hydroxide	0.2 gm.
80% ethyl alcohol	100.0 ml.

Hematoxylin, page 125.

[7] Hartman Leddon Co., Philadelphia.

PROCEDURE:

1. Deparaffinize slides, transfer through absolute, 95%, and into 50% alcohol.
2. Stain with Congo red: 1–5 minutes.
3. Differentiate in potassium hydroxide: 1–3 minutes.
4. Rinse in tap water.
5. Stain in Mayer's hematoxylin (or the like): 2–3 minutes.
6. Wash in tap water: 5 minutes.
7. Dehydrate, clear, and mount.

RESULTS:

amyloid—red
nuclei—blue

COMMENTS:

Amyloid is a hyaline material that appears in connective tissue as a result of disease and methods should be on hand for pathological study.

See also Metachromatic Method, page 278.

Fluorescent Method (VASSAR AND CULLING, 1959)

FIXATION: 10% formalin or alcohol. The latter gives a crisper differential picture.

SOLUTIONS:

Thioflavine:

thioflavine *T*, C.I. 49005	1.0 gm.
distilled water	100.0 ml.

Acetic acid, 1%:

glacial acetic acid	1.0 ml.
distilled water	99.0 ml.

PROCEDURE:

1. Place frozen sections in distilled water.
2. Stain sections in thioflavine: 3 minutes.
3. Differentiate in 1% acetic acid: 10 minutes.
4. Wash briefly, blot, and mount in *Harleco Fluorescence Oil Mountant*,[8] or *Apathy Mountant* (page 119).

RESULTS:

amyloid—yellow fluorescence

[8] Hartman Leddon Co., Philadelphia.

COMMENTS:

Treatment with acetic acid enhances differentiation and reduces fluorescence of normal tissue without affecting the fluorescence of amyloid. *Vassar and Culling* suggest that the nuclear fluorescence can be quenched by prestaining with hematoxylin (2 minutes), then proceeding with step 2 above.

For details concerning fluorescent microscope and equipment, see page 102.

Mast Cell Staining

Mast cells are of common occurrence in connective tissue. Because of their cytoplasmic granules, however, staining methods for these cells have been included in this cytoplasmic element section. The specific staining of these granules is the primary means of identification of mast cells.

Neutral Red (ALLEN, 1960)

FIXATION: 10% formalin

SOLUTION:

neutral red, C.I. 50040	0.5 gm.
50% ethyl alcohol	100.0 ml.

PROCEDURE:
1. Deparaffinize and run slides down to 70% alcohol.
2. Stain in alum hematoxylin: 3 minutes.
3. Wash, blue, and wash.
4. Stain in neutral red: 10 minutes.
5. Differentiate in 70% alcohol: 2–10 minutes.
6. Dehydrate in 95% alcohol: 3 minutes.
7. Dehydrate in *n*-butyl alcohol, 2 changes: 5–10 minutes in each.
8. Clear and mount.

RESULTS:

mast cell granules—red
cartilage matrix—red
nuclei—blue

COMMENTS:

Color is paler than with metachromatic methods, page 281.

Bismarck Brown (SPATZ, 1960)

FIXATION: 10% formalin.

SOLUTION:

Bismarck brown:

Bismarck brown, C.I. 21000	0.5 gm.
absolute ethyl alcohol	80.0 ml.
1% aqueous hydrochloric acid	20.0 ml.

PROCEDURE:

1. Deparaffinize and transfer sections to absolute alcohol: 3 minutes.
2. Dip in 95%, then 70% alcohol.
3. Stain in Bismarck brown: 30 to 90 minutes.
4. Differentiate in 3 changes 70% alcohol: 2 seconds each.
5. Transfer to 95% alcohol: 2 seconds.
6. Dehydrate in absolute alcohol: 30 seconds.
7. Clear in xylene: 1 second; mount.

RESULTS:

mast cell granules—yellow brown

COMMENTS:

If counterstaining is desirable, follow the 70% differentiation by 3 minutes in hematoxylin (Harris, Mayer's, etc.); dip in 70% alcohol: 2 seconds, and continue into step 5 above.

Chrysoidin (HARADA, 1957)

FIXATION: any general fixative.

SOLUTION:

chrysoidin Y, C.I. 11270	0.5 gm.
distilled water	100.0 ml.

PROCEDURE:

1. Deparaffinize and run slides down to 80% alcohol; remove $HgCl_2$ if present.
2. Stain in chrysoidin: 5–10 minutes.
3. Rinse in distilled water.
4. Dehydrate, clear, and mount.

RESULTS:

mast cell granules—deep brown to black
other elements—yellowish

COMMENTS:

Staining with chrysoidin can be preceded with hematoxylin or PAS. The author likes this method.

Metachromasia

A certain few tissue elements are stainable by a particular group of cationic dyes, changing in the tissues from blue (the usual **orthochromatic** form) to a purplish-red or reddish-purple hue. Such a dye, called **metachromatic** (see page 110), is of considerable value in the study of specific elements of connective tissue. Among the metachromatic dyes most commonly used are toluidine blue *O*, thionin, methylene blue, azures, crystal violet, cresyl violet, methyl violet, safranin *O*, celestin blue, gallocyanin, and pinacyanol. Some of the tissues identified by this means are mast cells, amyloid, cartilage, and mucus materials (*Schubert and Hamerman, 1956*).

The methods are tricky and a technician must learn to distinguish a true metachromasia from a false one. The difficulty in preserving metachromasia lies in the dehydration of the tissue after staining. Increasing strengths of alcohol (ethyl) revert the dye back to the orthochromatic form. Sections can be examined in an aqueous condition, but this produces at best a semipermanent preparation. Some workers use acetone or tertiary butyl alcohol for dehydration, then follow with one of the clearing agents. *Padawer (1959)* uses Ether 181 (page 282) and *Levine (1928)* used oil of cloves for dehydration (page 281).

Amyloid [9]

Crystal Violet (LIEB, 1947)

FIXATION: 10% formalin or alcoholic fixative.

SOLUTION:

Crystal violet stock solution:

    crystal violet, C.I. 42555 (14.0–15.0 gm.); saturated in 95% ethyl alcohol .... 100.0 ml.

Working solution:

    stock solution .... 10.0 ml.

    distilled water .... 300.0 ml.

    hydrochloric acid, concentrated .... 1.0 ml.

[9] See Amyloid Staining, page 274.

PROCEDURE:

1. Run frozen sections or deparaffinized paraffin sections down to water.
2. Stain in working solution: 5 minutes to 24 hours.
3. Rinse in water.
4. Mount in *Abopon,* page 122

RESULTS:

amyloid—purple
other tissue elements including hyalin—blue

COMMENTS:

Acid in the staining solution makes it self-differentiating and staining time is flexible. Lieb suggests that if there is only a small amount of amyloid in the tissue, thicker sections should be cut to make the color reaction more clearly visible. Slides mounted in *Abopon* have retained their color for 2 years. *Abopon* mounts must be sealed with ringing cement for permanency.

Gomori (1953) outlines a simple method for permanent mounts:

1. Float paraffin sections on dye solution: 15–20 minutes.
2. Float sections on distilled water to remove excess dye.
3. Float on 1–2% acetic acid, aqueous, to differentiate.
4. Mount on slides in usual fashion and dry.
5. Remove paraffin with xylene and mount.

This preserves the metachromasia of the crystal violet.

Mucin[10]

Toluidine Blue (LILLIE, 1929)

FIXATION: any general fixative, but alcohol preferred.

SOLUTION:

toluidine *O*, C.I. 52040	2.0 gm.
distilled water	100.0 ml.

PROCEDURE:

1. Deparaffinize and hydrate slides to water; remove $HgCl_2$.
2. Stain in toluidine blue: 1 minute.
3. Wash in water: 2–3 minutes.
4. Dehydrate in acetone, 2 changes: 3–5 minutes each.
5. Clear in xylene and mount.

[10] See Mucin Staining, page 273.

RESULTS:

mucin—reddish violet
nuclei and bacteria—deep blue
cytoplasm, fibrous tissue—bluish green
bone—bluish green
cartilage matrix—bluish violet
muscle—light blue
cell granules—blue violet
hyalin and amyloid—bluish green

Thionin (MALLORY, 1938)

FIXATION: any general fixative, but alcoholic preferred.

SOLUTION:

thionin, C.I. 52000	1.0 gm.
25% ethyl alcohol	100.0 ml.

PROCEDURE:

1. Deparaffinize and hydrate slides to water; remove $HgCl_2$.
2. Stain in thionin: 15 minutes to 1 hour.
3. Differentiate in 95% alcohol.
4. Dehydrate in absolute alcohol, clear, and mount.

RESULTS:

mucin—light to dark red or purple

Acid Mucopolysaccharides[11]

Thionin (GURR, 1958)

FIXATION: 10% formalin or other general fixative.

SOLUTIONS:

Thionin:

thionin, C.I. 52000, saturated aqueous	0.5 ml.
distilled water	100.0 ml.

Molybdate-ferricyanide solution:

ammonium molybdate, 5% aqueous	50.0 ml.
potassium ferricyanide, 1% aqueous	50.0 ml.

Make up solutions fresh each time.

PROCEDURE:

1. Deparaffinize and hydrate slides to water.

[11] See Acid Mucopolysaccharides under Saccharides, page 269.

2. Stain in thionin: 5–15 minutes.
3. Rinse in distilled water.
4. Treat with molybdate-ferricyanide: 2 minutes.
5. Wash in distilled water: 2–3 minutes.
6. Dehydrate, clear, and mount.

RESULTS:

acid mucopolysaccharides—purple
other cell elements—bluish

COMMENTS:

The molybdate-ferricyanide solution prevents loss of metachromasia.
See *Kuyer (1957)* for suggestions concerning fluorescent methods
for mucopolysaccharides.

Mast Cells[12]

Thionin Method (LEVINE, 1928)

FIXATION: any general fixative.

SOLUTIONS:

Thionin:

thionin, C.I. 52000 .... 1.0–2.0 gm.
distilled water .... 100.0 ml.

Orange G:

orange G, C.I. 16230, saturated solution in oil of cloves. It goes into
solution slowly; stir frequently. Allow to stand 24 hours before using.
Good until it becomes discolored by thionin.

PROCEDURE:

1. Deparaffinize and hydrate slides to water; remove $HgCl_2$.
2. Stain in thionin: 2–3 minutes for light stain; 10–15 minutes for
   an intense stain.
3. Rinse briefly in water for light stain; blot around sections for intense stain.
4. Dehydrate by dropping a few drops of absolute alcohol on sections.
5. Stain with orange G-clove oil: 1–2 minutes. Repeat orange G until
   thionin disappears from cytoplasm, leaving it orange. Mast cells
   remain unchanged.
6. Clear thoroughly in xylene, and mount.

[12] See Mast Cell Staining, page 276.

RESULTS:

mast cells—deep blue or purple blue

cytoplasm—light gold-orange

nuceli—faint blue

Quick Toluidine Blue Method [13]

FIXATION: any general fixative.

SOLUTION:

toluidine blue *O*, C.I. 52040	0.2 gm.
60% ethyl alcohol	100.0 ml.

PROCEDURE:

1. Deparaffinize and run slides down to 60% alcohol. Remove $HgCl_2$ if present.
2. Stain in toluidine blue: 1–2 minutes.
3. Rinse quickly in tap water.
4. Dehydrate in acetone, 2 changes: 2–3 minutes in each.
5. Clear in xylene and mount.

RESULTS:

mast cells—deep reddish purple

background—faint blue

Toluidine Blue (PADAWER, 1959)

FIXATION: formalin-alcohol preferred, 10% formalin satisfactory.

formalin	10.0 ml.
95% alcohol	90.0 ml.

SOLUTIONS:

toluidine blue *O*, C.I. 52040	0.05 gm.
ether 181 [14]	50.0 ml.
distilled water	50.0 ml.

Dissolve dye in water, add ether 181. Filter. Use within 24 hours.

PROCEDURE:

1. Deparaffinize and transfer into absolute methyl alcohol, 2 changes: 10 minutes each.
2. Transfer to ether 181, 50% aqueous: 10 minutes.
3. Stain in toluidine blue: 20–60 minutes.
4. Dehydrate in ether 181, 50% aqueous: 10–15 minutes.
5. Dehydrate in ether 181, 100%, 2 changes: 20 minutes each.
6. Clear in xylene and mount.

[13] Personal communication from Miss Marlies Natzler, U.C.L.A.

[14] Tetra methylene glycol ether, Ansul Chemical Co., Marinette, Wis.

RESULTS:

mast cell granules—reddish purple

background—faintly blue

cartilage—reddish purple (will be the only other tissue staining meta-chromatically)

COMMENTS:

The toluidine blue in many methods reverts to its orthochromatic (blue) color during dehydration; therefore it is the usual practice to prepare an aqueous or glycerine mount to produce only semi-permanent results. *Padawer* suggests that partial hydration is required for metachromasia and ether 181 does not completely hydrate the tissue. A specific concentration is used in which both mast cell polysaccharides and toluidine blue are poorly soluble.

Belanger and Hartnett (1960) use the following solution:

potassium acid phthalate-tartaric acid	1.0 gm.
distilled water	100.0 ml.
toluidine blue *O*, C.I. 52040	0.5 gm.

The dye requires 24 hours to dissolve. Filter before use. Good for one week.

PROCEDURE: Stain for 10 minutes; rinse in fresh phthalate-tartaric acid buffer (1 gm./100 ml. water): 2 minutes; dehydrate in tertiary butyl alcohol, 4 changes: 2 minutes each; clear and mount.

Pituitary and Pancreas

The staining of the cytoplasm and its elements is used to characterize and differentiate the cells of the anterior PITUITARY. The glandular cells are classed as either **chromophils** or **chromophobes.** Seventy-five per cent of the chromophils are normally acidophilic (**acidophils,** sometimes called *alpha* cells) and twenty-five per cent are basophilic (**basophils).** The latter group is made up of **gonadotrophs** (*delta* cells) and **thyrotrophs** (*beta* cells). Every few months a new method seems to appear in the literature, suggesting that the ideal procedure is being elusive. Certain reactions seem to be specific for certain cells. Thyrotrophs and gonadotrophs have an affinity for Schiff's reagent, thyrotrophs also stain with Gomori's aldehyde fuchsin or aldehyde thionin. Acidophil granules differentiate sharply in *Elftman's (1960)* method. Orange *G* also stains them. *Paget and Eccleston (1959, 1960)* use luxol fast blue to distinguish them.

Five methods have been included here. For additional information some of the following authors may be of assistance: *Elftman* (*1957 A*; *1959 A and B*; *1960*); *Gomori* (*1951*); *Kerenyi* (*1959*); *Landing* (*1954*); *Landing and Hall* (*1955*); *Lazarus* (*1958*); *Paget and Eccleston* (*1959, 1960*);*Pearse* (*1949, 1950*); *Shanklin, Nassar, and Issidorides* (*1959*).

Characteristic staining of cells types is also used to differentiate the various cells of the islets of Langerhans of the PANCREAS. *Gomori's* (*1941 B*), method is recommended, but the Heidenhain Azan method (page 149) also is excellent and brilliant.

Trichrome PAS [1] (PEARSE, 1950)

FIXATION: Helly's is best.

SOLUTIONS:
Periodic acid:

periodic acid	0.4 gm.
M/5 sodium acetate	5.0 ml.
95% ethyl alcohol	35.0 ml.
distilled water	10.0 ml.

Reducing solution:

potassium iodide	1.0 gm.
sodium thiosulfate	1.0 gm.
95% ethyl alcohol	30.0 ml.
distilled water	20.0 ml.
2N HCl (page 408)	0.5 ml.

A precipitate of sulfur forms; do not filter out. Make fresh just before use.

Schiff's reagent, see page 294.

Sulfite baths:

sodium metabisulfite, $Na_2S_2O_5$	0.5 gm.
distilled water	100.0 ml.

Celestin blue solution:

celestin blue *B*, C.I. 51050	0.5 gm.
ferric ammonium sulfate (iron alum)	5.0 gm.
distilled water	100.0 ml.

Dissolve alum in water, add celestin blue; boil 3 minutes. Cool and filter. Add:

glycerine	14.0 ml.

---

[1] Concerning PAS technics, see page 298.

Mayer's hematoxylin, see page 125.

Orange *G* Solution:

orange *G*, C.I. 16230 .... 2.0 gm.

phosphotungstic acid, 5% (5 gm./100 ml. water) 100.0 ml.

Allow to stand 48 hours. Use supernatant fluid.

PROCEDURE:
1. Deparaffinize and hydrate slides to water; remove $HgCl_2$.
2. Transfer to 70% alcohol: 2 minutes.
3. Oxidize in periodic acid: 5 minutes.
4. Rinse in 70% alcohol.
5. Place in reducing solution: 1 minute.
6. Rinse in 70% alcohol.
7. Treat with Schiff's reagent: 10–30 minutes.
8. Treat with sulfite solutions, 3 changes: 1 minute, 2 minutes, and 2 minutes.
9. Wash in running water: 10 minutes.
10. Stain in celestin blue: 2 minutes.
11. Stain in Mayer's hematoxylin: 2 minutes.
12. Wash in running water: 5 minutes.
13. Stain in orange *G*: 10 seconds.
14. Wash in running water until orange color is differentiated: about 10–15 seconds. Check under microscope.
15. Dehydrate, clear, and mount.

RESULTS:
colloid of stalk and parenchyma, and vesicles of vesiculate chromo-phobes—magenta
basophil (*beta*) granules—dark red
acidophil (*alpha*) granules—orange
erythrocytes—orange
nuclei—dark blue

Trichrome PAS (LAZARUS, 1958)

FIXATION: Zenker-formol (Helly's). Bouin's unsatisfactory.

SOLUTIONS:
Schiff's reagent, see page 294.
Sulfurous acid:

sodium metabisulfite, $Na_2S_2O_5$ .... 0.5 gm.

distilled water .... 100.0 ml.

Weigert's hematoxylin, see page 126.

Ponceau-orange *G*:

ponceau *2R*, C.I. 16150	0.2 gm.
orange *G*, C.I. 16230	0.1 gm.
distilled water	100.0 ml.
glacial acetic acid	1.0 ml.

Light green:

light green *SF* yellowish, C.I. 42095	1.0 gm.
distilled water	100.0 ml.
glacial acetic acid	1.0 ml.

Phosphomolybdic acid solutions:

phosphomolybdic acid	1.0 gm.
distilled water	100.0 ml.

To make 0.5% solution, use above 1%

phosphomolybdic acid	50.0 ml.
distilled water	50.0 ml.

PROCEDURE:

1. Deparaffinize and hydrate slides to water: remove $HgCl_2$.
2. Treat with periodic acid, 0.6% (0.6 gm./100 ml. water): 20 minutes.
3. Wash in running water: 5 minutes.
4. Treat with Schiff's reagent: 20 minutes.
5. Transfer through 3 sulfurous acid rinses: 0.5 minute each.
6. Wash in running water: 5–10 minutes.
7. Rinse in distilled water.
8. Stain in Weigert's ferric chloride hematoxylin (24 hours old): 10 minutes.
9. Rinse in 95% alcohol.
10. Differentiate in acidic alcohol (0.5 ml. HCl/100 ml. water).
11. Wash in running water: 10 minutes.
12. Stain in ponceau-orange G: 2 hours.
13. Rinse in distilled water.
14. Differentiate in phosphomolybdic acid, 1% until delta cells and collagen are colorless.
15. Rinse briefly in distilled water.
16. Stain in light green: 5–30 minutes.
17. Wash well in acetic acid, 1% (1 ml./99 ml. water): 1–2 minutes.
18. Differentiate in phosphomolybdic acid, 0.5%: 0.5–5 minutes.
19. Wash in acetic acid, 1%: 20 minutes.

20. Dehydrate in absolute alcohol, 2 changes: 3–5 minutes each.
21. Clear and mount.

RESULTS:

beta cell granules—pale yellow orange
beta cell cytoplasm—pale yellowish green
alpha cells—deep orange
delta cells—translucent green
glycogen, mucus, glycoproteins—dark red to purplish
nuclei—black
collagen—green
PAS-positive elements—magenta
erythrocytes—yellow

Aldehyde fuchsin-PAS Method (ELFTMAN, 1959 A and B)

FIXATION: overnight or week end in:

mercuric chloride, 5% aqueous	100.0 ml.
potassium chromium sulfate	5.0 gm.
formalin	5.0 ml.

Prepare fresh. Wash in 70% alcohol.

SOLUTIONS:

Aldehyde fuchsin:

basic fuchsin, C.I. 42500	0.5 gm.
70% ethyl alcohol	100.0 ml.
paraldehyde	0.75 ml.
hydrochloric acid, concentrated	1.25 ml.

Put in 37°C oven early in morning, and will be ready by noon of succeeding day.

Schiff's reagent, see page 294.

Orange G:

orange G, C.I. 16230	3.0 gm.
distilled water brought to pH 2.0 with few drops of glacial acetic acid or hydrochloric acid	100.0 ml.

PROCEDURE:

1. Deparaffinize and run slides down to 70% alcohol; remove $HgCl_2$ in iodine-70% alcohol.
2. Stain in aldehyde fuchsin: 30 minutes.
3. Rinse in 95% alcohol.
4. Oxidize in periodic acid, 1% (1 gm./100 ml. water); 15 minutes.

5. Rinse in distilled water, 3 changes: 2 minutes each.
6. Treat with Schiff's reagent: 20 minutes.
7. Rinse in tap water.
8. Stain acidophils in orange *G*: 10 minutes.
9. Rinse rapidly in water.
10. Dehydrate, clear, and mount.

RESULTS:

thyrotrophs (*beta*)—deep purple
gonadotrophs (*delta*)—red
acidophils, erythrocytes—orange
nuclei—unstained

COMMENTS:

If aldehyde is overstained, treat for about 4 minutes with 0.1% dilution of Clorox. Check under microscope. Wash thoroughly 10 or more minutes.

If oxidation of tissues is desired before staining, treat with equal parts of 0.2 potassium permanganate and 1% sulfuric acid: 5 minutes. Bleach in 5% oxalic acid. Wash.

Rhodacyan Method (GLENNER AND LILLIE, 1957)

FIXATION: Formalin or Zenker-formalin, not acetic formalin or Bouin's.

SOLUTION:

eosin, C.I. 45400, 1% (1 gm./100 ml. water)	8.0 ml.
anilin blue, C.I. 42780, 1% (1 gm./100 ml. water)	2.0 ml.

*p*H 4.5 buffer composed of

0.1M citric acid	1.1 ml.
0.2M disodium phosphate	0.9 ml.
distilled water	28.0 ml.

PROCEDURE:

1. Deparaffinize and hydrate slides to water; remove $HgCl_2$.
2. Stain, start staining at room temperature, and place at once in oven at 60°C: 1 hour.
3. Wash in running water: 5 minutes.
4. Dehydrate and clear through 50%, 80% and anhydrous acetone, acetone-xylene (1:1), xylene, 2 changes, and mount.

RESULTS:

beta cell granules—blue-black
acidophil granules—dark red

chromophobe granules—slate grey to pale pink
colloid—red to blue-violet
red cells—orange
collagen—blue

Cameron and Steele (1050) Method

FIXATION: any good fixative.

SOLUTIONS:

Potassium permanganate, 0.3%:

potassium permanganate	0.3 gm.
distilled water	100.0 ml.

Sodium bisulfite, 2.5%:

sodium bisulfite	2.5 gm.
distilled water	100.0 ml.

Aldehyde-fuchsin, page 168 and 287.

Halmi's mixture (1952):

distilled water	100.0 ml.
lightgreen *SF*, yellowish, C.I. 42095	0.2 gm.
orange *G*, C.I. 16230	1.0 gm.
chromotrope *2R*, C.I. 16570	0.5 gm.
phosphotungstic acid	0.5 gm.
glacial acetic acid	1.0 ml.

Keeps indefinitely.

PROCEDURE:

1. Deparaffinize and hydrate slides to water; remove $HgCl_2$.
2. Oxidize in potassium permanganate: 1 minute.
3. Rinse in distilled water.
4. Bleach in sodium bisulfite until permanganate color is removed.
5. Wash in running water: 5 minutes.
6. Transfer to 70% alcohol: 2 minutes.
7. Stain in aldehyde-fuchsin: 5–10 minutes.
8. Wipe off back of slide and rinse in 95% alcohol.
9. Differentiate in 95% alcohol until no more aldehyde-fuchsin comes out of sections.
10. Transfer to 70% alcohol: 2 minutes.
11. Rinse in distilled water: 1 minute.
12. Stain in Halmi's mixture: 45 seconds.

13. Wipe off back of slide, differentiate in 95% alcohol plus 0.2% of acetic acid: 2–3 minutes.
14. Rinse in fresh 95% alcohol.
15. Dehydrate in absolute alcohol, clear, and mount.

RESULTS:

granulation of beta cells—dark purple
delta cells—green
acidophilic granules—orange
nucleoli—bright red
coagulated contents of cytoplasmic granules—orange

Pancreas

Chromium-Hematoxylin-Phloxine (GOMORI, 1941 B)

FIXATION: Bouin's preferred. Stieve's satisfactory. Zenker's, Carnoy, and formalin unsatisfactory.

SOLUTIONS:

Bouin's solution, see page 13.
Potassium dichromate-sulfuric acid:

Can be made up as separate 0.3% solutions and mixed or:

potassium dichromate .... 0.15 gm.
distilled water .... 100.0 ml.
sulfuric acid, concentrated .... 0.15 ml.

Hematoxylin solution:

hematoxylin .... 0.5 gm.
distilled water .... 50.0 ml.

When dissolved, add:

potassium chromium sulfate (chrome alum) 3%,
(1.5 gm./50 ml. water) .... 50.0 ml.

Mix well and add:

potassium dichromate, 5% (5 gm./100 ml.
water) .... 2.0 ml
N/2 sulfuric acid (about 2.5 ml./100 ml. water) 2.0 ml.

Ripen for 48 hours. Can be used as long as a film with a metallic luster forms on its surface after 1 day's standing. Filter before use.

Phloxine:

phloxine *B*, C.I. 45410 .... 0.5 gm.

distilled water .... 100.0 ml.

PROCEDURE:

1. Deparaffinize and hydrate slides to water; remove $HgCl_2$.
2. Refix in Bouin's solution: 12–24 hours.
3. Wash in running water: 5 minutes.
4. Treat with potassium dichromate-sulfuric acid: 5 minutes.
5. Decolorize in sodium bisulfite, 5% (5 gm./100 ml. water): 3–5 minutes.
6. Wash in running water: 5 minutes.
7. Stain in hematoxylin solution until beta cells are deep blue. Check under microscope. 10–15 minutes.
8. Differentiate in hydrochloric acid, 1% (1 ml./99 ml. water): about 1 minute.
9. Wash in running water until clear blue: 5 minutes.
10. Stain in phloxine: 5 minutes.
11. Rinse briefly in distilled water.
12. Treat with phosphotungstic acid, 5% (5 gm./100 ml. water): 1 minute.
13. Wash in running water: 5 minutes. Sections turn red again.
14. Differentiate in 95% alcohol. If the sections are too red and the alpha cells do not stand out clearly, rinse 15–20 seconds in 80% alcohol.
15. Dehydrate in absolute alcohol, clear, and mount.

RESULTS:

beta cells—blue

alpha cells—red

delta cells (not present in all animals)—pink to red, actually indistinguishable from alphas

COMMENTS:

Also see Heidenhain's Azan method, page 149.

If the zymogen granules (acidophilic) are to be preserved in the acinar cells of the pancreatic lobules avoid fixatives containing acetic acid.

For fluorescent differentiation of the alpha and beta cells, see *Hartroft (1951)*.

Chapter 19

Feulgen and PAS
Technics, and
Related Reactions

Feulgen and PAS technics involve two chemical reactions: (1) the oxidation of 1,2 glycols and/or *a*-amino alcohol groups to aldehydes, and (2) the reaction of resulting aldehydes with Schiff reagent (page 294) to form a purple-red color. Among the polysaccharides are glycogen, starch, and cellulose having 1,2 glycol groups which develop a positive Schiff reaction. Cartilage has a polysaccharide compound making this tissue react positively; and among the mucoproteins, the mucins are carbohydrates and thus react positively. Other structures of unknown chemical composition, but containing polysaccharides, will show a positive reaction: striated and brush borders and reticulin fibers, for example. The two oxidizers most commonly used are chromic and periodic acids. The latter breaks the carbon chains of the polysaccharides containing the 1,2 glycol groupings and oxides the broken ends into aldehyde groups. Chromic acid is a weaker oxidizer with its action limited almost exclusively to glycogen and mucin (the principle of the Bauer method, page 301). If necessary, glycogen and starch can be demonstrated to the exclusion of other reactants, by iodine or Best's Carmine (page 267), and mucin by Mayor's mucicarmine (page 273) or metachromatic methods (page 278). If it is desirable to prevent the reaction of glycogen or starch, the saliva or diastase treatment is simple and effective.

Among the nucleic acids, oxidation will not form aldehydes and acid hydrolysis is required. The two kinds of nucleic acid are (1) **thymo-nucleic acid** (desoxyribose or deoxyribose nucleic acid, desoxypentose or deoxypentose ribonucleic acid, or **DNA**), the principle component of nuclei and containing desoxyribose (desoxypentose) sugar; and (2) **ribose nucleic acid** (pentose nucleic or plasmo nucleic acid, or **RNA**), found in cytoplasmic structures, with ribose (pentose) as the sugar component. When nucleic acids are treated with warm HCl, aldehyde groups are released from the desoxypentose sugars, but not from the pentose sugars. Thus, when treated with Schiff reagent, DNA reacts positively, but RNA reacts negatively. Both, however, can be demonstrated at the same time by selective dyeing with pyronin and methyl green (page 297).

Schiff's reagent. In an acid solution and with excess of SO_2 present, **basic fuchsin** (a mixture of several related phenyl methane dyes, rosanilins, and pararosanilins built on the quinoid ring) is reduced to form a colorless N-sulfinic acid (fuchsin sulfurous acid). This reagent, with the addition of aldehydes, forms a new phenyl methane dye, slightly different from basic fuchsin since the color is more purple-red than pure red. The chemical reaction is not wholly understood. Thus, areas rich in DNA, after hydrolysis, show deep coloration. Schiff's is stable so long as an excess of SO_2 is present and high acidity. Anything removing these conditions restores the original dye and produces a pseudo-reaction. But when regenerated by an aldehyde, the dye becomes extremely resistant to such agents. Schiff's reagent is not a dye; it lacks a chromophore and is, therefore, colorless. *Baker (1958)* considers this an example of *localized synthesis* of a dye; when the Schiff's (colorless) comes in contact with an aldehyde, the chromophore of the triaryl-methane (quinoid ring structure) dye is reconstituted. The additive compound of the aldehyde with the Schiff could be called a dye.

Schiff's deteriorates rapidly at temperatures over 40°C, but at 0° and −5°C, if kept tightly stoppered, the deterioration is slow. Under these conditions it will keep as long as six months.

References: Atkinson (1952); Baker (1958); Bensley (1959); Glegg, Clermont and Leblond (1952); Gomori (1952); Lhotka and Davenport (1949); Lillie (1951A, 1953, 1954A and B); and Stowell (1945).

Feulgen Reaction

FIXATION: one containing $HgCl_2$ is preferred.

SOLUTIONS:

N hydrochloric acid, see page 408.

Schiff's reagent (Lillie, 1951 B):

basic fuchsin, C.I. 42500	0.5–1.0 gm.
distilled water	85.0 ml.
sodium metabisulfite, $Na_2S_2O_5$	1.9 gm.
N HCl	15.0 ml.

Place in bottle with approximately 50–60 ml. of free air space. Shake at intervals for at least 2 hours or overnight. Add 200 mg. activated charcoal: 2 minutes; shake occasionally. Filter. If solution is not water-white the charcoal is old. Try a fresh batch and refilter. Store Schiff reagent in a bottle with a minimum of air space above the solution and keep in refrigerator. This will decrease loss of SO_2 (*Elftman, 1959*).

Bleaching solution (sulfurous acid):

N HCl (page 408)	5.0 ml.
potassium or sodium bisulfite, 10% aqueous	
$K_2S_2O_5$ or $Na_2S_2O_5$	5.0 ml.
distilled water	100.0 ml.

or:

HCl, concentrated	1.0 ml.
potassium or sodium bisulfite	0.4 gm.
distilled water	100.0 ml.

For best results, make up bleach fresh each time.

Fast Green:

fast green *FCF*, C.I. 42053	0.05 gm.
95% ethyl alcohol	100.0 ml.

PROCEDURE:

1. Deparaffinize and hydrate slides to water; remove $HgCl_2$. (Leaving slides in 95% alcohol overnight will remove lipids which might cause a plasmal reaction.)
2. Rinse at room temperature in N HCl: 2 minutes.
3. Hydrolyze at 50°C in N HCl: 20 minutes or 5 minutes at 60°C.
4. Rinse at room temperature in N HCl; rinse in distilled water.
5. Stain in Schiff's reagent: 2 hours in dark.
6. Drain and transfer quickly into bleaching solution, 3 changes: 1.5–2 minutes in each.
7. Wash in running water: 10–15 minutes.

8. Rinse in distilled water.

9. Counterstain in fast green: 10 seconds.

10. Dehydrate, clear, and mount.

RESULTS:

thymonucleic-acid-containing substances—red-violet

other tissue elements—shades of green

COMMENTS:

1. *Kasten and Burton (1959)* make the following Schiff reagent. It is quickly prepared, colorless, does not stain the hands, and does not require refrigeration. It can be made more sensitive by boiling it for 1 minute.

basic fuchsin, C.I. 42500	0.05 gm.
distilled water	300.0 ml.
sodium hyposulfite, $Na_2S_2O_4$	6.0 gm.

Solution should decolorize immediately. Filter if necessary. Ready for immediate use.

2. Pink solutions of Schiff reagent may have lost their potency. Test by pouring a few drops into 10 ml. of 40% formalin. A good solution changes rapidly to reddish purple, but if the color changes slowly and becomes blue-purple, the solution is breaking down.

3. *Chen (1943)* uses the following weak Flemming's fixative for Avian parasites. It gives beautiful results on any kind of smear preparation and very small pieces of tissue.

FIXATION: 1–4 hours.

chromic acid, 1% in normal saline	25.0 ml.
acetic acid, 1% in normal saline	10.0 ml.
osmic acid, 2% in normal saline	5.0 ml.
normal saline	60.0 ml.

WASHING: smears—1 hour in running water and proceed to step 2, hydrolysis: *pieces of tissue*—overnight before proceeding to embed for sectioning.

4. The first of the series of three bleaching solutions (step 6) will begin to accumulate Schiff's reagent and turn pink. Then it is advisable to remove that solution, shift number 2 and number 3 along into positions 1 and 2, and add a new number 3 solution.

Desoxyribonucleic Acid (DNA) Fluorescent Technique
(CULLING AND VASSER, 1961)

FIXATION: 10% formalin for sections; methyl alcohol for smears. (Other fixatives may require a different time for hydrolysis.)

SOLUTIONS:

Fluorescent Schiff's reagent:

acriflavine dihydrochloride	1.0 gm.
potassium metabisulfite	2.0 gm.
distilled water	200.0 ml.
N hydrochloric acid	20.0 ml.

Dissolve acriflavine and potassium metabisulfite in distilled water; add hydrochloric acid. Keep overnight before using.

Periodic acid:

periodic acid	1.0 gm.
M/15 sodium acetate	10.0 ml.
absolute ethyl alcohol	90.0 ml.

Acid alcohol:

70% ethyl alcohol	99.0 ml.
hydrochloric acid, concentrated	1.0 ml.

PROCEDURE:

1. Deparaffinize and hydrate sections to water. Smears can be carried directly into next step.
2. Transfer to pre-heated N hydrochloric acid, 60°C: sections, 10 minutes; smears, 3–4 minutes (or 1% periodic acid: 10 minutes for PAS).
3. Wash briefly in distilled water.
4. Transfer to fluorescent Schiff reagent: 20 minutes.
5. Wash in acid alcohol: 5 minutes.
6. Wash in fresh acid alcohol: 10 minutes.
7. Dehydrate in absolute alcohol: 1 minute.
8. Clear in xylene: 1 minute, and mount.

RESULTS:

DNA—bright golden fluorescence
other elements—dark green to black

COMMENTS:

The advantage of this method over the conventional one is that smaller amounts of dye molecules are more easily observed.

Culling and Vasser warn that previously heated hydrochloric acid is important; cold hydrochloric acid can produce negative results.

Also timing is important; the reaction may weaken if slides are left in hydrolysis too long.

For details concerning fluorescent microscope and equipment, see pages 102.

Pyronin-Methyl Green for Nucleic Acids (KURNICK, 1952)

FIXATION: absolute alcohol, Carnoy or cold acetone. If formalin is used, it must be adjusted to pH 7 and used only briefly before the solution turns acid and produces a faint green staining of cytoplasm. Picric acid depolymerizes DNA and shows no green chromatin.

SOLUTIONS·

Methyl green:

      methyl green, C.I. 42590 .... 0.2 gm.

      0.1M acetate buffer (pH 4.2) or distilled water   100.0 ml.

Before making solution, methyl green should be purified by extraction with chloroform. Add approximately 10 gm. methyl green to 200 ml. of chloroform in 500 ml. Erlenmeyer flask and shake. Filter with suction and repeat with smaller amounts of chloroform until the solution comes off blue-green instead of lavender (usually requires at least 3 extractions). Dry and store in stoppered bottle. Purified dye is stable.

Pyronin:

pyronin *Y* saturated in acetone, or for lighter color in 10% acetone. The *British Pyronin Y* for RNA (*G. T. Gurr* or *Edward Gurr*) is recommended.

PROCEDURE:

1. Deparaffinize and hydrate slides to water.
2. Stain in methyl green solution: 6 minutes.
3. Blot and immerse in *n*-butyl alcohol: several minutes in each of 2 changes.
4. Stain in pyronin: 30–90 seconds. Shorten to a few dips if stain is too dark.
5. Clear in cedar oil, xylene, and mount.

RESULTS:

RNA containing cytoplasm—red

nucleoli—red

chromatin—bright green

erythrocytes—brown

eosinophilic granules—red

cartilage matrix—green

osseous matrix—pink with trace of violet

COMMENTS:

These two dyes distinguish between states of polymerization of nucleic acids, not between the acids themselves. Highly polymerized nucleic acid stains with methyl green; low polymers of both DNA and RNA stain with the pyronin. The usual technics resulted in too pale a methyl green, or if excess staining was tried, water rinses removed the methyl green and acetone removed the pyronin. Dehydrating with ethyl alcohol removes most of the color; isopropyl and tertiary butyl are no improvement. So *Kurnick* developed the above method, when he found that *n*-butyl alcohol differentiated the methyl green, but it removed the pyronin. He, therefore, decided to leave the pyronin out of the first solution (it was lost anyway) and tried following the methyl green with pyronin saturated in acetone. The acetone must be free of water, so always use a fresh solution.

Later *Kurnick (1955)* published a method in which he did combine the two stains:

SOLUTION:

pyronin *Y*, 2% (2 gm./100 ml. water)	12.5 ml.
methyl green, 2% (2 gm./100 ml. water)	7.5 ml.
distilled water	30.0 ml.

PROCEDURE:

1. Deparaffinize and hydrate slides to water.
2. Stain in methyl green-pyronin: 6 minutes.
3. Blot carefully with filter paper.
4. Dehydrate, *n*-butyl alcohol, 2 changes: 5 minutes each.
5. Clear in xylene: 5 minutes; transfer to cedarwood oil: 5 minutes.
6. Mount.

Flax and Pollister (1949) used 0.1% aqueous Azure *A*, and differentiated overnight in absolute alcohol. The stain was specific for nucleic acids; chromatin, nucleoli, and cytoplasmic regions high in nucleoprotein concentrations, but it also stained mast cells, mucus and cartilage matrix. The latter could be checked by applying ribonuclease.

Periodic Acid-Schiff (PAS) Reaction

Two methods are outlined; one (*A*) with alcoholic solutions, the other (*B*) with aqueous solutions.

FIXATION: any general fixative, but if glycogen or other soluble polysaccharides are to be demonstrated, fixation and washing should be done
in alcoholic fluids of no less than 70% alcoholic content.

A. SOLUTIONS (alcoholic):

Periodic acid:

periodic acid, HIO_4	0.8 gm.
distilled water	30.0 ml.
sodium acetate, hydrated	0.27 gm.
(or 10 ml. M/5 sodium acetate)	
absolute ethyl alcohol	70.0 ml.

Reducing rinse:

potassium iodide	2.0 gm.
sodium thiosulfate, $Na_2S_2O_3$	2.0 gm.
distilled water	40.0 ml.
add with stirring:	
absolute ethyl alcohol	60.0 ml.
2N HCl (page 408)	1.0 ml.

If a precipitate forms, allow it to settle and use solution immediately.

Schiff's reagent, see page 294.

Sodium bisulfite:

sodium metabisulfite, $Na_2S_2O_5$	0.5 gm.
distilled water	100.0 ml.

PROCEDURE:
1. Deparaffinize and run slides down to 70% alcohol; remove $HgCl_2$
   if present, using iodine in 70% alcohol.
2. Treat with alcoholic periodic acid: 10 minutes.
3. Rinse with 70% alcohol.
4. Treat with reducing rinse: 5 minutes.
5. Rinse in 70% alcohol.
6. Treat with Schiff's reagent: 10 minutes.
7. Transfer through sulfite solutions, 3 changes: 1.5–2 minutes in
   each (see Comment 4, page 295).
8. Wash in running water: 5 minutes.
9. Counterstain if desired (see Comments, number 3).
10. Dehydrate, clear, and mount.

B. SOLUTIONS (aqueous):

Periodic acid:

periodic acid (HIO_4)	0.6 gm.
distilled water	100.0 ml.
nitric acid, concentrated	0.3 ml.

Schiff's reagent, see page 294.

Sulfite solution, see above procedure.

PROCEDURE:

1. Deparaffinize and hydrate slides to water; remove $HgCl_2$.
2. Treat with periodic acid, aqueous: 5 minutes.
3. Wash in running water: 5 minutes.
4. Treat with Schiff's reagent: 10 minutes.
5. Transfer through sulfite solutions, 3 changes: 1.5–2 minutes in each.
6. Wash in running water: 5 minutes.
7. Counterstain, if desired (see Comments, number 3).
8. Dehydrate, clear, and mount.

RESULTS:

Many tissues give positive PAS reactions: glycogen, starch, cellulose, mucins, colloid of thyroid, cartilage matrix, chitins, reticulum, fibrin, collagen—rose to purplish-red

fungi—red

nuclei and other tissue elements—colors of counterstain

COMMENTS:

1. When preparing slides, avoid excessive use of egg albumen; it contains sufficient carbohydrate to react with the Schiff.

2. *Control Slides:*

   To remove *glycogen,* run the slides down to water and subject them to the saliva test. Saliva contains a diastatic enzyme which dissolves glycogen and starch. Instead of saliva, a 1% solution of salt or animal diastase can be used for 20 minutes to overnight at room temperature.

   To remove *mucin,* treat slides with Lysozyme, 0.1 mg. to 10.0 ml. of Sorensen M/15 phosphate buffer (page 417), pH 6.24, room temperature: 40–60 minutes.

   To remove *RNA,* treat slides with 0.01 mg. RNase in 10.0 ml. 0.2M acetate buffer (page 414), pH 5.0 at room temperature: 10–15 minutes (or tris-HCl buffer, 0.05M, pH 7.5: 2 hours, 56°C).

3. *Counterstains:*

for nuclei—hematoxylin
for glycogen—fast green *FCF* as in Feulgen method
for mucin or acid polysaccharides—an acid dye (fast green)
for other polysaccharides—a basic dye (malachite green)

4. If it is necessary to remove the PAS from the tissue, treat it with potassium permanganate until all the color is removed, followed by oxalic acid bleaching of the permanganate.

Glycogen[1]

Bauer-Feulgen Reaction

FIXATION: avoid aqueous media (see McManus and Mowry, 1958).

absolute ethyl alcohol	9 parts.
formalin	1 part.

Start dehydration for embedding in 95% alcohol. Mount slides with 95% alcohol.

SOLUTIONS:

Chromic acid:

chromic acid, CrO_3	4.0 gm.
distilled water	100.0 ml.

Schiff's reagent, see page 294.
Sodium bisulfite:

sodium bisulfite, meta, $Na_2S_2O_5$	1.0 gm.
distilled water	100.0 ml.

PROCEDURE:

1. Deparaffinize and hydrate slides to water; remove $HgCl_2$ if present.
2. Oxidize in chromic acid: 1 hour.
3. Wash in running water: 5 minutes.
4. Treat with Schiff's reagent: 10–15 minutes.
5. Transfer through sodium sulfite, 3 changes: 1, 2, and 2 minutes (see Comment 4, page 295).
6. Wash in running water: 5 minutes.
7. Counterstain in hematoxylin, if desired.
8. Wash and blue in Scott's, and wash.
9. Dehydrate, clear, and mount.

[1] See also Best's Carmine reaction for glycogen, page 267.

RESULTS:

glycogen—red
nuclei—blue

Desoxyribonucleic Acid, Polysaccharides and Proteins

Triple Stain (HIMES AND MORIBER, 1956)

FIXATION: any good general fixative.

SOLUTIONS:

N HCl, see page 408.
Azure *A*-Schiff reagent:

azure *A* (azure I), C.I. 52005	0.5 gm.
bleach solution (below)	100.0 ml.

Lasts several weeks, but add a few drops of 10% potassium metabisulfite before reusing.

Bleach:

potassium or sodium metabisulfite, 10% aqueous	5.0 ml.
N HCl	5.0 ml.
distilled water	90.0 ml.

Make up fresh each time.

Periodic acid:

periodic acid (HIO_4)	0.8 gm.
0.2M sodium acetate	10.0 ml.
distilled water	90.0 ml.

Make up fresh each time.

Basic fuchsin-Schiff's reagent, page 294.

Naphthol yellow *S*:

Stock solution:

naphthol yellow *S*, C.I. 10316	1.0 gm.
acetic acid, 1% aqueous	100.0 ml.

Working solution:

stock solution	2.0 ml.
acetic acid, 1% aqueous	100.0 ml.

Keeps indefinitely.

PROCEDURE:

1. Deparaffinize and hydrate slides to water; remove $HgCl_2$.
2. Hydrolyze in N HCl, 60°C: 12 minutes, no more.
3. Rinse in distilled water.
4. Treat with Azure *A*-Schiff: 5 minutes.
5. Rinse in distilled water.
6. Bleach, 2 changes: 2 minutes each.
7. Rinse in distilled water.
8. Oxidize in periodic acid: 2 minutes.
9. Rinse in distilled water.
10. Treat with basic fuchsin-Schiff: 2 minutes.
11. Rinse in distilled water.
12. Bleach, 2 changes: 2 minutes each.
13. Rinse in distilled water.
14. Stain in Naphthol yellow: 2 minutes.
15. Rinse briefly in distilled water.
16. Dehydrate in tertiary or isopropyl alcohol, 2 changes.
17. Clear and mount.

RESULTS:

nuclei—blue to green (DNA)
polysaccharides—red
proteins—yellow

Chapter **20**

Microorganisms

In this chapter, to simplify the specificity of staining methods, the microorganisms will be broken down into three groups: bacteria, viruses, and fungi.

BACTERIA. Bacteria are customarily studied by direct microscopic observation and differentiated by shape, grouping of cells, presence or absence of certain structures, and the reaction of their cells to differential stains. Bacteria may be stained with aniline dyes; in a single dye, in mixed dyes, in polychromed dyes, or by differential methods. One of the most universally used stains was developed by the histologist *Gram* while he was trying to differentiate the bacteria in tissue. His method separates bacteria into two groups, (1) those that retain crystal violet and are said to be **Gram positive,** and (2) those that decolorize to be stained by a counterstain and are said to be **Gram negative.**

Some bacteria of high lipid content cannot be stained by the usual methods but require heat or long exposure to the stain. They are also difficult to decolorize and resist acid alcohol. These have been given the name **acid fast.** The spirochete forms will stain only faintly if at all and must be colored by silver methods.

Many bacteria form a capsule from the outer layer of the cell membrane, and the capsule appears like a halo around the organism, or over a chain of cells. This capsule will not stain in the customary stains; Hiss's stain (page 317), however, is simple and usually effective in this situation. Some bacteria are able to form spores that can be extremely resistant to injurious conditions (heat, chemicals). Boiling will destroy some of these, but many spores are more resistant. Some bacteria have flagella, filamentous appendages for locomotion.

Bacteria can be classified into three groups according to shape.

304

1. **Coccus:** *spherical;* may be found singly (micrococci), in pairs (diplococci), in clusters (staphylococci) or in chains (streptococci). The cocci cause food poisoning, infectious sore throat, scarlet fever, rheumatic fever, gonorrhea, pneumonia, and meningitis.

2. **Bacillus:** *rod-shaped;* elongate but oval, short, and thick (coccobacilli), attached end to end (streptobacilli). Bacilli cause typhoid fever, cholera, undulant fever, plague, tularemia, whooping cough, anthrax, tetanus, diphtheria, botulism, tuberculosis, and leprosy. *Bartonella,* a Gram-positive bacillus, causes infectious anemia in dogs, cats, mice, guinea pigs, cattle, sheep, and rats. The organism appears reddish violet in a Giemsa stain and is found in tissue macrophages and erythrocytes.

3. **Spiral forms:** *curved-rod;* a rigid spiral (spirillum) and a flexible spiral (spirochete). These forms can cause relapsing fever, Vincent's disease, syphillis, and yaws.

Rickettsia are very small, Gram-negative coccobacillary microorganisms associated with typhus and spotted fever and related diseases. They may appear as cocci or short bacilli, and may occur singly, in pairs, or in dense masses. They usually are found intracellularly, seldom living outside of body cells.

Some species are found only in the cytoplasm, others prefer the nucleus. Rickettsia stain best in a Giemsa-type stain or by Machiavello's method.

FUNGI: ACTINOMYCETES AND YEASTS. The fungus diseases are described in two groups.

1. Superficial mycoses: dermatophytes (ringworm).

2. Deep-seated mycoses: actinomycosis (cervico-facial, thoracic or abdominal infections, restricted mostly to agricultural workers).

The actinomycetes are characterized by fine branching filaments (**hyphae**) that form by intertwining and sometimes anastomosing a colony called a **mycelium.** Small oval or rod-shaped spores are formed by an aggregation of protoplasm of some of the hyphae. Sometimes the filaments themselves may break up and form bacillary-like bodies which are morphologically indistinguishable from bacteria. These spores are Gram positive and are considered by some as possible transition forms between bacteria and fungi.

There are two relatively well-defined groups of actinomycetes; one (including all the pathogenic forms) does not form aerial mycelium, but does show a tendency to segment into bacillary forms. The other group is characterized by formation of spores in aerial hyphae. Sometimes the actinomycetes are broken down into the *Actinomyces*—the anaerobic forms (live best without air), and *Nocardia*—the aerobic forms (must grow in air). *Burrows* (*1954*) uses the name *Actinomyces* for the pathogenic actinomycetes.

The fungi proper (Eumycetes) also form hyphae and mycelia. They give off two types of spores, sexual spores produced by the fusion of two cells and asexual spores formed by differentiation of the cells of the spore-bearing hyphae but without fusion. The so-called Fungi Imperfecti (part of the Eumycetes) form only asexual spores. These spores in some forms may be produced by the segmentation of the tips of the hyphae and are known as **conidia** (*Penicillium*).

Open or draining lesions are difficult to examine for fungi because of heavy bacterial contamination, but dermatophytes are easily demonstrated. Scrapings from horny layers or nail plate or hair can be mounted in 10–20% hot sodium hydroxide. This dissolves or makes transparant the tissue elements and then the preparation can be examined as a wet mount. Fungi in tissue sections are readily stained.

Yeast and Yeast-like Fungi. These are described as unicellular and nucleated. Some yeasts reproduce by budding and others by fission. Some can produce mycelium. Only a few are pathogenic, causing torula meningitis, European blastomycosis, and superficial infections of skin and mucus membranes.

Viruses. The viruses are microorganisms too small to be visible under the microscope and are capable of passing through filters. Viruses are responsible for many diseases, including yellow fever, poxes, poliomyelitis, influenza, measles, mumps, shingles, rabies, colds, infectious hepatitis, infectious mononucleosis, trachoma, psittacosis, and foot-and-mouth disease. In tissue sections and smears, viruses are characterized by **elementary** and **inclusion bodies.** Elementary bodies are infectious particles, and inclusion bodies are composed of numerous elementary bodies. Both types of bodies vary in size and appearance; some are located in the cytoplasm of infected cells (rabies, psittacosis, trachoma) and some are intranuclear (poliomyelitis). Special staining methods can demonstrate them effectively. (*Reference:* Burrows, 1954)

ANIMAL PARASITES. Protozoan, helminth, and arthropod infections: see Chapter 23.

Bacteria Staining

Gram Staining

When a gram staining procedure has been applied, a gram-positive cell or organism retains a particular primary dye. This process includes mordanting with iodine to form with the dye a precipitate which is insoluble in water and is neither too soluble nor insoluble in alcohol, the differentiator.

For the mechanism of gram reactions see Bartholomew and Mittwer (1950, 1951); Bartholomew *et al.* (1959); Mittwer *et al.* (1950).

Gram-Weigert Method (KRAJIAN, 1952)

FIXATION: 10% formalin or Zenker's formol.

SOLUTIONS:

Eosin:

eosin Y, C.I. 45380	1.0 gm.
distilled water	100.0 ml.

Sterling's gentian violet:

crystal violet, C.I. 42555 (gentian violet)	5.0 gm.
95% ethyl alcohol	10.0 ml.
aniline oil	2.0 ml.
distilled water	88.0 ml.

Mix aniline oil with water and filter. Add the crystal violet dissolved in alcohol. Keeps for several weeks to months.

Gram's iodine solution, see page 410.

PROCEDURE:

1. Deparaffinize and hydrate slides to water. Remove $HgCl_2$.
2. Stain in eosin: 5 minutes.
3. Rinse in water.
4. Stain in Sterling's gentian violet solution: 3 minutes for frozen sections; 10 minutes for paraffin sections.
5. Wash off with Gram's iodine and then flood with more of same solution: 3 minutes.
6. Blot with filter paper.
7. Flood with equal parts of aniline oil and xylene; reflood until color ceases to rinse out of sections.
8. Clear in xylene and mount.

RESULTS:

gram-positive bacteria, and fungi—violet
gram-negative organisms—not usually stained
fibrin—blue-black

Brown and Brenn Method (1931)

FIXATION: 10% formalin preferred.

SOLUTIONS:

Mayer's hematoxylin, see page 125.

Gentian violet:

crystal violet, C.I. 42555 (gentian violet) ...... 1.0 gm.
distilled water .... 100.0 ml.

Sodium bicarbonate:

sodium bicarbonate .... 5.0 gm.
distilled water .... 100.0 ml.

Gram's iodine, see page 410.

Basic fuchsin:

basic fuchsin, C.I. 42500 .... 0.25 gm.
distilled water .... 100.0 ml.

Dilute 0.1 ml. to 100 ml. distilled water for use.

Acetone-picric acid solution:

picric acid .... 0.1 gm.
acetone .... 100.0 ml.

PROCEDURE:

1. Deparaffinize and hydrate slides to water.
2. Stain in Mayer's hematoxylin: 2–3 minutes.
3. Wash in running water: 5 minutes.
4. Mix 26 drops of gentian violet and 5 drops of sodium bicarbonate solution. Flood slide, agitate occasionally: 2 minutes.
5. Rinse in water.
6. Treat with Gram's iodine: 1 minute.
7. Rinse in water and blot.
8. Decolorize with 1 part ether and 3 parts acetone, flooding slide until no more blue color comes off. Blot.
9. Stain in basic fuchsin: 5 minutes.
10. Rinse quickly in water, blot but do not dry.
11. Dip briefly in acetone, and immediately differentiate in acetone-picric acid until sections turn yellowish pink. Overdifferentiation may take out gram negative stain.
12. Rinse quickly in acetone, transfer to acetone-xylene (equal parts), then to xylene and mount.

RESULTS:

gram-positive organisms—deep violet or black
gram-negative organisms—bright red
cell nuclei—reddish brown

cytoplasm—yellowish
red blood corpuscles—yellow or reddish yellow
cartilage—pink
basophilic granules—red

COMMENTS:

The author finds it easier to differentiate step 8 by using a coplin jar of ether-acetone (1:3) and dunking the slide.

Glynn Method (1935)

FIXATION: Zenker's without acetic acid preferred.

SOLUTIONS:

Carbol-crystal violet:

crystal violet, C.I. 42555 (gentian violet)	1.0 gm.
phenol (carbolic acid) crystals	1.0 gm.
Work together in mortar, add	
absolute ethyl alcohol	10.0 ml.
distilled water	100.0 ml.

Allow to stand 48 hours. Filter.

Lugol's solution, see page 410.
Basic fuchsin:

basic fuchsin, C.I. 42500	0.05 gm.
HCl .05N or acetic acid .1N (page 408)	100.0 ml.

Solution should be pH 2–3.

PROCEDURE:

1. Deparaffinize and hydrate to water; remove $HgCl_2$.
2. Stain in carbol-crystal violet: 2 minutes.
3. Drain, but do not wash.
4. Treat with Lugol's solution: 1 minute.
5. Flush with acetone from dropping bottle until no more color is removed: 10–15 seconds.
6. Rinse in distilled water.
7. Stain in basic fuchsin: 3 minutes.
8. Drain, but do not wash.
9. Stain in saturated aqueous picric acid: 30 seconds to 1 minute.
10. Wash in running water till sections are light yellow.
11. Differentiate (some red is lost in sections) and dehydrate in acetone: 10–15 seconds.
12. Xylene and mount.

RESULTS:

gram-positive bacteria—deep violet
gram-negative bacteria—red
erythrocytes—yellow
nuclei—red
cytoplasm—faint yellow

COMMENTS:

Glynn suggests treating sections with .01N HCl before staining with basic fuchsin.

Lillie's Quick Method (1928)

FIXATION: any good general fixative.

SOLUTIONS:

Crystal violet solution:

crystal violet, C.I. 42555	2.0 gm.
95% ethyl alcohol	20.0 ml.
ammonium oxalate, 1% (1 gm./100 ml. water)	80.0 ml.

Filter. Keeps well.

Lugol's solution, see page 410.

Safranin:

safranin *O*, C.I. 50240	0.5 gm.
distilled water	100.0 ml.

PROCEDURE:

1. Deparaffinize and hydrate slides to water.
2. Stain in crystal violet solution: 30 seconds.
3. Wash in running water: 3–5 minutes.
4. Treat with Lugol's solution: 30 seconds.
5. Wash in running water: 2–3 minutes.
6. Flush with acetone from dropping bottle until no more color is removed: 10–15 seconds.
7. Wash in water.
8. Counterstain in safranin: 30 seconds.
9. Rinse in distilled water.
10. Dehydrate and differentiate in acetone. Some of red differentiates out of cells leaving nuclei red and cytoplasm pink.
11. Clear and mount.

RESULTS:

gram-positive bacteria—blue-black
gram-negative bacteria—red

cell nuclei—red

cytoplasm, fibrin, collagen—pink

COMMENTS:

For tubercle and lepra bacilli it may be necessary to stain for a longer period or heat for 90 seconds on a 50–52°C hot plate.

MacCallum-Goodpasture Method (MALLORY, 1944)

FIXATION: any good general fixative.

SOLUTIONS:

Goodpasture's fuchsin:

basic fuchsin, C.I. 42500	0.59 gm.
aniline oil	1.0 ml.
phenol (carbolic acid)	1.0 gm.
or melted	1.0 ml.
30% alcohol	100.0 ml.

Sterling's gentian violet:

crystal violet, C.I. 42500 (gentian violet)	5.0 gm.
95% ethyl alcohol	10.0 ml.
aniline	2.0 ml.
distilled water	88.0 ml.

Mix aniline and water and filter. Add crystal violet dissolved in alcohol. Keeps several weeks to months.

Gram's iodine, see page 410.

PROCEDURE:

1. Deparaffinize and hydrate slides to water; remove $HgCl_2$.
2. Stain in Goodpasture's fuchsin: 10–20 minutes.
3. Wash in water.
4. Differentiate in formalin (full strength): few seconds. Red color changes to rose.
5. Rinse in distilled water: few seconds.
6. Treat with picric acid, saturated aqueous: 3–5 minutes. Sections turn purplish yellow.
7. Wash in distilled water: few seconds.
8. Differentiate in 95% alcohol. Sections turn red; some of it washes out, also some of yellow.
9. Rinse in distilled water.
10. Stain in Sterling's gentian violet: 3–5 minutes.
11. Rinse in distilled water.
12. Treat with Gram's iodine: 1 minute.

13. Blot with filter paper. Do not dry.
14. Flood with equal parts of aniline oil and xylene, reflood until no color washes out of sections.
15. Xylene and mount.

RESULTS:

gram-positive bacteria—red
gram-negative bacteria—blue
fibrin—blue
other tissue elements—reds to purples

Acid-Fast Staining

Ziehl-Neelsen (MODIFIED FROM MALLORY, 1944)

FIXATION: any general fixative.

SOLUTIONS:

Carbol-fuchsin:

basic fuchsin, C.I. 42500, saturated in absolute ethyl alcohol (approximately 6 gm./100 ml. water)	10.0 ml.
carbolic acid, 5% (5 ml. melted carbolic acid/95 ml. water)	90.0 ml.

Store at room temperature. It is advisable to filter each time before use.

Acid alcohol:

hydrochloric acid, concentrated	1.0 ml.
70% ethyl alcohol	99.0 ml.

Methylene blue solution:

methylene blue chloride, C.I. 52015	0.5 gm.
glacial acetic acid	0.5 ml.
distilled water	100.0 ml.

PROCEDURE:

1. Deparaffinize and hydrate slides to water; remove $HgCl_2$.
2. Stain in carbol-fuchsin, 55°C: 30 minutes.
3. Wash in running water: 5 minutes.
4. Destain in acid alcohol until sections are pale pink; check under microscope.
5. Wash in running water: 3–5 minutes.
6. Dip one slide at a time into methylene blue, taking care that sections remain light blue; rinse briefly in distilled water.

7. Dehydrate, isopropyl alcohol, 99%, 2 changes: 3–5 minutes in each.
8. Clear and mount.

RESULTS:

acid-fast bacteria—red
nuclei—blue

Ziehl-Neelsen (PUTT'S MODIFICATION, 1951)

FIXATION: general fixative, but 10% formalin best.

SOLUTIONS:

New fuchsin:

new fuchsin, C.I. 42520 (magenta III)	1.0 gm.
phenol (carbolic acid)	5.0 gm.
ethyl or methyl alcohol (absolute)	10.0 ml.
distilled water to make	100.0 ml.

Acetic alcohol:

glacial acetic acid	5.0 ml.
absolute ethyl alcohol	95.0 ml.

Counterstain:

methylene blue chloride, C.I. 52015	0.5 gm.
absolute ethyl alcohol	100.0 ml.

PROCEDURE:

1. Deparaffinize and hydrate slides to water; remove $HgCl_2$.
2. Stain in new fuchsin, room temperature: 3 minutes.
3. Treat with lithium carbonate, saturated aqueous: 1 minute. Agitate gently, discard solution if it becomes blue.
4. Differentiate until pale pink in acetic alcohol.
5. Rinse in absolute alcohol, 2 changes: 1–2 minutes in each.
6. Counterstain.
7. Decolorize in absolute alcohol, 2 changes: $\frac{1}{2}$ minute each.
8. Clear and mount.

RESULTS:

acid-fast bacteria—red
red blood corpuscles—pink
mast cell granules—deep blue
other bacteria—blue
nuclei—blue

Kinyoun's Carbol-Fuchsin Method (MARTI AND JOHNSON'S MODIFICATION, 1951)

FIXATION: any general fixative, 10% formalin preferred.

SOLUTIONS:

Carbol-fuchsin:

basic fuchsin, C.I. 42500	4.0 gm.
phenol (carbolic acid) crystals	8.0 gm.
95% ethyl alcohol	20.0 ml.
distilled water	100.0 ml.

Add 1 drop Tergitol #7 to every 30 ml. of above.

Acid alcohol:

nitric acid, concentrated	0.5 ml.
95% ethyl alcohol	95.0 ml.

Malachite green:

malachite green oxalate, C.I. 42000	1.0 gm.
distilled water	100.0 ml.

PROCEDURE:

1. Deparaffinize and hydrate slides to water.
2. Stain in carbol-fuchsin: 30 minutes, room temperature.
3. Wash in running water: 5 minutes.
4. Decolorize in acid alcohol: 3 minutes. Mixture should not be yellow.
5. Wash in running water: 5 minutes.
6. Rinse in 95% alcohol: 1 minute.
7. Wash in running water: 2 minutes.
8. Stain in malachite green: 0.5 minute.
9. Wash in running water: few minutes.
10. Rinse in 95% alcohol, 10 dips.
11. Dehydrate, absolute alcohol; clear and mount.

RESULTS:

acid-fast bacteria—red
tissue elements—shades of green

COMMENTS:

Instead of malachite green, Lillie's (1944) methylene blue can be used; 1% methylene blue in 0.5% aqueous acetic acid: 3 minutes.

Fite-Formaldehyde Method (WADE'S MODIFICATION, 1957)

FIXATION: Zenker's preferred; removal of $HgCl_2$ not necessary, it disappears during processing.

SOLUTIONS:

Phenol new fuchsin:

new fuchsin, C.I. 42520 (Magenta III)	0.5 gm.
phenol (carbolic acid)	5.0 gm.
ethyl or methyl alcohol	10.0 ml.
distilled water to make	100.0 ml.

Van Gieson, modified:

acid fuchsin, C.I. 42685	0.01 gm.
picric acid	0.1 gm.
distilled water	100.0 ml.

PROCEDURE:

1. Deparaffinize in turpentine-paraffin oil (2:1) 2 changes: 5 minutes total.
2. Drain, wipe off excess fluid, blot to opacity, place in water.
3. Stain overnight in phenol-fuchsin, room temperature.
4. Wash in tap water.
5. Treat with formalin (full strength): 5 minutes (turns blue).
6. Wash in running water: 3–5 minutes.
7. Treat with sulfuric acid, 5% (5 ml./95 ml. water): 5 minutes.
8. Wash in running water: 5–10 minutes.
9. Treat with potassium permanganate, 1% (1 gm./100 ml. water): 3 minutes.
10. Wash in running water: 3 minutes.
11. Treat with oxalic acid, 2–5% (2–5 gm./100 ml. water) individually with agitation: not more than 30 seconds. Slides can remain in water while others are being treated.
12. Stain with modified Van Gieson: 3 minutes. *No wash.*
13. Rinse for few seconds in 95% alcohol.
14. Dehydrate, clear, and mount.

RESULTS:

acid-fast bacteria—deep blue or blue black
connective tissue—red
other tissue elements—yellowish

COMMENTS:

Beamer and Firminger (1955) emphasize care in the use of formalin. Old formalin yields poor results, while a redistilled form produces the most brilliant staining. The reagent grade in 16 oz. brown bottles, if kept tightly closed, give a good stain.

Tilden and Tanaka (1945) outline a method for frozen sections, essentially the same as the one above after mounting the sections with celloidin protective coat. They also emphasize the need for good formalin; if the sections fail to turn blue, try a different batch.

Tubercle Bacilli Staining

Fluorescent Method (RICHARDS, *et al.*, 1941; RICHARDS, 1941; BOGEN, 1941)

FIXATION: 10% formalin for sections; smears by heat.

SOLUTIONS:

Auramin stain:

auramin *O* C.I. 41000	0.3 gm.
distilled water	97.0 ml.
melted phenol (carbolic acid)	3.0 ml.

Shake to dissolve dye or use gentle heat. Solution becomes cloudy on cooling, but is satisfactory. Shake before using.

Decolorizing solution:

hydrochloric acid, concentrated	0.5 ml.
70% ethyl alcohol	100.0 ml.
sodium chloride	0.5 gm.

PROCEDURE:

1. Deparaffinize and hydrate sections to water.
2. Stain in auramin, room temperature: 2–3 minutes.
3. Wash in running water: 2–3 minutes.
4. Decolorize: 1 minute.
5. Transfer to fresh decolorizer: 2–5 minutes.
6. Wash in running water: 2–3 minutes.
7. Dry smear and examine. Mount sections in fluorescent mountant (page 122) or Harleco fluorescent mountant for examining.

RESULTS:

bacilli—golden yellow

COMMENTS:

Bogen counterstains with Loeffler's alkaline methylene blue solution before mounting:

methylene blue C.I. 52105	3.0 gm.
absolute ethyl alcohol	30.0 ml.
potassium hydroxide, 0.01% aqueous	100.0 ml.

Capsule Staining

Hiss' Method (BURROWS, 1954)

FIXATION: any good general fixative, 10% formalin is satisfactory.

SOLUTIONS:

Either of 2 following stain solutions may be used:

A. basic fuchsin, C.I. 42500	0.15–0.3 gm.
distilled water	100.0 ml.
B. crystal violet, C.I. 42555	0.05–0.1 gm.
distilled water	100.0 ml.

Copper sulfate solution:

copper sulfate crystals	20.0 gm.
distilled water	100.0 ml.

PROCEDURE:

1. Deparaffinize and hydrate slides to water.
2. Flood with either staining solution and heat gently until the stain steams.
3. Wash off the stain with copper sulfate.
4. Blot, but do not dry.
5. Dehydrate in 99% isopropyl alcohol, 2 changes: 1 minute each.
6. Clear and mount.

RESULTS:

capsules—light pink (basic fuchsin) or blue (crystal violet)
bacterial cells—dark purple surrounded by the capsule color

Spirochete Staining

Dieterle's Method (MODIFIED BY BEAMER AND FIRMINGER, 1955)

FIXATION: 10% formalin.

SOLUTIONS:

Dilute gum mastic:

gum mastic, saturated in absolute alcohol	30 drops
95% ethyl alcohol	40.0 ml.

Developing solution:

distilled water	20.0 ml.
hydroquinone	0.5 gm.
sodium sulfite	0.06 gm.

While stirring add:

formalin	4.0 ml.
glycerol	5.0 ml.

When thoroughly mixed add, drop by drop, with constant stirring:

equal parts of gum mastic saturated in absolute	
alcohol and absolute alcohol	8.0 ml.
pyridine	2.0 ml.

PROCEDURE:

1. Deparaffinize and hydrate slides to water.
2. Remove any formalin pigment in 2% ammonium hydroxide (2 ml./98 ml. water): few minutes.
3. Transfer to 80% alcohol: 2–3 minutes.
4. Wash in distilled water: 5 minutes.
5. Treat with uranium nitrate 2–3% (2–3 gm./100 ml. water), previously warmed to 60°C: 10 minutes.
6. Wash in distilled water: 1–2 minutes.
7. Transfer to 95% alcohol: 1–2 minutes.
8. Treat with dilute gum mastic: 5 minutes.
9. Wash in distilled water, 3–4 changes, until rinse is clear.
10. Impregnate with silver nitrate, 2% (2 gm./100 ml. water), previously warmed to 60°C: 30–40 minutes.
11. Warm developing solution to 60°C. Dip slide up and down in solution until sections turn light tan or pale brown.
12. Rinse in 95% alcohol, then in distilled water.
13. Treat with silver nitrate, 2% (2 gm./100 ml. water): 1–2 minutes.
14. Wash in distilled water: 1–2 minutes.
15. Dehydrate, clear and mount.

RESULTS:

spirochetes—black
background—yellow

COMMENTS:

Use thin sections, 4–5 microns.

The uranium nitrate prevents the impregnation of nerve fibers and reticulum.

Warthin-Starry Silver Method (KERR, 1938; FAULKNER AND LILLIE, 1945A; BRIDGES AND LUNA, 1957)

FIXATION: 10% formalin.

Notes of caution:

All glassware must be cleaned with potassium dichromate-sulfuric acid.

No contamination; coat forceps with paraffin.

Solutions must be fresh (no more than 1 week old) and made from triple distilled water.

Carry a known positive control slide with test slide through the process, or preferably a control section on the same slide.

SOLUTIONS:

Acidulated water:

triple distilled water	1000.0 ml.
citric acid	10.0 gm.

*p*H 3.8–4.4

2% Silver nitrate (for developer):

silver nitrate	2.0 gm.
acidulated water	100.0 ml.

1% Silver nitrate:

dilute a portion of above with equal volume of acidulated water.

0.15% Hydroquinone:

hydroquinone	0.15 gm.
acidulated water	100.0 ml.

5% gelatine:

sheet gelatine or granulated of high degree of purity	10.0 gm.
acidulated water	200.0 ml.

Developer:

2% silver nitrate	1.5 ml.
5% gelatine	3.75 ml.
0.15% hydroquinone	2.0 ml.

Warm solutions to 55–60°C and mix in order given, with stirring. Use immediately.

PROCEDURE:

1. Deparaffinize and hydrate slides to acidulated water.
2. Impregnate in 1% silver nitrate, 55–60°C: 30 minutes.
3. Place slides on glass rods, pour on warm developer (55–60°C). When sections become golden brown or yellow and developer brownish-black (3–5 minutes) pour off. The known positive can be checked under microscope for black organisms.
4. Rinse with warm (55–60°C) tap water, then distilled water.
5. Dehydrate, clear, and mount.

RESULTS:

spirochetes—black

background—yellow to light brown

melanin and hematogenous pigments—may darken

underdevelopment will result in pale background, very slender and pale spirochetes

overdevelopment will result in dense background, heavily impregnated spirochetes, obstructed detail, sometimes precipitate

COMMENTS:

Faulkner and Lillie (1945) use water buffered to *p*H 3.6–3.8 with Walpole's M/5 sodium acetate-M/5 acetic acid buffer (page 415).

Levaditi Method for Block Staining (MALLORY, 1944)

FIXATION: 10% formalin.

SOLUTIONS:

Silver nitrate:

silver nitrate	1.5–3.0 gm.
distilled water	100.0 ml.

Reducing solution:

pyrogallic acid	4.0 gm.
formalin	5.0 ml.
distilled water	100.0 ml.

PROCEDURE:

1. Rinse blocks of tissue in tap water.
2. Transfer to 95% ethyl alcohol: 24 hours.
3. Place in distilled water until tissue sinks.
4. Impregnate with silver nitrate, 37°C, in dark: 3–5 days.
5. Wash in distilled water.
6. Reduce at room temperature in dark: 24–72 hours.
7. Wash in distilled water.
8. Dehydrate, clear in cedarwood oil, and infiltrate with paraffin.
9. Embed, section at 5 microns, mount on slides and dry.
10. Remove paraffin with xylene, 2 changes, and mount.

RESULTS:

spirochetes—black

background—brownish yellow

Fungi Staining

Hotchkiss-McManus Method (MCMANUS, 1948)

FIXATION: 10% formalin or any geneal fixative.

SOLUTIONS:

Periodic acid:

periodic acid	1.0 gm.
distilled water	100.0 ml.

Schiff's reagent, see page 294.

Differentiator:

potassium metabisulfite, 10% aqueous	5.0 ml.
N HCl (page 408)	5.0 ml.
distilled water	100.0 ml.

Light green:

light green *SF* yellowish, C.I. 42095	0.2 gm.
distilled water	100.0 ml.
glacial acetic acid	0.2 ml.

PROCEDURE:

1. Deparaffinize and hydrate slides to water; remove HgCl₂ if present.
2. Oxidize in periodic acid: 5 minutes.
3. Wash in running water: 15 minutes.
4. Treat with Schiff's reagent: 10–15 minutes.
5. Differentiate, 2 changes: total 5 minutes.
6. Wash in running water: 10 minutes.
7. Stain in light green: 3–5 minutes. If too dark, rinse in running water.
8. Dehydrate, clear, and mount.

RESULTS:

fungi—red. Not specific, however—glycogen, mucin, amyloid, colloid and others may show rose to purplish red

background—light green

COMMENTS:

To remove glycogen, starch, mucin, or RNA, see page 300.

Gridley Method (1953)

FIXATION: any good general fixative.

SOLUTIONS:

Chromic acid:

chromic acid	4.0 gm.
distilled water	100.0 ml.

Schiff reagent, see page 294.

Sulfurous rinse:

sodium metabisulfite, 10% (10 gm./100 ml. water)	6.0 ml.
N hydrochloric acid (page 408)	5.0 ml.
distilled water	100.0 ml.

Aldehyde-fuchsin, see pages 168 and 287.

Metanil yellow:

metanil yellow	0.25 gm.
distilled water	100.0 ml.
glacial acetic acid	2 drops

PROCEDURE:

1. Deparaffinize and hydrate slides to water; remove $HgCl_2$.
2. Oxidize in chromic acid: 1 hour.
3. Wash in running water: 5 minutes.
4. Place in Schiff's reagent: 15 minutes.
5. Rinse in sulfurous acid, 3 changes: 1.5 minutes each.
6. Wash in running water: 15 minutes.
7. Stain in aldehyde-fuchsin: 15–30 minutes.
8. Rinse off excess stain in 95% alcohol.
9. Rinse in water.
10. Counterstain lightly in metanil yellow: 1 minute.
11. Rinse in water.
12. Dehydrate, clear, and mount.

RESULTS:

mycelia—deep blue
conidia—deep rose to purple
background—yellow
elastic tissue, mucin—deep blue

Gomori's Methenamine Silver Nitrate Method (GROCOTT'S ADAPTATION, 1955; MOWRY'S MODIFICATION, 1959)

FIXATION: 10% formalin or any good general fixative.

SOLUTIONS:

Methenamine silver nitrate. Stock solution:

silver nitrate, 5% (5 gm./100 ml. water)	5.0 ml.
methenamine, 3% (3 gm./100 ml. water)	100.0 ml.

Working solution:

borax, 5% (5 gm./100 ml. water)	2.0 ml.
distilled water	25.0 ml.
methenamine silver nitrate stock solution	25.0 ml.

Light green, Stock solution:

light green *SF*, yellowish, C.I. 42095	0.2 gm.
distilled water	100.0 ml.
glacial acetic acid	0.2 ml.

Working solution:

light green stock solution	10.0 ml.
distilled water	100.0 ml.

PROCEDURE:

1. Deparaffinize and hydrate slides to water; remove $HgCl_2$.
2. Oxidize in periodic acid, 0.5% (0.5 gm./100 ml. water): 10 minutes.
3. Wash in running water: 3 minutes.
4. Oxidize in chromic acid, 5% (5 gm./100 ml. water): 45 minutes.
5. Wash in running water: 2 minutes.
6. Treat with sodium bisulfite, 2% (2 gm./100 ml. water): 1 minute to remove chromic acid.
7. Wash in running water: 5 minutes.
8. Rinse in distilled water, 2–3 changes: 5 minutes total.
9. Place in methenamine silver nitrate, 58°C: 30 minutes. Do not use metal forceps. Sections appear yellowish brown.
10. Wash thoroughly, several changes distilled water.
11. Tone in gold chloride (10 ml. stock solution/90 ml. water) until sections turn purplish grey, fungi are black.
12. Rinse in distilled water.
13. Fix in sodium thiosulfate, 5% (5 gm./100 ml. water): 3 minutes.
14. Wash in running water: 5 minutes.
15. Counterstain in light green: 30 seconds.
16. Dehydrate, clear, and mount.

RESULTS:

fungi—black
background—light green

COMMENTS:

Mowry's method uses oxidation with both periodic and chromic acid (former methods use only the latter) with the result that the final staining is stronger and more consistent than that of the original Gomori method.

Fluorescent Method (PICKETT *et al.*, 1960)

FIXATION: 10% formalin, Zenker's, alcohol and others.

SOLUTIONS:

Acridine orange:

acridine orange	0.1 gm.
distilled water	100.0 ml.

Weigert's hematoxylin, see page 126.

PROCEDURE:

1. Deparaffinize and hydrate sections to water.
2. Stain in Weigert's hematoxylin: 5 minutes.
3. Wash in running water: 5 minutes.
4. Stain in acridine orange: 2 minutes.
5. Rinse in tap or distilled water: 30 seconds.
6. Dehydrate in 95% alcohol: 1 minute.
7. Dehydrate in absolute alcohol, 2 changes: 2–3 minutes.
8. Clear in xylene, 2 changes: 2–3 minutes.
9. Mount in a nonfluorescing medium.

RESULTS:

all fungi fluoresce except *Nocardia* and *Rhizopus;* colors of the fluorescing genuses appear as follows:
Coccidioides, Rhinosporidum—red
Aspergillus—green
Actinomyces, Histoplasma—red to yellow
Candida, Blastomyces dermatitids, Monosporium—yellow-green
Blastomyces brasiliensis—yellow

COMMENTS:

Old hematoxylin and eosin slides may be decolorized and restained as above.

The Weigert's hematoxylin staining is necessary as a quenching agent, because some fungi are difficult to see against a background which also fluoresces. With the hematoxylin, the fungi fluoresce brightly against a dark setting.

Rickettsia and Inclusion Bodies

Modified Pappenheim Stain (CASTAÑEDA, 1939)

FIXATION: any general fixative, Regaud recommended.

SOLUTIONS:

Stock Jenner stain:

Jenner's stain	1.0 gm.
methyl alcohol, absolute	400.0 ml.

Stock Giemsa stain:

Giemsa stain	1.0 gm.
glycerol	66.0 ml.

Mix and place in oven 2 hours, 60°C. Add

methyl alcohol, absolute	66.0 ml.

Working solution *A*:

distilled water	100.0 ml.
glacial acetic acid	1 drop
Jenner stock solution	20.0 ml.

Working solution *B*:

distilled water	100.0 ml.
glacial acetic acid	1 drop
Giemsa stock solution	5.0 ml.

PROCEDURE:
1. Deparaffinize and hydrate slides to water.
2. Stain in solution *A*, 37°C: 15 minutes.
3. Transfer directly to solution *B*, 37°C: 30–60 minutes.
4. Dehydrate quickly, 2 changes absolute alcohol.
5. Clear and mount.

RESULTS:
rickettsiae—blue to purplish blue

Castañeda's Method (GRADWOHL, 1956)

FIXATION: a general fixative, but Regaud recommended.

SOLUTIONS:
Buffer solutions:
Solution *A*:

di-basic sodium phosphate, $Na_2HPO_4 \cdot 12H_4O$	23.86 gm.
distilled water	1000.0 ml.

Solution *B*:

monobasic sodium phosphate, anhydrous, NaH_2PO_4	11.34 gm.
distilled water	1000.0 ml.

Working solution:

solution *A*	88.0 ml.
solution *B*	12.0 ml.
formalin	0.2 ml.

Methylene blue solution:

Dissolve methylene blue, C.I. 52015	21.0	gm.
in 95% ethyl alcohol	300.0	ml.
Dissolve potassium hydroxide	0.1	gm.
in distilled water	1000.0	ml.

Mix the two solutions and let stand 24 hours.

Staining solution:

Mix buffer working solution with methylene blue solution.

PROCEDURE:

1. Deparaffinize and hydrate slides as far as 50% alcohol.
2. Stain in methylene blue: 2–3 minutes.
3. Wash in running water: 30 seconds.
4. Counterstain in 1% safranin (1 gm./100 ml. water): 1–2 minutes.
5. Dip briefly in 95% alcohol.
6. Dehydrate in 2 changes absolute alcohol, clear, and mount.

RESULTS:

rickettsiae—light blue

COMMENTS:

Burrows (1954) recommends this as one of the best methods for rickettsia.

Ordway-Machiavello Method (GRADWOHL, 1956)

FIXATION: Regaud recommended.

SOLUTION:

Staining solution:

Poirrier's blue (C.C.), 1% aqueous	10.0	ml.
eosin bluish, C.I. 45400, 0.45% aqueous	15.0	ml.
Mix just before use. Add slowly with constant shaking:		
distilled water	25.0	ml.

Use within 24 hours.

PROCEDURE:

1. Deparaffinize and hydrate slides to water.
2. Stain: 6–8 minutes.
3. Decolorize in 95% ethyl alcohol until slides appear pale bluish pink.
4. Dehydrate in absolute alcohol: 1 minute.
5. Clear and mount.

RESULTS:

rickettsiae, also inclusion bodies—bright red
nuclei and cytoplasm—sky blue

Giemsa Method (AMERICAN PUBLIC HEALTH ASSOCIATION, 1956)

FIXATION: general fixative, Regaud recommended.

SOLUTIONS:

Giemsa stock solution, see page 225.

Buffer solutions:

A. dibasic sodium phosphate, anhydrous, Na_2
    HPO_4 .... 9.5 gm.
    distilled water .... 1000.0 ml.
B. monobasic sodium phosphate, $NaH_2PO_4 \cdot$
    H_2O .... 9.2 gm.
    distilled water .... 1000.0 ml.

Working solution, pH 7.2:

solution A .... 72.0 ml.
solution B .... 28.0 ml.
distilled water .... 900.0 ml.

Giemsa working solution:

Dilute 1 drop Giemsa stock solution with 5 ml. of buffer working solution.

PROCEDURE:

1. Deparaffinize and hydrate slides to water. (Smears can be carried directly to water: wash well in running water: 5–10 minutes.)
2. Leave slides in Giemsa working solution overnight, 37°C.
3. Rinse thoroughly in distilled water. Dry between blotters.
4. Dip rapidly in absolute alcohol. If overstained, use 95% alcohol to decolorize them, dip in absolute alcohol.
5. Clear and mount. (Smears, after treatment with absolute alcohol, can be washed in distilled water: 1–2 seconds, and blotted dry. Examine with oil or mount with a cover glass.)

RESULTS:

rickettsiae and inclusion bodies (psittacosis)—blue to purplish blue

Modification for trachoma.

SOLUTION:

Giemsa working solution:

Dilute 1 drop of stock Giemsa with 2 ml. of buffer solution above.

PROCEDURE:
1. Hydrate slides to water (these will be smears).
2. Stain in working solution, 37°C: 1 hour.
3. Rinse rapidly, 2 changes 95% ethyl alcohol.
4. Dehydrate in absolute alcohol, clear, and mount.

RESULTS:
inclusion bodies—blue to purplish blue

Negri Bodies (Rabies)

Schleifstein (1937) Method

FIXATION: Zenker's preferred.

SOLUTIONS:
Staining solution:

basic fuchsin, C.I. 42500	1.8 gm.
methylene blue, C.I. 52015	1.0 gm.
glycerol	100.0 ml.
methyl alcohol	100.0 ml.

Keeps indefinitely.

For use add about 10 drops to 15–20 ml. of dilute potassium hydroxide (1 gm./40,000 ml. water). Alkaline tap water may be used.

PROCEDURE:
1. Deparaffinize and hydrate slides to water; remove $HgCl_2$.
2. Rinse in distilled water and place slides on warm electric hot plate.
3. Flood amply with stain and steam for 5 minutes. Do not allow stain to boil.
4. Cool and rinse in tap water.
5. Decolorize and differentiate each slide by agitating in 90% ethyl alcohol until the sections assume a pale violet color. This is important.
6. Dehydrate, clear, and mount.

RESULTS:
Negri bodies—deep magenta red
granular inclusions—dark blue
nucleoli—bluish black
cytoplasm—blue-violet
erythrocytes—copper

COMMENTS:
Schleifstein outlines a rapid method for fixing and embedding so the

entire process can be handled in 8 hours, including fixing embedding, and staining.

Massignani and Malferrari (1961) Method

FIXATION: 10% formalin or saturated aqueous mercuric chloride-absolute alcohol (1:2).

EMBEDDING and SECTIONING: paraffin method, 4 microns.

SOLUTIONS:

Harris hematoxylin, see page 125.

Dilute hydrochloric acid:

hydrochloric acid, concentrated	1.0 ml.
distilled water	200.0 ml.

Dilute lithium carbonate:

lithium carbonate, saturated aqueous	1.0 ml.
distilled water	200.0 ml.

Phosphotungstic acid-eosin stain:

Grind together 1 gm. eosin Y (C.I. 45380) and 0.7 gm. phosphotungstic acid. Mix thoroughly into 10.0 ml. of distilled water and then bring volume up to 200.0 ml. with distilled water. Centrifuge at 1,500 rpm: 40 minutes. Pour off supernatant solution but do not throw it away. Dissolve the precipitate in 50 ml. of absolute alcohol. When dissolved, add to the supernatant solution. The solution is ready to use. If the eosin and phosphotungstic acid are not ground together and then dissolved it requires 24 hours for the dye-mordant combination to form.

PROCEDURE:

1. Deparaffinize and hydrate sections to water, remove $HgCl_2$.
2. Stain in hematoxylin: 2 minutes.
3. Wash in running water: 5 minutes.
4. Dip 8 times in dilute hydrochloric acid.
5. Wash in running water: 5 minutes.
6. Blue in dilute lithium carbonate: 1 minute.
7. Wash in running water: 5 minutes.
8. Dehydrate to absolute alcohol.
9. Stain in phosphotungstic acid-eosin: 8 minutes.
10. Rinse in distilled water.
11. Dehydrate by quick dips in 50%, 70%, 80%, and 90% alcohol, then follow with 95% alcohol: 1 second.
12. Complete dehydration in absolute alcohol: 2–3 changes: 4 minutes each.
13. Clear and mount.

RESULTS:

Negri bodies—deep red

COMMENTS:

Massignani and Refinetti in their paper (1958) adapted the Papanicolaou stain for Negri bodies. Further study, however, led to the
discovery that eosin combined with phosphotungstic acid is responsible for Negri body staining and the above stain was developed
specifically for these bodies.

Antigen-Antibodies

The subject of immunity is complex and has filled several large textbooks. It is mentioned briefly here to bring to mind certain principles
used in this field, and to highlight one of the most important technics
developed for locating antigens and antibodies in tissues.

If foreign materials, living or nonliving—bacteria and viruses, for
instance—invade the body, certain substances are formed in body fluids
to combat these foreign materials and "neutralize" them. The defense
substances are proteins called **antibodies** that have the power to combine specifically with the invading foreign materials **(antigens)** which
induced the formation of the antibodies. Eventual immunity to an
infection can be brought about either by entrance of the antigen naturally or artificially—by "shots," for instance. In the latter case, serum,
called **antiserum** (immune serum) from an artificially immunized animal can be injected into a nonimmune animal to induce immunity.
Antiserum can be used in this way to combat an infection already
present (mumps, measles, anthrax, tetanus) or it can be used to prevent
infection (measles, poliomyelitis, tetanus, diphtheria).

If the fluid portion of blood plasma is allowed to clot (fibrinogen
precipitates out) a relatively stable serum remains. This is made up of
two protein fractions: albumin and globulin. The globulins consist of
two alpha globulins, one beta globulin, and one **gamma globulin.** It is
the latter globulin which is associated with immunity. Antibodies have
been classically identified with gamma globulin (to a lesser extent with
the other globulins, also) and are considered modified serum globulin.
It has become a common practice to use for immune serum the gamma
globulin fraction, which can be isolated from the other serum proteins
and used in a concentrated form. The difference, therefore, between
immune and normal serum globulin lies in the ability of the former to
combine with an antigen.

Coons' Fluorescent Technic

If antigens can be labeled, sources of antibody production in tissues can be seen microscopically. Coons and his associates have coupled antibodies with fluorescein isocyanate and isothiocyanate to form fluorescent carbamide-proteins. The **conjugates** thus formed from dye and antibodies still retain the specific reaction of the antibody for the antigen that causes its formation. Labeled antibodies are poured over the tissues or cells and will leave a labeled protein in the tissues which can be observed under a fluorescent-adapted microscope.

Some of the solutions, antisera (immune serum), and conjugates have to be prepared in the laboratory; some can be purchased,[1] but it is recommended that all conjugates be purified by absorption against tissue powders. For reasons and means of doing this, see *Coons et al.* (*1955*); *Coons* (*1958*); and *Mellors* (*1959*). The method is complicated and should not be undertaken without a thorough study of the source material.

With a few exceptions (some polysaccharides) chemical fixatives must be avoided to retain specific activity of the antigen. Smears, touch preparations, tissue cultures, and cell suspensions can be used. If sections are preferred, freeze-dried or unfixed frozen sections cut in a cryostat (page 337) are mandatory. Tissues may be quick-frozen in petroleum ether previously chilled to $-65°C$ with dry ice-alcohol mixture in a Dewar flask. When completely frozen, blot and store in tightly stoppered test tube at $-20°C$ to $-70°C$ until used. Long storage is to be avoided; the tissues dehydrate (*Tobie, 1958*). *Coons et al.* (*1955*) place small pieces of tissue against the wall of a small test tube and plunge it into alcohol cooled to $-70°C$ with solid carbon dioxide. Store at $-20°C$ until used.

After sectioning by either method, the tissue sections must be fixed before applying the antigen-antibody solution. Fixation depends on the antigen.

FIXATION: *proteins:* 95% ethyl alcohol, sometimes absolute methyl alcohol; *polysaccharides:* can be fixed in the block by picric acid-alcohol-formalin (Rossman fluid, page 20) and paraffin-embedded; *lipids:* 10% formalin; *viruses:* acetone.

DIRECT METHOD (staining directly with fluorescein-labeled antibody against specific antigen).

Slides are dried after fixation, rinsed in buffered saline (0.8% sodium

---

[1] Arnel Products Co., N.Y. (Sylvania Chemicals) Baltimore Biological Laboratory, Baltimore, Maryland.

chloride with 0.01M phosphate, *p*H 7.0) and the excess saline wiped off except over the sections. Labeled antibody is pipetted over the section; the slides, covered with a petri dish with moist cotton or filter paper attached to its undersurface, are allowed to stand, room temperature: 20–30 minutes. The slide is wiped dry except for the section and mounted in buffered glycerol (anhydrous glycerol, 9 parts, buffered saline, 1 part), then covered with a cover glass. Examination is made under the fluorescent microscope.

INDIRECT METHOD (layering).

A tissue section containing antigen is covered with unlabeled specific antiserum to allow the antibody molecules to react with it and be fixed *in situ* (humid environment): 20 minutes. The slide is rinsed off in buffered saline: 10 minutes, then wiped dry except for the section, and fluorescein-labeled antiglobulin serum (prepared against the species which furnished the specific serum) added: 20 minutes. The slide is washed in buffered saline and mounted in buffered glycerol. Cells that reacted with the antiserum will be covered with antibody (globulin) and will have reacted with the labeled antiglobulin. This has been termed layering because the bottom layer is antibody, the middle layer the antigen, and the labeled antibody lies on top.

Coons (1958) recommends control slides and uses a blocking technique. Unlabeled specific antiserum is added to a slide and allowed to react for 20 minutes. Then, if washed with buffer solution and treated with a drop of labeled antibody, only a faint fluorescence, if any, should be exhibited.

Silverstein (1957) described a means of applying contrasting fluorescent labels for two antibodies using rhodamin *B* with fluorescein.

The *Coons* methods have been applied for the detection of viruses, rickettsiae, epidemic typhus, mumps, influenza, canine hepatitis, chicken pox, canine distemper, measles, psittacosis, and poliomyelitis.

This description is intended as only a brief résumé of *Coons'* technics in order to acquaint the technician with their potentialities. The following references contain extensive and pertinent discussions of the procedures: *Coons (1956 and 1958)* and *Mellors (1959)*.

A tremendous bibliography is developing in this field; the following references will lead to many others: Buckley *et al.* (1955); Cohen *et al.* (1955); Coons *et al.* (1942, 1950, 1951, 1955); Coons and Kaplan (1950); Kaplan *et al.* (1950); Lacey and Davis (1959); Leduc *et al.* (1955); Mellors *et al.* (1955); Noyes (1955); Noyes and Watson (1955); Tobie (1958); Watson (1952); and White (1955).

HISTOCHEMISTRY AND MISCELLANEOUS SPECIAL PROCEDURES

Chapter 21

Histochemistry

By definition the field of **histochemistry** is concerned with the localization and identification of a chemical substance in a tissue. In a broad sense this might include staining, combining chemical and physical reactions, instances where acidic and basic methods demonstrate basic and acidic properties of the tissue. But strictly speaking, histochemistry is being applied only to chemical methods immobilizing a chemical at the site it occupies in living tissue. These methods can apply to inorganic substances: calcium, iron, barium, copper, zinc, lead, mercury, and others; they also apply to organic substances: saccharides, lipids, proteins, amino acids, nucleic acid, enterochromaffin substance, and some pigments. Some substances are soluble and react directly, others are insoluble and must be converted into soluble substances before a reaction takes place. *Occult* or *masked* materials are part of a complex organic molecule. This has to be destroyed by an unmasking agent before the chemical can react. Some chemicals may be fixed in place, others which are soluble or diffusible have to be frozen quickly and prepared by the freeze-drying method involving no liquid phase. Sometimes it is advisable to make control slides, thereby preventing confusion between a genuine reaction and a nonspecific one giving a similar effect.

A sharp distinction between staining and histochemical methods has proved difficult and not wholly practical. Some will disagree with the present arrangement of methods, but a sequence according to similar tissue or cell types seemed adaptable to general laboratory application, the primary intent of this book. The section "Histochemistry," therefore, will cover mainly procedures used to identify enzymatic activity.

The field is a tremendous and puzzling one of increasingly extensive activity. It is impossible and impractical to include all histochemical methods and their variations in this type of manual. There are available many excellent books in the field. Also there are journals that describe the newest methods and modifications; therefore, only the most familiar (at least to the author) methods are being incorporated in this text.

For greater detail start with: Cassellman (1959); Danielli (1953); Davenport (1960); Glick (1949); Gomori (1952); Gurr (1958); Lillie (1954); and Pearse (1960).

Freezing-Drying Method for Embedding

Sometimes enzymes, proteins or other substances can be lost during fixation, dehydration and embedding, and a freezing-drying method must be used. Small pieces (approximately 1 mm.) are frozen solid instantly with isopentane cooled by liquid nitrogen to a temperature of $-150°C$. The tissue must be frozen rapidly to prevent large crystal formation which would disrupt the cells. The initial freezing is commonly called quenching; it stops all chemical reactions that have been going on in the tissues. Immediately after freezing (it must not thaw) the tissue is dehydrated in a drying apparatus *in vacuo* at a temperature of -30 to $-40°C$ and the ice is sublimed into water vapor and removed.[1] There is no liquid phase present at any time, and therefore no diffusion of enzymes.

When the material is dry, it is allowed to rise to room temperature, is infiltrated with degassed paraffin or carbowax and embedded. The advantages of this method are that shrinkage and diffusion artifacts are reduced to a minimum, and enzymes and chemical structures are preserved. There are some disadvantages; the equipment is bulky and expensive, and only small pieces can be used in order to prevent distortion by ice crystals. Because of sensitivity to water, the sections cannot be floated on water, but must be applied directly to warm albumenized slides (*Mendelow and Hamilton, 1950*). Embedded blocks have to be kept stored in a desiccator.

Carbowax or paraffin can be cut at room temperature, but many enzymes and other tissue constituents necessitate sectioning at low temperatures of -25 to $-20°C$ or they are lost. Since embedding is

---

[1] See new "Unitrap," Fisher Scientific Co.

impractical at these temperatures, tissue is frozen in isopentane ($-160°C$) or in dry ice-ethyl alcohol mixtures ($-70°C$). The tissue must be maintained at least at dry ice temperature ($-20°C$) and sectioned and mounted at this temperature. This is performed inside a cold chamber cryostat[2] (-25 to $-20°C$). The object holder is precooled and the block frozen to it with a few drops of water. The knife must be sharp and kept as dry as possible. After the section is cut, dip a clean cooled slide in ethyl alcohol or isopentane ($-20°C$) and pick up section by touching slide against it (*Louis, 1957*). A cover glass can be used in the same manner. (Slides sometimes must be albumenized.) Dry in a cold room at 0 to $-2°C$: 1 hour with fan. *Mellors (1959)* thaws them quickly at room temperature for 15 minutes, aided by a warm finger against the undersurface of the slide. If slides must be stored (but only for a short time) place them over desiccant ($CaSO_4$) in refrigerator.

Fitz-William et al. (*1960*) recommend that immediately before each section is cut the tissue block be coated with 20% polystyrene dissolved in methylene chloride (volatile at cryostat temperature). Wait until a highly reflecting surface, which forms, disappears and then cut section. Curling of sections is minimal and they can be picked up with fine forceps. The polystyrene solution should be stored in the cryostat. These authors also include complete directions on the care of the microtome used in the cryostat.

See also *Greenbaum (1956)* and *Coons et al. (1951)*.

Ice-Solvent (freeze-substitution) Method

Freeze-dry methods can be troublesome and costly. A simpler and cheaper method with excellent results is the ice-solvent procedure wherein the tissue is rapidly frozen and then the ice formed within the tissue is slowly dissolved in a fluid solvent such as ethyl or methyl alcohol. (Other polar solvents also have been tried. See *Patten and Brown, 1958*.) When the tissue is free of ice and completely permeated by the cold solvent, it is brought to room temperature and embedded. In addition to being simpler than freeze-drying, other advantages are: no disruptive streaming movements in the tissue—the ice simply dissolves—and the substitution solution can sometimes be chosen to contain a specific precipitant for a specific substance. The method can be used for radioautography, fluorescent preparations, many enzymes, and other cyto-histochemical methods. There can, however, be cases in which the freeze-drying procedure is preferred—for instance an enzyme

[2] Linderstrom-Lang Cryostat, manufactured by Harris Refrigeration Co., Cambridge, Mass.; also, Fisher & Lipshaw advertise Cryostats.

might be damaged by the denaturing action of the alcohol as it warms up.

PROCEDURE: (*Feder and Sidman, 1958; Hancox, 1957; Patton and Brown, 1958*).

1. Cool a beaker of liquid propane-isopentane (3:1) to −170°C–175°C with liquid nitrogen.
2. Place tissue specimen (small pieces, 1.5–3 mm.) on thin strip of aluminum foil and plunge into the cold propane-isopentane (**quenching**). Stir vigorously with a 12″ ruler: 30 seconds.
3. Transfer frozen specimen to ice-solvent (see Comments) (already chilled to −60 to −70°C). After a few minutes the tissue can be shaken loose from the foil. Store in dry ice chest for 1 to 2 weeks. (52 days did no harm; *Patten and Brown*)
4. Remove fluid and tissue to refrigerator, wash 12 hours or longer in 3 changes of absolute alcohol.
5. Transfer to chloroform: 6–12 hours in refrigerator, to remove any traces of water. (This step may be omitted in most cases.)
6. Transfer to cold xylene (or similar agent), −20°C; and remove to room temperature for 10 minutes.
7. Transfer to fresh xylene, room temperature: 10 minutes.
8. Transfer to xylene: tissuemat, 56°C, vacuum: 15 minutes.
9. Infiltrate, tissuemat #1, vacuum: 15 minutes.
10. Transfer to tissuemat #2, vacuum: 15 minutes.
11. Transfer to tissuemat #3, vacuum: 15 minutes.
12. Embed.

COMMENTS:

Ice-solvents used with best results by *Patten and Brown* (*1958*) were absolute methyl and absolute ethyl alcohol. *Hancox* (*1957*) used *n*-butyl alcohol and could infiltrate directly from the ice-solvent, thereby bypassing the xylene step. *Feder and Sidman* (*1958*) used 1% solution of mercuric chloride in ethyl alcohol, and osmic acid in acetone, trying to combine a chemical and physical fixing action. The latter authors include complete directions concerning obtaining, storing and disposing of liquid nitrogen, isopentane and propane, also details about equipment.

Hancox (*1957*) obtained his best sections in a cryostat. He tried dry mounting, 85% alcohol flotation and water flotation of sections. The latter gave inferior results; certain cell inclusions had disappeared, and the cytoplasm resembled a vacuolated reticulum. *Patten and Brown* (*1958*) found that mounting on water gave the most distinct and intense sections, but they were chiefly interested in fluorescence. So perhaps the best suggestion is to try all methods and discover which serves the particular investigation being undertaken.

Blank et al. (1951) use glycols if fixation is to be avoided, alcohol or acetone if fixation is permissible. This method is as follows:

PROCEDURE:

1. Place slices (2–3 mm.) of tissue in cold propylene glycol in deep freeze below —20°C: 1–2 hours.
2. Transfer to mixture of carbowax, 55°C: 2–3 hours.

   carbowax 4000 .... 9 parts
   carbowax 1500 .... 1 part
3. Prepare blocks, page 81.
4. Cut sections and float on slides according to Blank and McCarthy, page 81.
5. Stain or use for autoradiographs. Water-soluble substances have not leached out. For autoradiographs, before each cut coat the block face with thin molten wax. Press wax-reinforced sections against emulsion for exposure. *See also: Freed (1955); Meryman (1959, 1960); Woods and Pollister (1955).*

References: Blank *et al.* (1951); Feder (1958); Freed (1955); Gersh (1932); Glick and Malstrom (1952); Hancox (1957); Hoerr (1936); Ibanez *et al.* (1960); Jennings (1951); Louis (1957); Mellors (1959); Meryman (1959, 1960); Packer and Scott (1942); Patten and Brown (1958); Simpson (1941); and Woods and Pollister (1955).

Acetone Fixation and Embedding

Gomori (1952) Method

Chilled alcohol (95% or absolute) and acetone are used for preservation of tissues to be used for many kinds of enzyme localization. Acetone is generally preferred, being applicable to more enzyme techniques. Keep a tightly stoppered bottle of it stored in the refrigerator, ready for any occasion (*see also Burstone, 1958*).

PROCEDURE:

1. If possible chill tissue for a short time before immersing in acetone. It may prevent some shrinkage artifacts. But fix within 10 minutes of death for best results.
2. Fix in cold acetone, 3 changes: 12 hours each.
3. Transfer to ether-absolute alcohol (1:1): 2 hours, refrigerator.

4. Infiltrate with dilute celloidin or nitrocellulose (approximately 10%): overnight, refrigerator.
5. Drain on cleansing tissue. Place in benzene or chloroform: 0.5–1 hour. Stirring on a mag-mix aids penetration of fluid.
6. Infiltrate with paraffin, 56°C (52°C is better): 15–20 minutes in oven without vacuum.
7. Infiltrate with paraffin, 56°C (or 52°C): 30 minutes with vacuum.
8. Infiltrate with paraffin, 56°C (or 52°C): 10–15 minutes without vacuum.
9. Embed. Store in refrigerator.
10. Section. Float on lukewarm water, briefly (10 minutes maximum). Drain off water and dry. If kept for some time, put in oven 5–10 minutes to melt paraffin forming protective coat against atmospheric influence. Store in cold room or refrigerator. Safest way to store tissues is in uncut paraffin block in refrigerator.

COMMENTS:

Novikoff et al. (1960) find acetone fixation is good for some cryostat preparations.

Control Slides: Most enzyme reactions should be accompanied by a control slide in order to help detect false positives. An enzyme can be inactivated by one of the following methods:
1. Place slide in distilled water and bring to boil: 10 minutes.
2. Immerse in 1N HCl: 15 minutes; wash in tap water: 0.5 hour.
3. Incubate slide in substrate medium containing an inhibitor. NaCN or KCN.
4. Incubate untreated slide in a medium backing substrate.

Preservation of incubation media: Klionsky and Marcoux (1960) prepared twelve different media, froze them in dry ice-acetone mixture, and stored them in a dry ice chest. Within at least 6 months, the solutions remained as good as freshly prepared solutions. The types of media tested were:
1. azo dye and metal precipitate methods for acid and alkaline phosphotases.
2. alpha-naphthyl and indoxyl acetate for esterase.
3. 5-nucleotidase.
4. nitro-BT for succinic dehydrogenase.
5. post-coupling technic for beta-glucuronidase.
6. triphosphopyridine nucleotide and diphosphopyridine nucleotide diaphorase.

Alkaline Phosphatase

Sections containing active phosphatase are incubated in a mixture of calcium salt and phosphate ester, usually sodium glycerophosphate, so calcium phosphate is precipitated at the sites. The enzyme liberates the phosphate ions, which are held on the spot by salts of metals whose phosphates are insoluble. (Magnesium ions are often required as an activator and are added in the form of magnesium sulfate or chloride. The mechanism of activation is unknown.) The insoluble phosphates are made visible either by (1) silver nitrate, producing silver phosphate and metallic silver; or (2) cobalt nitrate and ammonium sulfide, producing cobalt phosphate and finally black cobalt sulfide.

Phosphatase is dissolved or destroyed by ordinary fixatives, but alcohol or acetone will preserve it. Celloidin or paraffin embedding can be used safely, but paraffin sections must be covered with a film of celloidin to protect against dissolution of enzyme. See *Burstone (1960)* for fluorescent demonstration of alkaline phosphatase.

FIXATION: Thin slices (1–2 mm) are fixed at once in chilled acetone, 3 changes: 24–48 hours. Other fixatives may be 80%, 95%, and absolute alcohol, or cold formalin (4°C) followed by freezing method.

INFILTRATION AND EMBEDDING: For paraffin embedding use chloroform and paraffin at no higher than 58°C melting point, preferably 52°C. Cut sections 6–10 microns. Do not dry slides at higher than 37°C. Store all blocks at 6°C until needed.

SOLUTION:
Incubating Solution:

sodium barbital	knife-point full
	(regulates alkalinity, only a bit raises it)
3% sodium glycerophosphate (3 gm./100 ml. water) Keep in refrigerator	5–10 ml.
2% calcium chloride (2 gm./100 ml. water)	20–25 ml.
1% magnesium sulfate (1 gm./100 ml. water) ..	10 drops
distilled water to make	50.0 ml.

*p*H should be 9.4; if solution is turbid, filter out free phosphate.

PROCEDURE:

1. Deparaffinize (light petroleum can be used), pass through acetone and coat with 0.25–0.5% celloidin; continue hydration.

2. Place in incubating solution, 37°C: 0.5–3 hours. (Warm solution up to 39°C before starting incubation.)
3. Rinse in distilled water.
4. Change to colored form by either of following methods:
   A. Immerse in 1–2% cobalt salt (chloride, nitrate, acetate or sulfate) (1–2 gm./100 ml. water): 3–5 minutes.
   Rinse thoroughly, distilled water, 3 changes.
   Immerse in fresh dilute solution of yellow ammonium sulfide (5–6 drops in coplin jar of distilled water).
   Rinse in distilled water, 3–4 changes.
   Counterstain if desired, dehydrate, clear, and mount.
   B. Immerse in 5% silver nitrate (5 gm./100 ml. water) under ultraviolet lamp: 30 minutes. Or use 0.5% silver nitrate (0.5 gm./100 ml. water) in direct sunlight, depending on light intensity.
   Rinse in distilled water.
   Fix in 1–2% sodium thiosulfate: 2 minutes.
   Rinse, counterstain, dehydrate, clear, and mount.

Counterstains may be phloxine-methylene blue, **PAS**, eosin, safranine, or the like.

RESULTS:

cobalt method—brownish black
silver method—golden brown

COMMENTS:

False positives can be due to hemosiderin or melanin and these pigments should be checked for presence.

References: Ackerman (1958); Gomori (1941A, 1946); Kabot and Furth (1941); and Moffat (1958)

Azo-Coupling Method

The sections are incubated in a solution of sodium alpha naphthyl phosphate and a diazonium salt. The phosphatase activity liberates alpha naphthol to couple with the diazonium salt and form an insoluble pigment.

FIXATION: cold 10% formalin (4°C): 8–16 hours.

Frozen sections, 10–15 microns: mount on clean slides with no adhesive, air-dry 1–3 hours.

SOLUTION:
Incubating solution:

sodium *a*-naphthyl phosphate	10–20 mg.
O.1 M veronal acetate buffer, *p*H 9.2	20 ml.
stable diazotate of 4-benzoyl amino-2:5-dimeth-oxyaniline (fast blue *RR*)	20.0 gm.

PROCEDURE:
1. Filter enough incubating solution onto slides to cover sections adequately. Incubate, room temperature: 15–60 minutes.
2. Wash in running water: 1–3 minutes.
3. Counterstain, Mayer's hematoxylin: 4–6 minutes.
4. Wash in running water: 15–30 minutes.
5. Mount in glycerol jelly.

RESULTS:
sites—black

COMMENTS:
Alcohol fixation can be used, but is of no great advantage for frozen sections.

References: Gomori (1951), Manheimer and Seligman (1949), and Pearse (1960)

Acid Phosphatase

Most methods lack uniformity and some loss occurs during fixation and preparation for sectioning. *Gomori (1956)* considered the lead sulfide method "capricious," producing artifacts, and that the benzoylnaphthol phosphate post-coupling method of *Rutenburg and Seligman (1955)* was best. Since then *Burstone's (1959B)* method has appeared. Both of the latter are included.

FIXATION:
Rutenburg and Seligman Method:
1. Cold neutral 10% formalin: 24–48 hours (neutralize with NaCl). Wash in 0.85% NaCl 2 changes: 30 minutes.
   Cut frozen sections.
2. Fresh frozen sections (6–10 microns) cut in cryostat, mounted on uncoated slides, air-dried.

Immerse 3 minutes in 3 solutions of NaCl (0.85%, 1% and 2%) before incubation.

Burstone Method:

Fix in cold acetone, 8–24 hours. Pieces 3 mm. thick. Double-embed (page 339).

SOLUTIONS:

Rutenburg and Seligman Method:

Solution *A*:

sodium 6-benzoyl-2-naphthyl phosphate[3]	25.0 mg.
distilled water	80.0 ml.
acetate buffer (0.5M) *p*H 5.0	20.0 ml.

make hypertonic by adding 2 gm. NaCl to each 100 ml. of solution.

Solution *B*:

tetrazotized diorthoanisidine	50.0 mg.
distilled water	50.0 ml.

make alkaline with Na_2CO_3.

Burstone Method:

Either of two substrates may be used.[4]

a. Naphthol AS-MX phosphate
b. 6-benzoyl-2-naphthyl phosphate

Dissolve 5 mg. in 0.25 ml. DMF (N, N-dimethyl formamide)[5] and add distilled water	25.0 ml.
0.2M acetate buffer, *p*H 5.2	25.0 ml.
diazotized 4-amino-2,5-diethoxybenzanilide, C.I. 37175 (fast blue *BBN* salt)[6]	30.0 mg.
manganese chloride, 10%	2 drops

Shake and filter.

PROCEDURE:

Rutenburg and Seligman Method:

1. Transfer frozen sections or cryostat sections to substrate (solution *A*) room temperature: 1–2 hours.
2. Wash, 3 changes: 10–5 minutes each, in cold saline (fresh tissues) or water (fixed tissues).

[3] Dajac Laboratories.
[4] Dajac Laboratories.
[5] Matheson, Coleman and Bell.
[6] General Dyestuff Corporation.

3. Transfer to cold (4°C) freshly prepared solution *B*, agitate: 3–5 minutes till blue dye produced.
4. Wash, 3 changes of cold 0.85% NaCl or water (fixed tissues): 10 minutes each.
5. Mount in glycerol jelly.

Burstone Method: (simultaneous dye and substrate procedure)
1. Deparaffinize in petroleum ether, 3 changes: 4 minutes each.
2. Acetone, 2 changes: 4 minutes each.
3. Acetone-water (1:1): 2 minutes.
4. Rinse in distilled water: 30 seconds.
5. Incubate, room temperature: 45–60 minutes.
6. Rinse in distilled water.
7. Mount in glycerol jelly.

RESULTS:
sites—blue

COMMENTS:

If decalcification is necessary, *Schajowicz and Cabrini (1959)* say that 2% formic acid and 20% sodium citrate (1:1), *p*H 5 is satisfactory up to 15 days. There is loss of enzyme if versene is used.

References: Burstone (1959B); Burton (1954); Goetsch and Reynolds (1951); Gomori (1950A, 1956); Rutenburg and Seligman (1955); and Tandler (1953).

Aminopeptidase

Burstone and Folk (1956)

FIXATION and EMBEDDING:
1. Cold acetone fixation and paraffin embedding, page 339.
2. Freeze drying and embedding in vacuum gives better retention of enzyme.

SOLUTIONS:
Substrate and Dye:
Stock solution of substrate:

L-leucyl-*b*-naphthylamide	1.0 gm.
distilled water	100.0 ml.

Tris buffer, *p*H 7.19:

0.2 M tris (hydroxymethyl) aminomethane	25.0 ml.
0.1N HCl	45.0 ml.
dilute with distilled water to	100.0 ml.

Working solution:

stock substrate	1.0 ml.
distilled water	40.0 ml.
tris buffer	10.0 ml.
Garnet *GBC*[7] (diazotized *o*-aminoazotoluene) ..	30.0 mg.

Shake and filter.

For substrate, the alanyl compound may be substituted: 10 mg. in 40 ml. hot distilled water (90°C). Cool and add 10 ml. of tris buffer and 30 mg. garnet GBC.

PROCEDURE:
1. Chloroform or petroleum ether, 2 changes: 4 minutes each.
2. Absolute acetone: 1 minute.
3. 95% acetone: 1 minute.
4. 85% acetone, several dips.
5. Distilled water, few dips.
6. Substrate: 15 minutes to 1 hour, room temperature.
7. Tap water: 5 minutes.
8. Hematoxylin: 3 minutes.
9. Tap water: 10 minutes.
10. Glycerol jelly.

RESULTS:

sites—red

COMMENTS:

If necessary to purify *GBC* salt (not *Imperial Chemical Industries* product):
1. Dissolve 10 gms. salt in 50 ml. methyl alcohol. Let stand 0.5 hour. Filter.
2. Repeat with residue.
3. Dissolve second residue in 500 ml. ether. Let stand 2–3 hours.
4. Filter. Wash residue 2–3 times with ether. Store dry powder in refrigerator.

[7] Imperial Chemical Industries, Manchester, England, recommended.

Esterases and Lipases

These terms are used in reference to enzymes which hydrolyze esters of carboxylic acids. There is an overlapping between enzyme types and some seem to occupy intermediate positions between lipases and esterases, and react like both forms. (*Chessick, 1953; Gomori, 1952*) Broadly speaking, esters of short-chained fatty acids are acted on by esterases, long-chained esters by lipases.

Esterases or lipases are not destroyed by acetone fixation, are resistant to heat and can be embedded in paraffin if not used excessively (3 hours, maximum, 58°C). They can be incubated with the long-chained fatty acid esters of sorbitan and mannitan, water-soluble commercial products by the name of "Tween." On hydrolysis, the liberated fatty acids form insoluble calcium soaps deposited at the sites. These are converted into lead soaps and then into brown sulfide of lead.

Esters of naphthols also are used and naphthol is liberated and demonstrated by azo-coupling.

Esterase, Azo-Coupling (GOMORI, 1953)

FIXATION: cold acetone, paraffin embedding, page 339.

SOLUTIONS:

Barbital buffer:

sodium diethyl barbiturate (10.3 gm./500 ml. water)	66.5 ml.
0.1 M HCl	33.5 ml.

Shake and filter.

Substrate:

dissolve *a* or *b*-naphthylacetate	10.0 mg.
in acetone	1.0 ml.

add to solution of:

a-naphthyl diazonium naphthalene-1,5-disulfonate	40.0 mg.
2M NaCl	50.0 ml.
barbital buffer, *p*H 7.8	20.0 ml.
distilled water	29.0 ml.

PROCEDURE:

1. Xylene, 2 changes: 3 minutes each.
2. Absolute acetone: 1 minute.

3. 95% acetone: 1 minute.
4. 85% acetone: 1 minute.
5. 50% acetone, 1 minute.
6. Water: 1 minute.
7. Incubate, room temperature: 3–20 minutes.
8. Wash in tap water: 2 minutes.
9. Hematoxylin: 3 minutes.
10. Wash, tap water: 5 minutes.
11. Glycerol jelly.

RESULTS:
sites—red

COMMENTS:

Nachlas and Seligman (1949) prefer *b* over *a*-naphthylacetate, saying that it gives greater brilliance of reaction.
Wachstein and Wolf (1958) incubate 30–90 minutes in:

1% propylene glycol (in 0.2M phosphate buffer at *p*H 6.9)	40.0 ml.
1% naphthol-AS acetate in acetone	0.4 ml.
fast blue *BB* salt (C.I. 37175)	80.0 mg.

Lipase (GOMORI, 1950E, 1952)

FIXATION: chilled acetone: 24 hours (2mm. sections: prechill tissue to lessen shrinkage; trim thinner when tissues have gained some consistency). Embed by double embedding, page 339. Temperature should not exceed 58°C. If sections refuse to flatten completely, blot onto slides, dry at room temperature, then melt in paraffin oven.

SOLUTIONS:
Substrate:

Tween 60 (or product #81, *Onyx Oil and Chemical Co.*, or G2151, *Atlas Powder Co.*)	5.0 gm.
distilled water	100.0 ml.

Tris buffer, *p*H 7.2–7.4:

maleic acid	29.0 gm.
tris (hydroxymethyl) aminomethane	30.3 gm.
distilled water	500.0 ml.
add charcoal	2.0 gm.

Shake, let stand 10 minutes, and filter.

Buffer working solution:

stock solution	40.0 ml.
N NaOH (4%)	20.0 ml.
dilute to a total of	100.0 ml.

(Preserve substrate and buffer with $\frac{1}{4}\%$ chloretone or crystal of thymol.)

Calcium chloride:

calcium chloride	10.0 gm.
distilled water	100.0 ml.

Working solution:

buffer working solution	5.0 ml.
calcium chloride	2.0 ml.
substrate	2.0 ml.
distilled water	40.0 ml.

If solution becomes turbid, filter through fritted glass or porcelain filter of medium density.

PROCEDURE:

1. Deparaffinize and transfer slides to absolute alcohol.
2. Flood with 0.5% celloidin to protect against loss of enzyme.
3. Hydrate to water.
4. Incubate: 12–48 hours.
5. Wash in distilled water.
6. Treat with 1% lead nitrate (1 gm./100 ml. water): 15 minutes (calcium stearate transformed to lead stearate).
7. Wash in several changes distilled water.
8. Treat with dilute ammonium sulfide (1:5): few minutes (brown sulfide produced).
9. Rinse in tap water.
10. Counterstain lightly, hematoxylin and eosin if desired.
11. Dehydrate.
12. Clear in crude gasoline or tetra-chloroethylene (avoid xylene, fades stain).
13. Mount, using resin in one of above; not xylene.

RESULTS:

sites—golden brown

COMMENTS:

Sources of error: brownish pigment or calcareous deposits, pigments visible in unincubated section. These may be *hemosiderin* (perform Prussian blue reaction) or *calcium deposits* (remove before incubation in citrate buffer of *p*H 4.5±: 10–20 minutes).

George and Thomase (1960) coat sections with thin layer of 5–10% aqueous solution of pure gelatine (preserve with thymol not phenol). Place in refrigerator freeze chamber to solidify coating. Place in 6% cold neutral formalin to harden. Wash and proceed to incubate.

Eapen (1960) proved that lipase is activated by gelatine and coated sections to give better results.

Succinic Dehydrogenase

The **succinic oxidase system** is responsible for the oxidation of the majority of tissue **substrates** and is a part of the oxidation-reduction system in tissues. It is widely distributed, particularly in heart muscle and kidney.

Succinic dehydrogenase is demonstrated by the reduction of tetrazolium salts. The tetrazolium (colorless) acts as a hydrogen acceptor and becomes reduced to a blue water-insoluble pigment, *diformazon.*

Tetrazolium salts:

TPT—2,3,5-triphenyl tetrazolium chloride: simplest, with limited sensitivity.

BT—2,2′,5,5′-tetraphenyl-3,3′ (3,3′-dimethoxy-4,4′-biphenylene) ditetrazolium chloride: better pigment qualities.

Nitro BT—2,2′-di-*p*-nitrophenyl-5,5′-diphenyl-3,3′-(3,3′-dimethoxy-4,4′-biphenylene) ditetrazolium chloride.

Most methods require **anerobic** (absence of oxygen) to prevent atmospheric oxygen from competing with the tetrazolium for the electrons of the dye and thus decrease reduction. Sodium succinate is the substrate.

Sections must be fresh frozen, cut at 30 microns (not less than 20 microns) and are improved by cutting in a cryostat. They may be floated on a beaker of the incubating fluid inside the cryostat or mounted on slides and air dried in the cryostat. For anerobic conditions remove air from the solution with vacuum, or boil the substrate and then cool to 37°C. In either case, keep in full, tightly closed bottles (small weighing bottle are excellent). Sections are dropped in and the bottle immedi-

ately closed. Slides may be placed in fluid in covered coplin jars with
nitrogen bubbling through.

SOLUTIONS:

   Substrate:

      Stock buffered succinate; equal volumes of:
         0.2M phosphate buffer, pH 7.6
         0.2M sodium succinate
      Incubating solution; equal volumes of:
         buffered succinate
         nitro BT (10 mg./10 ml. distilled water)

PROCEDURE:

   1. Place sections or slides in incubating solution, 37°C: 1–2 hours or
      until sufficient color is present.
   2. Wash in physiological saline: 1 minute.
   3. Fix in 10% formalin: 1–24 hours.
   4. Mount loose sections in glycerol jelly, or mount on slides and pro-
      ceed to step 5.
   5. Dehydrate, clear, and mount.
   Sections may be counterstained in safranine or hematoxylin.

RESULTS:

   sites—blue

References: Farber and Bueling (1956); Farber and Louviere (1954);
Friede (1958); Nachlas *et al.* (1957); Novikoff *et al.* (1960); Pearson
(1958); Rosa and Velarde (1954); and Rutenburg *et al.* (1950, 1956)

Dopa Oxidase Reaction

The **Dopa reaction** is considered specific for melanoblasts and mye-
logenous leucocytes which are supposed to contain an intracellular fer-
ment, *dopa-melanase.* The latter converts the 3,4 dioxyphenylalanine
into a blackish brown pigment, the black condition of the reacting cell.

Laidlaw's Method (GLICK, 1949)

FIXATION: only fresh tissue with no fixation (or 5% formalin for no
   longer than 3 hours, but results are inferior to those from fresh tissue).

SOLUTIONS:

Dopa stock solution:

DL *b* (3,4 dioxyphenylalanine) phenyl tyrosine[8]	0.3 gm.
distilled water	300.0 ml.

Store in refrigerator. Discard when it turns red.

Buffer solutions:

A. disodium hydrogen phosphate	11.0 gm.
distilled water	1000.0 ml.
B. potassium dihydrogen phosphate	9.0 gm.
distilled water	1000.0 ml.

Buffered Dopa solution:

stock Dopa solution	25.0 ml.
buffer solution *A*	6.0 ml.
buffer solution *B*	2.0 ml.

Filter through fine filter paper. Should be *p*H 7.4.

Buffered control solution:

distilled water	2.0 ml.
buffer solution *A*	6.0 ml.
buffer solution *B*	2.0 ml.

Cresyl violet:

cresyl violet acetate	0.5 gm.
distilled water	100.0 ml.

PROCEDURE:

1. Cut frozen sections, 10 microns.
2. Wash in distilled water: few seconds.
3. Treat with buffered Dopa solution, 30–37°C. The solution becomes red in about 2 hours, and gradually becomes sepia brown in 3–4 hours. Do not allow sections to remain in a sepia-colored solution; they may overstain. After first 30 minutes, change to a new solution.
4. Wash in distilled water.
5. Counterstain in cresyl violet.
6. Dehydrate, clear and mount.

RESULTS:

Dopa oxidase—black
leukocytes, melanoblasts—grey to black
melanin—yellow brown

[8] Eastman Kodak Co. #4915.

COMMENT:

Freeze-dried and embedded tissues give a good Dopa reaction.

Arginine Test

The arginine reaction uses the reaction of *a*-naphthol with guanidine derivatives in the presence of hypochlorite or hypobromite to produce an orange-red color. The reaction proceeds with guanidine derivatives in which one hydrogen atom of one of amino groups is substituted by alkyl, fatty acid or cyano radical. Proteins containing arginine give the color, and in tissue fixed by ordinary methods the reaction is specific for protein-bound arginine and other guanidine derivatives such as glycocyamine or agmatine. Guanidine, urea, creatine, creatinine, and amino acids, other than arginine, do not give the color.

Thomas (1950); **Liebman** (1951)

FIXATION: Bouin's or Stieve's.

SOLUTIONS:

a-Naphthol stock solution:

a-naphthol (Eastman #170)	1.0	gm.
absolute ethyl alcohol	100.0	ml.

Keep in refrigerator.

Working solution:

stock solution	5.0	ml.
distilled water	100.0	ml.

Hypochlorite and potassium hydroxide:

N sodium hypochlorite	15.0	ml.
distilled water	80.0	ml.
N potassium hydroxide	5.0	ml.

Urea, potassium hydroxide:

urea	10.0	gm.
distilled water	15.0	ml.
N potassium hydroxide	5.0	ml.

Shake until urea is in solution, add:

tertiary butyl alcohol, anhydrous	70.0	ml.

PROCEDURE:

Reagents above are kept in ice bath and allowed to cool well before use. Keep in bath during procedure. Other reagents at room temperature.

1. Deparaffinize slides and run down to 70% alcohol.
2. Place in *a*-naphthol: 15–30 minutes.
3. Transfer (no wash) into hypochlorite-potassium hydroxide: 1.5 minutes.
4. Transfer quickly into urea-potassium hydroxide, 2 changes.
   First change: 10 seconds, agitate slides.
   Second change: 2 minutes.
5. Transfer into absolute tertiary butyl alcohol, 2 changes.
   First change: 10 seconds, agitate.
   Second change: 3.5 minutes.
6. Transfer into xylene, 3 changes.
   First change: 10 seconds, agitate.
   Second change: 1–2 minutes.
   Third change: 2–3 minutes.
7. Drain off xylene, but do not dry. Mount in mineral oil.

RESULTS:

arginine—orange to red. Good for about 6 months.

COMMENTS:

Make all transfers as quickly as possible without allowing slides to drain. Turn jars so slides do not hit lugs on sides.

The first changes in steps 4, 5, and 6 are intended to wash off the previous fluid, and the slides should be moved gently back and forth to facilitate the process. This may be done in the second changes, but more slowly. Timing must be accurate; a stop watch is advisable.

Change solutions frequently; the reagents must be fresh. Carry not more than 5 slides through the *a*-naphthol and hypochlorite-potassium hydroxide and not more than 30 through any of the other solutions.

Solidification of the tertiary butyl alcohol may be caused by the transfer of cold slides into it, so it is advisable to warm it to 30–40°C before use. Change the alcohol frequently. Carry about 10 slides through 1 change; the first solution may then be discarded and replaced by the second change. The latter is then replaced by a fresh solution.

Before mounting, drain off the xylene thoroughly, but do not dry. Apply several drops of mineral oil, and add cover glass. Draw off excess mineral oil with filter paper. (The excess oil is desirable because it dilutes the xylene to a minimum.) The cover glasses tend to slip, so seal them with one of the ringing cements (page 123).

Mounting Media

Burstone (1957A) recommends for some azo-dye methods:
1. Mount directly from 75–80% alcohol in 20% solution of polyvinyl acetate (*Gelva 2.5, Shawinigan Resins Corporation, Springfield, Massachusetts*) in 80% alcohol. It is soluble also in glacial acetic acid, *n*-butanol (90%), aniline, pyridine, and ethyl cellosolve.
2. It preserves the following:
   esterase, alkaline phosphatase, PAS, hematoxylin, celestin blue, aldehyde fuchsin, eosin.
3. Cover glass is immovable after 1 hour. No bubble formation. Index of refraction, 1.3865, but increases after evaporation of alcohol and water.

Chapter **22**

Special Procedures I

Exfoliative Cytology

Exfoliative **cytology** (study of cells as opposed to *Histology*, study of tissues) concerns the preparation and examination of **desquamated** cells. These are cells which have been shed or pulled off from a superficial epithelium, mucus membranes, renal tubules, or the like. For example, the horny layer of epidermis is shed normally, but in disease or inflammation the process may become exaggerated and form abnormal sized flakes or scales. These may be placed on slides, stained, and examined.

Methods in this field have reached high priority among diagnostic procedures for Pathology. By screening slides made from smears (vaginal, cervical, prostatic, or the like) or from body fluids (peritoneal, pleural, gastric, urine, spinal, etc.), rapid diagnosis of malignancies is made possible.

The cells in question degenerate rapidly and smears should be made and fixed immediately, in equal parts of 95% alcohol and ether, for a minimum of 15 minutes. The slides may remain in this fluid as long as a week before staining.

Add to body fluids an equal volume of 95% alcohol and centrifuge as soon as possible, medium speed, 2000 rpm., 3 minutes. Remove supernatant fluid. (If smears cannot be made immediately, cover the sediment with absolute alcohol and place in refrigerator.) Drop some of the sediment on an albumen-coated slide and, using another slide, smear the sediment as evenly as possible over the albumenized area. Allow the smear to begin to dry around the edge but still remain moist in the center. Fix in ether-alcohol, 1 hour.

356

After fixation, the slides should not be allowed to dry at any time before or during the staining procedure. In emergencies, they can be shipped dry, but if possible some protection for the smear is advisable. *Ehrenrich and Kerpe (1959)* add 5% of polyethylene glycol to the fixative. Following complete fixation, allow the slides to dry 5–10 minutes, and then prepare them for shipping. *Papanicolaou (1957)* protects smears for shipping by covering the fixed smears with Diaphane[1] solution: 2 parts of Diaphane to 3 parts of 95% alcohol. Allow to dry, 20–30 minutes, and prepare for shipping. The polyethylene glycol or the Diaphane forms a protective coating over the smear.

Richardson (1960) uses the following solution for shipping purposes; it is economical, noncombustible, and nonvolatile. Either biopsy pieces or slides can be shipped in it.

monoethylene glycol	344.6 ml.
diethylene glycol	18.1 ml.
borax	3.6 gm.
water	577.6 ml.
glacial acetic acid	50.0 ml.

Papanicolaou Method (1942, 1947, 1954, 1957)

Excellent preparations of the following solutions can be purchased from the *Ortho Pharmaceutical Corporation, Raritan, N.J.* (Harris Hematoxylin, *EA 65, EA 50* and *OF 6*). Otherwise the stains can be prepared as follows:

SOLUTIONS:

Harris Hematoxylin, page 125 (omit acetic acid).
Orange G 6 (*OG 6*):

orange *G 6*, 0.5% (0.5 gm./100 ml. 95% alcohol)	100.0 ml.
phosphotungstic acid	0.015 gm.

Eosin—azure *36* (*EA 36* or *EA 50*, the commercial designation):

light green *SF* yellowish, C.I. 42095, 0.5% (0.5 gm./100 ml. 95% alcohol)	45.0 ml.
bismarck brown, C.I. 21000, 0.5% (0.5 gm./100 ml. 95% alcohol)	10.0 ml.
eosin *Y*, C.I. 45380, 0.5% (0.5 gm./100 ml. 95% alcohol)	45.0 ml.
phosphotungstic acid	0.2 gm.
lithium carbonate, saturated aqueous	1 drop

[1] Obtained from Will Corp., Rochester, N.Y.

Note: EA65 is the same, except for the light green content; 0.25% in 95% alcohol is used. This gives a lighter, more transparent stain, which sometimes is desirable in smears containing much mucus. Differentiation between acidophilic and basophilic cells is better, however, with *EA 36* (*EA 50*) and therefore is preferable for vaginal, endocervical, and endometrial smears.

PROCEDURE:

1. Out of fixative, hydrate slides to water. Rinse in distilled water. A few seconds in each solution is adequate, or dip slides up and down until their surface has a homogeneous appearance.
2. Stain in Harris hematoxylin, either of following methods:
   (*a*) Papanicolaou dilutes Harris with an equal amount of distilled water: 8 minutes.
   (*b*) Harris hematoxylin without acetic acid: 4 minutes.
3. Wash in tap water, running water if flowing only slightly; do not wash off or loosen parts of smear: 3–5 minutes.
4. Differentiate nuclei in 0.5% hydrochloric acid in 70% alcohol (0.5 ml./100 ml.) until nuclei are sharp against a pale blue cytoplasm.
5. Wash in slightly running tap water: 5 minutes or until nuclei are a clear blue.
6. Rinse in distilled water.
7. Transfer through 70%, 80%, and 95% alcohol: few seconds in each or until surface appears homogeneous.
8. Stain in *OG 6*: 1–2 minutes.
9. Rinse in 95% alcohol, 3 changes: few seconds each.
10. Stain in *EA 36* (or *EA 50*): 2–3 minutes.
11. Rinse in 95% alcohol, 3 changes: few seconds in each.
12. Dehydrate in absolute alcohol, 2 changes: 1 minute each.
13. Clear and mount.

RESULTS:

nuclei—blue
acidophilic cells—red to orange
basophilic cells—green or blue green
cells or fragments of tissue penetrated by blood—orange or orange
  green

COMMENTS:

Papanicolaou cautions against agitating slides excessively, or crowding them while staining. If parts should float off from a positive slide onto a negative one, a false positive can occur.

Johnson and Klein (1956) apply the method to paraffin sections.

Carson (1959) substitutes *Technicon dehydrant*[2] for ethyl alcohol, thereby eliminating the need for revenue-taxed ethyl alcohol which is difficult for some laboratories to obtain.

MacLean (1960) describes processing Papanicolaou smears on the Technicon.

Fluorescent Method

Provided the proper equipment is available, the fluorescent procedure requires less time for preparation and less skill on the part of the examiner than the Papanicolaou method. The polychrome staining is so brilliant that cells are seen in sharp contrast against a black background, rendering mass screening simple and quick. Under low power atypical cells show increased amounts of fluorescence and suspicious malignant cells are a brilliant flaming reddish orange (they seem to glow) in contrast to normal cells, which may be greenish grey with whitish yellow nuclei. The method is based on the differentiation of RNA and DNA by acridine orange *NO (AO)*. The RNA in the cytoplasm and the nucleolus fluoresces red, while the DNA of the nucleus fluoresces green.

von Bertalanffy and Bickis (1956); von Bertalanffy, Masin and Masin (1958)

SOLUTIONS:

Acridine orange (*AO*):

Stock solution:

acridine orange, C.I. 46005	0.1 gm.
distilled water	100.0 ml.

Keep in dark bottle in refrigerator.

M/15 phosphate buffer, *p*H 6:

M/15 sodium phosphate, dibasic, $Na_2H_2PO_4$ (11.876 gm./1000 ml. water)	7.0 ml.
M/15 potassium phosphate, KH_2PO_4 (9.078 gm./1000 ml. water)	43.0 ml.

Keep in refrigerator.

Working solution:

AO stock solution	5.0 ml.
buffer solution	45.0 ml.

[2] Technicon Chemical Co., Chauncey, N.Y.

Calcium chloride, M/10:

calcium chloride .... 11.0 gm.

distilled water .... 1000.0 ml.

PROCEDURE:

1. Smears are fixed by Papanicolaou method, ether-95% alcohol: at least 15 minutes.
2. Hydrate to water: few seconds in each solution.
3. Rinse briefly in acetic acid, 1% (1 ml./99 ml. water), followed by wash in distilled water: few minutes.
4. Stain in acridine orange: 3 minutes.
5. Destain in phosphate buffer: 1 minute.
6. Differentiate in calcium chloride: 30 seconds. Wash with buffer.
7. Repeat step 6. If smear is very thick, a longer differentiation may be necessary. Nuclei should be clearly defined.
8. Wash thoroughly with phosphate buffer. Calcium chloride must be removed.
9. Blot carefully and mount with a drop of buffer.

Frozen Sections, Method I.

1. Wash out ether-alcohol, freeze, and cut.
2. Omit step 2 and proceed as usual. Use small shallow dishes, mounting sections on slide after staining.

Frozen Sections, Method II.

1. Section immediately after biopsy or wrap tissue in saline-soaked gauze and wax paper surrounded by ice. Keep in refrigerator, 4°C until processed. Cut, transfer to slides, and fix in alcohol or Carnoy's fluid.
2. Hydrate and stain.

RESULTS:

DNA of chromatin of nucleus—green from whitish to yellowish hues
connective tissue fibrils, cornified epithelia; structures—greenish
mucus—dull green
leukocytes—bright green
RNA of basophilic structures of cytoplasm, main portion of nucleoli
    —red and orange fluorescence
sites of strongly acidic groups—deep carmine
malignant cells under low power—brilliant flaming red-orange
proliferating malignant cells under high power—intense fluorescence
    cytoplasm—flaming red-orange containing reddish granules,
    patches, or fine granules

nuclei—yellowish hues, yellow-orange to yellow-green

nucleoli—brilliant orange-red

degenerating and necrotic malignant cells—characterized by a gradual loss of cytoplasmic RNA and therefore of the flaming red-orange

cytoplasm—faint orange or brick red, RNA often concentrated at periphery in a rim of dark brick red

nuclei—brilliant green, green-yellow or pale yellow-grey

nucleoli—often enlarged and multiple, orange-red

COMMENTS:

Paraffin sections also can be stained by this method.

The buffer mount is a temporary mount, even when ringed. Upon the author's suggestion, the laboratory at Los Alamos has tried dissolving Elvanol 51-50[3] in the buffer until the solution is of thin syrup consistency. This has resulted in a clearer and more lasting mount. (See also page 122) Seal the cover slip, however, with one of the ringing cements (page 123). Many scientific supply houses are now advertising media for fluorescent mounting.

After the smear has been used for fluorescent examination, it can be stained by the *Papanicolaou* technique.

1. Remove cover glass in distilled water.

2. Transfer to 50% alcohol: approximately 1 minute, 2 changes.

3. Proceed to Papanicolaou method.

Bacteria and parasites will fluoresce and can confuse the picture; for example: bacteria—bright orange; *Trichomonas*, cytoplasm—bright orange and nucleus—whitish yellow. These are easily recognized in vaginal smears. See *Umiker and Pickle (1960)* for lung cancer diagnosis.

Dart and Turner (1959) Method

SOLUTIONS:

McIlvaine's buffer:

sodium phosphate, Na_2HPO_4	10.081 gm.
citric acid, monohydrate	13.554 gm.
distilled water	1000.0 ml.

Keep in refrigerator. Good for 1 week.

Buffered acridine orange:

Stock solution.

acridine orange, C.I. 46005	0.1 gm.
distilled water	100.0 ml.

---

[3] PVA, polyvinyl alcohol, E. I. DuPont de Nemours and Co., Wilmington, Del.

Add 2 ml. of "Tween 80" to 1000 ml. of stock.

  Working solution:

    acridine orange stock solution .... 1 part

    McIlvaine's buffer .... 9 parts

PROCEDURE:

1. Hydrate slides to water, 5 dips in each of 80%, 70% and 50% alcohol.
2. Dip 4 times in acetic acid, 1% (1 ml./99 ml. water).
3. Rinse in distilled water: 2 minutes.
4. Transfer to McIlvaine's buffer: 3 minutes.
5. Stain in buffered acridine orange: 3 minutes.
6. Differentiate in McIlvaine's buffer: 4 minutes.
7. Wipe excess material from ends of slides, gently blot with coarse blotting paper.
8. Apply cover glass with buffer. Let stand 2 minutes before examining.

Can be restained, as above, with Papanicolaou. After this, can be decolorized and restained with acridine orange.

Sex Chromatin

Greenblatt and Manautou (1957)

FIXATION: peripheral blood smears in methyl alcohol: 1–2 minutes.
  See Comments below for "buffy coat" suggestion.
  Oral mucosal and vaginal smears in absolute alcohol-ether (1:1): 2–24 hours.

SOLUTION:

  Pinacyanole:

    pinacyanole[4] .... 0.5 gm.

    70% ethyl or methyl alcohol .... 100.0 ml.

  Wright's buffer:

    monobasic potassium phosphate .... 6.63 gm.

    dibasic sodium phosphate .... 3.20 gm.

    distilled water .... 1000.0 ml.

PROCEDURES

1. Cover with pinacyanole; blood smears: 30 seconds; oral mucosal and vaginal smears: 45 seconds.

[4] Eastman Kodak Co.

2. Dilute with Wright's buffer (equal to amount of stain); blood smears: 30 seconds; oral mucosal and vaginal smears: 45 seconds.
3. Wash in running water: 2–3 minutes.
4. Decolorize in 50%, 70%, 95%, and absolute alcohol: 30 seconds each.
5. (a) Air-dry blood smears and they are ready for use.
   (b) Clear oral mucosal and vaginal smears in xylene, 2 changes, and mount.

RESULTS:

Staining: chromatin—blue

Counting: oral mucosal and vaginal smears—6 cells out of 100 counted must be positive for female sex chromatin to be considered female. If less than 4 per 100, the specimen is male.

blood smears—at least 6 rich-staining "drumsticks" must be counted in 500 polymorph cells for a female count. No more than 2 drumsticks should appear in a male count. The tiny clubs and sessile nodules are found in about equal numbers in both sexes, but cannot be counted as sex chromatin bodies. (See excellent pictures in Greenblatt and Manaotou)

COMMENTS:

For sex chromatin counts, the preparation of a **"buffy coat"** is recommended by the present author. It gives the examiner a fighting chance at a relatively easy cell count. Place the collected blood in a glass tube plus an anticoagulant and allow it to stand for several hours or use mild centrifugation. The cellular elements will settle out and leave a straw-colored solution on top. The leukocytes are not as dense as the erythrocytes and will settle out last to remain as the so called "buffy coat" between the red cell layer and the plasma on top. Smear this "buffy coat" with its concentration of leukocytes on the slide and fix.

Klinger and Ludwig (1957)

FIXATION: 95% alcohol for smears and thin embryonic membranes: 30 minutes to 4 hours. Tissue blocks in Davidson's fixative (see below): 3–24 hours and transfer to 95% alcohol. If material was fixed in some other fixative, transfer immediately to 95% alcohol, but do not leave in first fixative for longer than 24 hours for good results.

SOLUTIONS:

Davidson's fixative:

95% ethyl alcohol	30.0 ml.
formalin	20.0 ml.
glacial acetic acid	10.0 ml.
distilled water	30.0 ml.

Buffered thionin:

A. thionin, C.I. 52000, saturated solution in 50% alcohol. Filter.

B. sodium acetate	9.714 gm.
sodium barbiturate	14.714 gm.
distilled water, CO_2 free	500.0 ml.
C. hydrochloric acid, sp. gr. 1.19	8.50 ml.
distilled water	991.5 ml.

Working solution (*p*H 5.7):

thionin solution (*A*)	40.0 ml.
buffer solution (*B*)	28.0 ml.
hydrochloric acid (*C*)	32.0 ml.

PROCEDURE:

1. Deparaffinize and hydrate slides to water.
2. Hydrolyze in 5N HCl (page 408), 20–25°C: 20 minutes.
3. Rinse thoroughly in distilled water, several changes; no acid should be carried over into thionin.
4. Stain in buffered thionin: 15–60 minutes.
5. Rinse in distilled water, and 50% alcohol.
6. Rinse in 70% alcohol until clouds of stain cease to appear.
7. Dehydrate, clear, and mount.

RESULTS:

sex chromatin—deep blue-violet
nuclear chromatin—lightly colored
cytoplasm—unstained
fibrin and related structures will show metachromasia

COMMENTS:

The *Feulgen technique* may be used for sex chromatin body identification, but the above method is simpler and quicker. The principle is the same in both methods: the sex chromatin body differentiates from nonspecific nuclear chromatin because of a higher content of DNA, which takes longer to extract. If the basophil shell of the nucleolus is not visible, no attempt at sexing should be made

(*Klinger and Ludwig*). In the Feulgen method, the sex chromatin stains more deeply than any other Feulgen-positive material present.

Skin biopsies are reliable if the sections are of good quality, but the simplest specimens are oral scrapings, easy to obtain and equally easy to stain. Scrape the mucosa of the check with a tongue depressor and smear scrapings on an albumen-coated slide. Fix immediately in Davidson's or alcohol. Papanicolaou fixative (equal parts of ether and 95% alcohol) also may be used.

Lennox (1956)

FIXATIVE: 10% formalin or mercuric chloride saturated formalin. Avoid Bouin's and dichromate fixatives.

SOLUTIONS:

Ribonuclease:

ribonuclease	1.0 gm.
distilled water, glass-distilled	100.0 ml.

Boil 3–5 seconds after dissolving. Keeps about 1 week in refrigerator.

Gallocyanin:

chrome alum	5.0 gm.
distilled water	100.0 ml.

Dissolve and add:

gallocyanin	0.15 gm.

Shake thoroughly, heat slowly and boil 5 minutes. Cool, filter and wash through filter with distilled water until filtrate reaches 100 ml. Usable at once. Keeps about 1 month.

PROCEDURE:

1. Deparaffinize and hydrate slides to water.
2. Incubate in ribonuclease solution, 37°C: 10–15 minutes.
3. Rinse in distilled water.
4. Stain in gallocyanin, 37°C: overnight.
5. Dip in acid alcohol (few drops HCl in 70% alcohol) to clean, not to differentiate.
6. Wash in tap water: 5 minutes or longer.
7. Dehydrate, clear and mount.

RESULTS:

By extracting with ribonuclease, the nuclear picture is sharpened against a colorless background, making it easier to distinguish the sex chromatin nodule.

Guard (1959)

FIXATION: Fix smears immediately in 9% alcohol; do not allow them to dry: 10 minutes.

SOLUTIONS:

Biebrich scarlet:

biebrich scarlet (water soluble) C.I. 26905	1.0 gm.
phosphotungstic acid	0.3 gm.
glacial acetic acid	5.0 ml.
50% ethyl alcohol	100.0 ml.

Fast green:

fast green *FCF* C.I. 42053	0.5 gm.
phosphomolybdic acid	0.3 gm.
phosphotungstic acid	0.3 gm.
glacial acetic acid	5.0 ml.
50% ethyl alcohol	100.0 ml.

Dilute hematoxylin:

Harris hematoxylin (page 125)	0.05 ml.
50% ethyl alcohol	100.0 ml.

PROCEDURE:

Short Method:

1. Transfer into 70% alcohol: 2 minutes.
2. Stain in biebrich scarlet: 2 minutes.
3. Rinse in 50% alcohol.
4. Differentiate in fast green: 1–4 hours. Check under microscope at hourly intervals for green cytoplasm and green vesicular nuclei in all cells.
5. Rinse in 50% alcohol; 5 minutes.
6. Dehydrate, clear, and mount.

Long Method:

1. Transfer to 70% alcohol: 2 minutes.
2. Stain in dilute hematoxylin: 15 seconds, or dip in solution 10 times.
3. No rinse, stain in Biebrich scarlet: 2 minutes.
4. Rinse in 50% alcohol.
5. Stain in fast green: 18–24 hours; no microscopic checking necessary.
6. Dehydrate, clear, and mount.

RESULTS:

sex chromatin—red

other nuclei, vesicular and cytoplasm—green

COMMENTS:

In the long method, the hematoxylin mordants the sex chromatin for biebrich scarlet and makes a firm binding, also slows down the fast green.

Makowski et al. (*1956*) identified sex chromatin in the cellular debris of amniotic fluid, spreading the centrifuged sediment on albumenized slides. *Vernino and Laskin* (*1960*) identified it in bone decalcified in EDTA. *Barr et al.* (*1950*) describe it in nerve cells. *See also:* Klinger (1958); Marberger *et al.* (1958); Marwah and Weinmann (1955); Moore and Barr (1955); and Moore *et al.* (1953).

Chromosomes

Squash and Smear Technics with Acetocarmine or Aceto-orcein Staining

FIXATION: sometimes desirable. Use small pieces, Carnoy's (page 16), freshly prepared, few minutes to several days.

SOLUTIONS:

Acetocarmine:

Stock solution.

Boil an excess (approximately 0.5 gm./100 ml.) of carmine in 45% acetic acid, aqueous: 2–4 minutes. Cool and filter.

Working solution:

Dilute stock solution with 45% acetic acid, aqueous, 1:2. An iron-mordanted stain often is favored because of darker, bluish-tinged red. *Belling* (*1926*) added a few drops of ferric hydrate in 50% acetic acid, but only a few drops. Too much iron produces a precipitate in a short time. *Moree* (*1944*) determined quantitatively the amount of ferric chloride to add and includes tables of various normalities and volumes.

Aceto-orcein:

Add 1–2 gm. orcein to 45 ml. of hot acetic acid. When cool, add 55 ml. of distilled water. *LaCour* (*1941*) used 2% orcein in 70% acetic acid.

PROCEDURE:

Temporary Mounts

1. Place material, fixed or fresh, on slide with small mount of either stain, just enough to reach edge of cover glass. Apply pressure. Sometimes it is advantageous to allow material to remain in stain 5–10 minutes, then remove to fresh batch before squashing. Fragments of animal tissue (ovaries, testes, biopsy bits) can be put in a tube with a large excess of stain for 2–7 days. Remove to fresh solution on slide and squash.

Methods of applying pressure:
   (*a*) Press with ball of thumb.
   (*b*) Tap or press with blunt or flat instrument.
   (*c*) Roll with glass rod or a vial.

   All methods are subject to ease and amount of spreading, some materials spread more easily than others. Avoid actual crushing.

Alternate squashing method: Use a large amount of stain and press out excess with a blotter, flattening cells at same time. Staining may be improved by passing slide 3–4 times through a small flame. Do not allow solution to boil.

2. Seal edges with paraffin or vaseline and allow to stand 1 day.

RESULTS:
   acetocarmine—red
   aceto-orcein—dark purple
   iron acetocarmine—deep bluish red

COMMENTS:
   Rothfels and Simonovitch (1958) use an air-drying technique for spreading chromosomes in cells grown in tissue culture, and recommend the method for material which is lumpy and contains debris making squashing difficult. The material growing on slides or cover glasses is fixed and at completion of fixation is placed horizontally to dry at room temperature with no airstream or humidity control. This produces uniform flattening of division stages and can be followed by acetocarmine or aceto-orcein staining.
   Puck (1958), Ruddle et al. (1958), Harnden (1959), and others first treat tissue cultures growing on cover-slip with hypotonic solutions (page 409), 37°C, 15 minutes to swell the cells, followed by fixation and then air drying. The combination of swelling and air drying helps to spread and flatten the chromosomes.

Colchicine pretreatment is efficacious, suppressing cell division, preventing spindle formation and allowing the chromosomes to spread. They shorten and thicken and become straight and can be fixed into almost a single plane when squashed. Use 0.01–0.02% aqueous solution of colchicine for 2–3 hours, and follow by fixation, etc. (*Burrell, 1939; O'Mara, 1939; Meyer, 1943*)

Permanent Mounts

If a slide is to be made into a permanent mount and there is a chance of losing the specimens, coat the slide with albumen before smearing.

A. Smith (1947) method:

1. Remove paraffin or vaseline seal with razor blade and xylene.
2. Soak in equal parts of acetic acid and 95% alcohol until cover glass comes off.
3. Place in equal parts of 95% ethyl alcohol and tertiary butyl alcohol: 2 minutes.
4. Transfer to tertiary butyl alcohol, 1–2 changes: 2 minutes each.
5. Briefly drain slide and cover glass against absorbent paper or blotter.
6. Add thin resin mountant to slide and return cover glass to same position as before.

   Step 2 can be followed by 2 changes of 95% ethyl alcohol; mount in Euparol or Diaphane.

B. Nolts (1948) method:

1. Place slide in covered dish so edge of cover glass dips into 95% alcohol: 6–12 hours.
2. Immerse in 95% alcohol: 1–2 hours.
3. With sharp needle, gently pry cover glass free while immersed.
4. Drain off excess alcohol and add drop of Euparol or Diaphane and replace cover glass.

C. Other permanent methods:

McClintock (1929); Celarier (1956); and Bradley (1948B). Peary (1955) uses a frozen method of dehydration, also counterstains with fast green.

Delamater (1951) describes a freezing method.

Conger and Fairchild (1953) freeze smears while in stain on a block of dry ice: 30 seconds. Pry off cover glass with razor blade. Place before thawing in 95% or absolute alcohol, 2 changes: 5 minutes. Mount in Euparol or Diaphane.

D. Lamination Method, page 394.

For additional Staining Methods, see:

> *Austin (1959):* iron alum modification with acetocarmine.
> *Bradley (1957):* sudan black with acetocarmine.
> *Griffin and McQuarrie (1942)* and *Chen (1944):* iron hematoxylin.
> *Melander and Wingstrand (1953):* Gomori's hematoxylin.
> *Rafalko (1946)* and *Sachs (1953):* Feulgen methods.
> *Carter et al. (1959)* recommend aceto-orcein squashing for cancer detection; mitotic figures are red and detailed. Sex chromatin is recognizable.
> *Sandberg et al. (1960)* describe in detail preparation of aspirated bone marrow for aceto-orcein staining.

Restoration of deteriorated slides (*Persidsky, 1954*)

If dye has precipitated as dark crystals because the preparation has dried:

1. Remove sealing material.
2. Place 1 drop of 2N HCl at one edge of cover glass. Apply blotter to opposite edge to help draw the acid under: 3–5 minutes.
3. Replace HCl with acetocarmine by same method.
4. Heat gently, do not boil. Crystals are redissolved and specimen restained.
5. Reseal.

References: Austin (1959); Belling (1926); Bradley (1948A & B, 1957); Carter *et al.* (1959); Celarier (1956); Chen (1944); Conger and Fairchild (1953); Griffin and McQuarrie (1942) ; LaCour (1935, 1941); McClintock (1929); Melander and Wingstrand (1953); Moree (1944); Nolte (1948); Peary (1955); Persidsky (1954); Rafalko (1946); Rothfels and Siminovitch (1956); Sachs (1953); Smith (1947) ; Warmke (1935); Zirkle (1937); and Zuck (1947).

Chapter 23

Special Procedures II

Preparation of Invertebrates for Whole Mounts and Sections

It is impossible to cover specifically all the members of this huge group of organisms, but certain generalizations can be made which will be applicable to the common forms and perhaps be adaptable to the less common ones. Fixatives can be applied directly to many of them, but not to others because of their propensity to contract or ball up, pulling in their tentacles or other appendages, and thereby making whole mounts or sections practically worthless. In the latter cases, careful anesthetizing or narcotizing must precede killing and fixation. As soon as the narcotization is complete, and before death if possible, fixation can be successful.

Anesthetizing and Narcotizing Agents

1. *Magnesium chloride* or *magnesium sulfate* is widely and successfully used on **sea anemones, corals, annelids, tunicates** and **nudibranchs** to name a few. Crystalline magnesium sulfate can be tied in a bag suspended above and just touching the water surface, or a 33% aqueous solution siphoned slowly in, controlled by a screw clamp. When the organisms are anesthetized (no reaction to the touch of a needle), siphon off the water until the animals are barely covered and carefully add fixative. Disturb the animals as little as possible. When partially hardened, transfer to fresh fixative.

371

2. *Cocaine* can be used for **ciliates, rotifers, bryozoa, hydra,** some **worms** and **nudibranchs.** A 1% aqueous solution is added to the water in proportions of about 1.0 ml. to 100.0 ml. of the water containing the animals. *Eucain hydrochloride* can be used in the same manner. Check for contraction and fix.

3. *Menthol.* Sprinkle on the water surface and leave overnight. Good for difficult to narcotize sessile marine animals, **coelenterates,** some **bryozoa, hydroids,** also **flukes.** It is more efficient when combined with *chloral hydrate* in proportions of 45.0 gm. menthol and 55.0 gm. chloral hydrate. Grind together in a mortar with a little water. Drop on surface of the water. Fix animals when they no longer contract. Large marine forms probably will require overnight treatment. Chloral hydrate can be used alone, sprinkled on water surface for **annelids, molluscs, tunicates, bryozoans** and **turbellaria.**

4. *Chloretone.* A 0.33 to 1% solution can be used, but it is slow acting.

5. *Chloroform* can be dropped on the water surface for many aquatic forms, and is used in special bottles for insects and arachnids (see below).

5. *Ether* and *alcohol* can be used by dropping on the water, or alcohol can be added gradually to the water by a tube controlled with a screw clamp until the proportion of alcohol to water is approximately 10%. It is particularly good for fresh water forms and **earthworms.** *Ether* can be used like chloroform for **insects.**

7. *Asphyxiation.* Boil water to remove the air and seal it in a jar. Particularly good for **gastropods** (snails); place them in the boiled water after it has cooled.

8. *Cold.* Partially freeze organisms in salt and ice mixture or in freezing compartment of refrigerator, or in ice water until they are relaxed. Good for **tapeworms.** Transfer to lukewarm water and then fix.

Tips on special handling

PORIFERA.

Small forms can be dropped directly into osmic-mercuric chloride (water, 250.0 ml.; osmic acid, 2.5 gm.; mercuric chloride, 9.0 gm.). Large forms fix better in alcoholic sublimate (Gilson; Carnoy).

Calcareous sponges can be decalcified in 70–80% alcohol plus 3% of hydrochloric or nitric acid. Silicious ones can be desilicified in 80% alcohol plus 5% hydrofluoric acid added gradually. Perform the latter in a glass dish coated inside with paraffin. After a few hours, transfer to 80% alcohol. Do not breathe hydrofluoric acid fumes. If sectioning sponges, small spicules will section easily without disilification.

COELENTERATES.

Hydra. Place in a small amount of water (few drops) in a shallow dish. When animals are extended, rapidly pipette warm mercuric chloride-acetic (saturated aqueous mercuric chloride, 95.0 ml.; glacial acetic acid, 5.0 ml.) at them. Work the fixative from base toward oral region, thereby preventing tentacles from contracting or curling.

Sea anemones. Anesthetize overnight with menthol; or thirty per cent magnesium chloride (50 to 100 ml.) can be added gradually over a period of one hour: leave in the solution until there is no more contraction of tentacles. Siphon off the solution until anemones are just barely covered. Add fixative (Susa, Bouin's, mercuric-chloride combinations, 10% formalin sea water) slowly down the side of the container. Also pipette some directly into the throats of the anemones. When partially hardened, transfer into fresh undiluted fixative.

Jellyfish. In sea water, while stirring, add fixative (10% formalin) down side of container until proportions are approximately 10 ml. or more to 100.0 ml. of sea water. Stir for 3 or 4 minutes. After 2–3 hours, change to fresh formalin.

Medusae. Must be anesthetized; cocaine is best. Allow them to expand in a small dish of water, add 3–4 ml. of 1% cocaine per 100.0 ml. of water. When they do not contract, add fixative (10% formalin) with stirring.

Corals with extended polyps. Narcotize with magnesium sulfate and fix in hot saturated mercuric chloride plus 5% acetic acid.

Freezing sometimes can be tried on **coelenterates.**

PLATYHELMINTHES.

Planaria. Starve for a few days before killing. Place in a small amount of water on a glass plate. When extended, add a drop of 2% aqueous nitric acid directly on it. Follow by pipetting fixative (Gilson or saturated mercuric chloride in saline) on it and then transfer into a dish of fixative.

Trematodes. Anesthetize large trematodes with menthol: $\frac{1}{2}$ hour. Then flatten by the following method: saturate filter paper with Gilson's and lay on a plate of glass. Lay worms on paper and quickly cover with another sheet of saturated paper and a second plate of glass. Add a weight, but not such a heavy one that the worms are crushed: 8–12 hours. Remove glass and paper and transfer worms to fresh fixative. A single specimen can be flattened between slides, tied together and dropped into fixative. After 2–3 hours, remove the string, but do not disturb the slides. Leave overnight. Remove slides and transfer animal to fresh fixative.

Small trematodes can be shaken in a small amount of 0.5–1.0% salt solution: 3 minutes. Add saturated mercuric chloride plus 2% acetic acid. Shake for several minutes. Change to fresh fixative: 6–12 hours. If they should be flattened, they can be laid on a slide and covered with another slide or, if very delicate, with a cover glass. Pipette fixative carefully along the side of the cover and then lower carefully into fixative.

Cestodes. Place a large tapeworm in ice water until relaxed (overnight). Then flatten between glass plates for microscope-slide whole mounts (as for trematodes—see above). For museum mounts, the worm can be wound on a tall bottle or 100 ml. graduate and fixative poured over it.

Small cestodes can be stretched from an applicator stick supported over a tall container and fixative poured down the length until they hang straight. Then immerse them completely. Then they can be flattened between microscope slides.

Nemertinea. Drop into saturated mercuric chloride-acetic acid (95/5).

NEMATHELMINTHES.

Nematodes (hookworms). Shake 3 minutes in physiological saline. Pour off and drop worms into hot glycerol alcohol (70–80% alcohol plus 10% of glycerol). A sublimate fixative can be used. (also for **ascaris**)

Very small nematodes can be relaxed and killed in a depression slide or watch glass by gentle heat. An incubator regulated to 50–52°C is most reliable. If using a flame or hot plate, be careful not to boil the worms. Transfer to fixative.

Formalin-acetic-alcohol is an excellent fixative for small nematodes:

95% ethyl alcohol	12–20.0 ml.
glacial acetic acid	1.0 ml.
formalin	6.0 ml.
distilled water	40.0 ml.

If a few drops of saturated aqueous picric acid is added, the worms take up a little color.

Slide whole mounts are easy to prepare. Place the worms in the alcohol glycerol mixture in an incubator (35–37°C) or on top of an oven to permit slow evaporation of the alcohol. When the solution is almost pure glycerine, mount in glycerine jelly (page 119). Helminth ova also can be mounted in this way. For other methods see Whole Mounts, page 379.

Microfilaria. Blood infected with microfilaria is smeared and dried as for any blood smear. Then fix in any mercuric chloride fixative and stain with Delafield's hematoxylin. If it is preferable to have the slides dehemoglobinized, after fixation treat them with 2% formalin plus 1% of acetic acid: 5 minutes. Wash and stain. An alternate method is to smear and dry; dehemoglobinize in 5% acetic acid and air dry; fix in methyl alcohol and stain with Giemsa (page 225).

BRYOZOA.

Anesthetize with menthol. Fix salt water forms in chromo-acetic (10% chromic acid, 7–10 ml.; 10% acetic acid, 10 ml.; water to make 100 ml.). Fix fresh-water forms in 10% formalin.

ANNELIDA.

Earthworms. If sections of worms (aquatic or terrestrial) are desired, the intestines must be freed of grit and other tough particles.

Several methods have been devised for earthworms. *Cocke (1938)* feeds them on cornmeal and agar (1:1) and some chopped lettuce for 3 days, changing the food every day. *Becker and Roudabush (1935)* recommend a container with the bottom covered with agar. Wash off the agar twice a day for 3–4 days. Moistened blotting paper can be used. When the animals are free from grit, place them in a flat dish with just enough water to cover them. Slowly siphon in 50% alcohol until the strength of the solution is about 10% of alcohol. Chloroform also can be used for narcotizing. Fix in Bouin's or mercuric chloride saturated in 80% alcohol plus 5% of acetic acid. The worms may be dipped up and down in the fixative and then supported by wire through a posterior segment, hanging down in the fixative, or placed in short lengths of glass tubing in fixative to keep them straight. This is necessary if perfect sagittal sections are to be cut. Embedding is probably most successful by the butyl alcohol method. After removal of mercuric chloride in iodized 80% alcohol, transfer to *n* or tertiary butyl alcohol: 24 hours (change once). Transfer to butyl alcohol saturated with paraffin (in 56–60°C oven): 24 hours. Pure paraffin: 24 hours and embed.

Sea worms can be kept in a container of clean sea water, changed every day for 2 or 3 days, then anesthetized with chloroform and fixed, using fast-penetrating fixative (Bouin's, or a mercuric chloride fixative).

ARTHROPODA.

Insects and **arachnids.** Ether, chloroform or potassium cyanide are used for killing. *Simplest method:* Place a wad of cotton in the bottom of a wide mouthed jar and cover the cotton with a piece of wire screen. Dampen the cotton with ether or chloroform or lay a few lumps of potassium cyanide on it before adding the screen wire. Keep tightly closed with a cork or screw cap. A piece of rubber tubing soaked in chloroform until it swells and placed under the screen wire will hold chloroform for several days. If the appendages should be spread when fixed, as soon as the insect is dead place it on a glass slide with another slide on top of it. Run fixative in between slides.

For *whole organisms,* rapidly penetrating fixatives should be used: picro-sulfuric, sublimate fixatives, mixtures containing nitric acid (Carnoy), alcoholic and ordinary Bouin's, or Sinha's (1953) fixative.

For *whole mounts,* the clearing of the exoskeleton is sometimes difficult. Body contents have to be made transparent, or sometimes have to be removed. Lactophenol (page 121) mounting will serve the purpose in the first case, but heavily pigmented arthropods probably will have to be bleached in hydrogen peroxide for 12 hours or longer. Fleas, ticks and the like make better demonstrations if not engorged; in any case they should be treated with 10% potassium hydroxide, 8–12 hours, to swell and dissolve the soft tissues, thus clearing out the body contents. Wash well to remove the potassium hydroxide. Acid corrosives are preferred by some because they do not soften the integument as much as alkaline corrosives.

Acid corrosive:

glacial acetic acid	1.0 ml.
chloral hydrate	1.0 gm.
water	1.0 ml.

Do not use a fixative containing alcohol or formalin if a corrosive is necessary. The organism will not clear.

For methods of mounting whole mounts, see page 378.

Because of chitin, sectioning of insects can be difficult. Avoid higher ethyl alcohols. Dioxane methods (page 39), butyl alcohol (above), or double embedding (page 83) must be used and will provide excellent results. Soaking the tissue blocks overnight or for several days in water (page 55) will simplify sectioning.

MOLLUSCA.

Snails. Place in boiled water until limp. Fix.

Mussels. Sections of undecalcified shell can be made by grinding.

Decalcification can be undertaken with 3–4% nitric acid. If the soft parts are to be fixed, wedge the valves apart with a small length of glass rod and place entire animal in fixative. Dissect out after it is fixed. Gills can be removed and fixed flat in a mercuric chloride fixative.

ECHINDODERMATA.

Inject fixative into the tip of the rays of starfish. This will extend the feet. Then drop the animal in fixative; mercuric chloride-acetic is good.

Staining Invertebrates

Sections can be stained in any manner, depending on the fixatives and the desired results.

For beautiful transparent whole mounts, the carmine stains (page 382) are the usual choice for most of the invertebrates: obelia, hydra and hydroids, Daphnia, bryozoa, medusae, flukes, tapeworms, small annelids, tunicate and ammocoetes larvae to name a few. But Kornhauser's hematein (page 384) is an excellent substitute, particularly for flukes and tapeworms.

If the cuticle and muscle layers of flukes and tapeworms tend to remain opaque and obscure the details of internal anatomy, either of the two methods can be tried to correct the condition. Dehydrate and clear in an oil, such as cedar oil. Place in a flat dish under a dissecting microscope and carefully scrape away some of the tissue from both surfaces. With care, this can free the animal of some of the dense tissue material and not harm the internal structures. An alternate method is to finish staining and then wash in water. Transfer to a potassium permanganate solution made from a few drops of 0.5% solution added to water until only a pink color develops. When the worm begins to show a greenish-brown sheen, remove it immediately to distilled water: 5 minutes. Transfer to 2–3% aqueous oxalic acid until bleached and the sheen is lost. Wash thoroughly in running water at least one hour. Dehydrate, clear, and mount.

References: Becker and Roudabush (1935); Galigher (1934); Gatenby (1950); Gray (1952); Guyer (1953); Hegner, Cort, and Root (1927), and Pantin (1946).

Preparation of Chick Embryos

The following procedure is a standard and simple one for removing, fixing, and staining chick embryos of any size, from primitive streak to age 96 hours:

With the handle of the scissors, break the shell at the air space end, turn scissors and cut the shell around the long axis, being careful to keep the tip of the scissors pressed against the inside of the shell while cutting. This will prevent penetration of the yolk or the embryo. With egg submerged in physiological saline at $37°C$ [5] in a finger bowl, remove top half of the shell. The chick will be found floating on the upper surface of the yolk. It can be a waste of time to remove the lower half of the shell, but many workers prefer to do so. This is a matter of individual preference and ease of preparation. With small scissors, cut quickly around the outside of the area vasculosa. Except for large embryos, do not cut through the vascular area. Keep one edge gripped by forceps, and slip a syracuse watch glass under the chick. Withdraw the watch glass and embryo with a little of the saline. Bring as little yolk as possible with the chick.

The vitelline membrane most likely will come with the embryo; occasionally it will float free. If not, wave the embryo gently back and forth in the saline until the membrane begins to float loose. Release grip on embryo and remove the membrane. Make certain that the embryo is wrong side up, that is, the side which was against the yolk is now uppermost. Straighten out the chick, with no folds. Sometimes washing with saline in a pipette across the top helps to clean and flatten it. Pull off remaining saline and yolk, carefully, not just from one edge but slowly and with gentle pressure on the pipette bulb around the area vasculosa. Do not get so close that the embryo is drawn up into the pipette.

Have a circle of filter paper cut with the inside hole approximately the size of the vascular area if it is to be retained, or a little larger than the embryo if it only is to be used. Being careful not to disturb the embryo, drop the circle of paper around it. Press gently around the paper to make it adhere to the blastoderm. With a pipette apply fixative (Gilson or Bouin's), carefully dropping it first directly on the embryo; ease it on, do not squirt it on, and then work outward toward and over the paper circle, finally adding enough fixative to completely immerse embryo and paper. Leave overnight. The embryo should remain adhering to the paper and can be transported in this fashion from solution to solution. Fixation is followed by proper washing, depending upon choice of fixative. Embryo is then stained in a carmine, hematoxylin or hematein stain (see whole mounts) and dehydrated. Remove the chick from the circle, clear and mount. The cover glass may have to be

---

[5] The author has found that with rapidity developed from experience, warm water serves just as well as saline, with no ultimate harm to the chick if it is to be fixed immediately.

supported (page 381) to protect the delicate embryo from destructive pressure. For sections, after washing the embryos can be dehydrated, cleared and embedded in paraffin.

Incubation time and determination of age can be puzzling. A perfectly aged chick sometimes is difficult to obtain, because the age is determined not only by the number of hours in, and the temperature of, the incubator, but the length of time the egg was in the hen and the temperature at which the egg was stored. The temperature of the incubator should be 37.5°C and it usually requires about 4 hours to warm up the egg once it is placed in the incubator. In other words, a 36 hour chick would require about 40 hours in the incubator for proper development. The accompanying chart (Figure 27) indicates how counting the number of pairs of **somites** in the chick will determine its age; thus 10 pairs indicates an age of 30 hours. This is the best criterion of development, rather than the number of hours in the incubator.

Any bird or reptilian embryo can be fixed as outlined for the chick. *Amphibian larvae* can be dropped directly into fixative, after first dissecting off any surrounding yolk or jelly.

Mammalian embryos should be dissected from the uteri and fixed in Bouin's. If the uterine site also is to be preserved, cut through the uterus on either side of the embryo and fix. A little fixative can be injected into the uterine cavity to quicken the fixing action.

Ascaris uteri are fixed in alcoholic Bouin's; sometimes Carnoy will give desired results.

Whole Mounts

Whole mounts are slide mounts of entire specimens small enough to be studied *in toto* and mounted in resins in toluene or water, in gums or glycerine as aqueous mounts, or as dry mounts. Some examples from the innumerable methods will follow, with the hope that a technician can adapt them to almost any whole-mount venture.

FIXATION: 95% alcohol, followed by bleaching if necessary. From 70% alcohol into bleaching fluid (3–4 drops of *Clorox* in 10 ml. 70% alcohol, or water plus H_2O_2 (1:1) with a trace of ammonia): 24 hours.

PROCEDURE:
  1. Wash with 70% alcohol, 3 changes.
  2. Dehydrate in 95% and absolute alcohol.
  3. Clearing is often difficult. Try mixture of zylene and beechwood

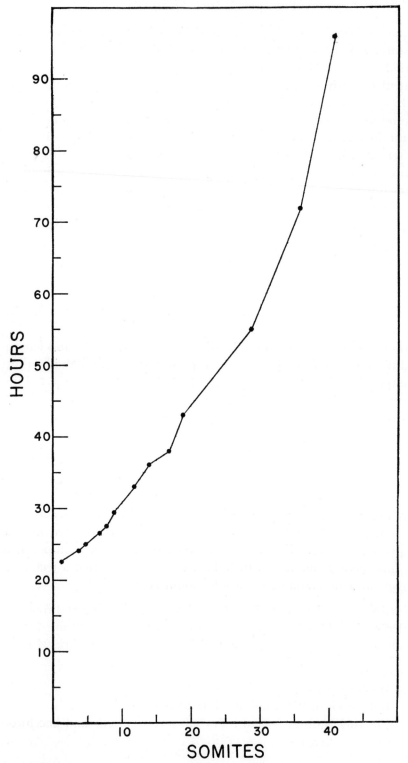

Figure 27. *Development of chick embryo.* [*From figures in Patten (1952).*]

380

creosote (or aniline or phenol) (prevents them from becoming brittle), 2 changes. If opaque patches persist, return them to absolute alcohol.

4. Impregnating with mountant can be difficult. Specimen may collapse and turn black or opaque when taken directly from alcohol or clearer to mountant. Impregnate gradually by adding each day a drop or two of mountant to the clearer containing the specimen. Carefully stir the mountant into the solution.

Galigher (1934) uses a cone of filter paper containing the mountant, and allows it to enter the solution gradually and continuously.

When the clearer has obviously thickened, allow concentration to continue by evaporation.

5. Mounting sometimes requires considerable experience (and patience) in judging the correct method and amount of mountant. Some specimens, large or delicate, should have supports under the cover glass, in the former case to prevent tilting of the cover glass, in the latter to lessen chances of smashed specimens. Various materials may be used to support the cover glass; bits of cover glass or slide, thin glass rods, circles, squares, or strips stamped or cut out of heavy aluminum foil, bits of glass wool.

Place a drop of mountant on slide and place specimen in it. Lower cover glass carefully; keep it flat (not tilted); have specimen in center of mount. If several specimens are to be mounted under one cover glass, chance of their slipping out of place is lessened by allowing the mountant to air dry for a few hours. Place a bit more mountant over them and add cover glass. Warming the cover glass aids in bubble prevention.

COMMENTS:

Demke (1952) embeds helminths in celloidin to support them. Dehydrate through absolute alcohol, alcohol-ether and into thin celloidin. Pour celloidin and specimens into flat dish (petri dish); allow solvent to evaporate slowly. Cut out squares of celloidin containing specimens, dehydrate, clear and mount. No other support of cover glass required.

Rubin (1951) uses PVA mounting medium, page 120. See other mounting media in that section.

Glycerol Jelly Mounts

Many materials, including frozen sections, may be mounted directly from water into glycerol jelly. If there is danger of an object collapsing, transfer it from 70% alcohol or water into a mixture of 10–15% glycerol in alcohol or water. Leave the dish uncovered until most of the alcohol or water has evaporated. Mount in glycerol jelly. Sections are mounted without cover glass support. Thicker specimens probably will require a supported cover glass. With a turntable spin a ring of gold size on the slide. Allow it to dry. If it is not high enough, add more layers to the height desired.

Melt glycerol jelly in water bath or in oven. Add a drop or two of jelly onto specimen inside ring. Use just enough to fill ring. Warm cover glass and ease horizontally into place. Carefully wipe off any glycerol jelly that works out from cover glass. After a few tries, it becomes relatively easy to estimate the correct amount of jelly to make a clean mount. Seal cover glass, supported or unsupported, with gold size or other cover glass sealer (page 123).

Hydra, Embryos, Flukes (stained whole mounts)

FIXATION: Many fixatives are suitable: Carnoy's or Gilson for worms, Bouin's or Zenker's for embryos, formol acetic or saturated $HgCl_2$ acetic (100/5). But before fixing consult the previous section on invertebrates or an authoritative source concerning the problem at hand.

Follow by proper washing and extraction of any undesirable pigments or crystals.

STAINING: Choice of stain also depends upon type of material. A few of wide usage will be included here.

Grenacher's Borax Carmine (GALIGHER, 1934)

SOLUTION:

carmine, C.I. 75470	3.0 gm.
borax	4.0 gm.
distilled water	100.0 ml.

Boil approximately 30 minutes or until carmine is dissolved. Mixture may be allowed to stand until this occurs. Add:

70% ethyl alcohol	100.0 ml.

Allow to stand 1–2 days. Filter.

PROCEDURE: (Hydra, flukes, tapeworms, small crustacea, etc.)

1. Transfer from 50% alcohol to borax carmine: 3–4 hours or overnight.

2. Add concentrated HCl, slowly, drop at a time, stirring, until carmine has precipitated and is brick red. Let stand 6–8 hours or overnight.

3. Add equal volume of 3% HCl in 70% alcohol and thoroughly mix. Let stand 2–3 minutes until specimens have settled. Draw off precipitated carmine with pipette. Add more acid alcohol, mix, allow to settle and draw off fluid. Repeat until most of carmine is removed.

4. Add fresh acid alcohol and allow to destain, checking at intervals under microscope: may require 2 hours or more. If exceedingly slow, increase percentage of acid in alcohol.

5. When destained, replace with 80% alcohol, several changes to remove acid: over a period of 1 hour.

6. Dehydrate, 90% alcohol: 30 minutes or more, depending on size of specimen; absolute alcohol: 30 minutes or more.

7. Clear. For delicate objects this probably should be done gradually through the following concentration of absolute alcohol and creosote (or aniline or carbol) xylene; and into pure creosote-xylene.

absolute alcohol	*creosote (aniline or carbol) xylene*
80 parts	20 parts
60	40
50	50
40	60
20	80
0	100

8. Mount. For exceedingly delicate objects and round worms, heed the warning above concerning slow impregnation with the mounting medium. Judgment concerning its use rests with experience, but slowness is invariably necessary for round worms.

Mayer's Carmalum (COWDRY, 1952)

SOLUTIONS:

Stock solution:

carminic acid (C.P. carmine) C.I. 75470	1.0 gm.
ammonium alum	10.0 gm.
distilled water	200.0 ml.

When dissolved, filter. Add:

formalin	1.0 ml.

Working solution:

carmalum stock .	5.0 ml.
glacial acetic acid	0.4 ml.
distilled water	100.0 ml.

PROCEDURE: stain for 48 hours, no destaining. Dehydrate as above. Carmalum is good and requires no destaining.

Hematein (KORNHAUSER, 1930)

SOLUTIONS:

Stock solution:

Grind 0.5 gm. hematein with 10 ml. 95% alcohol and add to 5% aqueous aluminum sulfate.

Working solution:

Dilute above 1:10 with distilled water.

PROCEDURE:
1. Stain overnight.
2. Transfer to 70% alcohol.
3. Destain in acid alcohol, 5% HCl in 70% alcohol.
4. Blue in alkaline alcohol, ammonia or sodium bicarbonate in 70% alcohol.
5. Dehydrate and mount as above.

Hematein is good for flatworms.
Alum cochineal used to be popular but has become largely replaced by carmine stains.
Alum hematoxylin may be used for small organisms if not too dense.
Celestin blue method, Demke (1952) may be used.

Protozoa

FIXATION: hot Schaudinn's, 50°C: 5–15 minutes. Other fixatives are formol Bouin's, acetic, or mercuric chloride acetic.

Organisms such as *Paramecium* should be concentrated by centrifuging. Quickly pour off some of the solution and add fixative. *Amoeba* will settle on the bottom of a clean culture dish. Decant off most of the culture media, leaving the bottom barely covered. Quickly pour hot Schaudinn's or Bouin's (50–60°C) over the organisms. After a few minutes add an equal amount of 85% alcohol. Carefully loosen any amoebae clinging to the bottom and collect the solution in a centrifuge tube. For both *Paramecium* and *Amoeba,* allow to settle or centrifuge down at low speed. Pour off fixative and wash several times with 70% alcohol, centrifuging after each wash. If a mercuric chloride fixative was used, one of the washes must contain some iodine.

The easiest method for handling is the cover glass method of *Chen* (*1944 A*).

PROCEDURE:
1. Follow the 70% washing with 80–85% alcohol: 10 minutes.
2. Smear cover glass with albumen fixative. Place them albumen-side up on slides with a bit of edge projecting beyond the slide. The projecting edge can be easily grasped with forceps when it becomes necessary to move the cover glass. With a pipette pick up a few drops of alcohol containing organisms. Drop them in the center of the cover glass, where they will spread over its surface. The alcohol will begin to evaporate and bring the specimens in contact with the albumen. Avoid complete drying; the edges may dry, but the center will remain slightly moist. Carefully add a couple of drops of 95% alcohol onto the specimens, and then transfer the cover glass to a petri dish of 95% alcohol. Slides lying in the bottom of the dish will help to handle the cover glasses, as above.
3. Carefully remove the cover glass from the 95% alcohol, dip it gently in absolute alcohol and then flood it with 1% celloidin or nitrocellulose. Drain off excess celloidin against filter paper. Wave it back and forth a few seconds until it begins to turn dull and place it in 70–80% alcohol. It can remain in this solution until ready for staining.
4. Any stain can be applied—hematoxylin, carmine, Feulgen—depending upon study to be undertaken.
5. The cover glasses are finally dehydrated, cleared, and mounted, albumen-specimen-side down on a drop of mounting resin.

COMMENTS:
The above method is excellent and rarely fails.

Smyth (*1944*) uses a quicker method and directly on slides. After fixation he carries the organisms through graded alcohols into absolute alcohol. This is dropped on a film of albumen on a slide. Place the slide in absolute alcohol and continue from there to the stain.

Agrell (*1958*) places suspensions of minute embryos on albumen-coated slide. Allowed to almost, but not quite, dry, they become flattened and in close contact with albumen. Dip into absolute alcohol, and then into fixative; place them horizontally in 95% alcohol vapor: 1 minute. Then fix. This coagulates the embryos and attaches them.

Animal Parasites

Animal organisms parasitic in or on man include protozoans, platyhelminths, nemathelminths, and arthropods. Clinical parasitology is extensive and therefore only a few methods which can expedite a tissue technician's work are incorporated here. Since the Romanowsky-type stains are used on blood parasites (malaria, trypanosomes, filaria, etc.) the preparation of smears is included in the section on hematologic elements (p. 218). Tissue sections can be stained in a similar manner. Parasitic roundworms (pinworms, *Trichuris, Ascaris,* hookworms), flatworms (lung, intestinal, bile duct and blood flukes, tapeworms) and arthropods (ticks, lice, mites) are discussed in the sections on invertebrates and whole mounts in this chapter. Methods given there can be adapted in most cases of parasitic helminths and arthropods. Sections of tissue parasitized by protozoans or helminths are effectively stained by hematoxylin methods, also by periodic acid-Schiff; protozoans and worms are strongly PAS positive due to stored glycogen in both forms, and PAS-positive cuticle in the helminths. The scolices hooks in hydatid disease (*Echinococcus*), however, do not show with PAS and are better demonstrated against a hematoxylin background. Ova and larvae can be handled according to directions given on page 374. Intestinal protozoa (amoebae, flagellates, ciliates, and coccidia) require the following special methods, both for smears and tissue sections.

Only permanent slide mounts are described. Consult clinical laboratory manuals for temporary and rapid examination methods for immediate diagnosis. *Gradwohl (1956)* is comprehensive.

Intestinal Protozoa: Smear Technics

Preparing Concentrate Smears (ARENSBURGER AND MARKELL, 1960)

PROCEDURE:

1. Add 1 ml. of feces to 10–15 times its volume of tap water. Mix well and strain through 2 layers of wet gauze in a funnel. Collect in a small centrifuge tube. Add 1–2 ml. of ether. Using a cork or thumb for a stopper, cautiously shake the tube. Fill with water to 1 cm. from top.

2. Centrifuge 45 seconds, 2500 rpm. Break up any plug at top and decant supernatant fluid.
3. Add 2–3 ml. of normal saline and shake to resuspend the sediment. Fill tube with normal saline to within 1 cm. of top and centrifuge.
4. Decant supernatant fluid. Take a small quantity of the original fecal specimen on the end of an applicator stick and mix well with sediment at bottom of tube.
5. With an applicator stick, transfer as much as possible of the material to a clean slide. Smear as for a conventionally made slide and fix immediately in Schaudinn's.
6. Stain as usual, hematoxylin, Lawless' method, etc.

Goldman (1949) Smears

FIXATION: Schaudinn's (page 21), 40°C: 5–15 minutes.

SOLUTIONS:

Stock solution *A*:

hematoxylin, 10% in 95% alcohol (10 gm./ 100 ml. 95% alcohol)	1.0 ml.
95% ethyl alcohol	99.0 ml.

Stock solution *B*:

ferric ammonium sulfate	4.0 gm.
glacial acetic acid	1.0 ml.
sulfuric acid, concentrated	0.12 ml.
distilled water	100.0 ml.

Working solution:

Equal parts of *A* and *B*. It turns purple, but within a few hours changes to dark brown. Then it should be filtered and is ready for use. If it turns greenish black, it is unsuitable for staining; the hematoxylin was too ripe and became overoxidized.

Hanson's Iron Trioxyhematein (page 127) may be used in same way.

PROCEDURE:

1. Rinse slides in 70% alcohol and treat with iodized alcohol.
2. Wash in several changes of 50% alcohol until brown color removed.
3. Stain in hematoxylin progressively: 3–5 minutes.
4. Wash in running water: 15–30 minutes.
5. Dehydrate, clear, and mount.

RESULTS:

protozoa—black nuclear stain

Kessel (1925) and Chen (1944A) Smears (modified)

FIXATION: Schaudinn's (page 21), 40°C: 10–15 minutes or more.

SOLUTIONS:

Iron alum:

ferric ammonium sulfate	4.0 gm.
distilled water	100.0 ml.

Hematoxylin.
Stock solution:

hematoxylin	1.0 gm.
absolute ethyl alcohol	10.0 ml.

Allow to ripen several months or hasten process (page 128).

Working solution:

hematoxylin stock solution	0.5 ml.
distilled water	99.5 ml.

Add 3 drops of saturated aqueous lithium carbonate. If the hematoxylin working solution looks rusty or muddy brown, it is unsatisfactory and will not stain efficiently.

PROCEDURE:

1. Transfer slides into 70% alcohol (from fixative): 2–3 minutes.
2. Treat with Lugol's solution: 2–3 minutes.
3. Wash in running water: 3 minutes.
4. Decolorize with 5% sodium thiosulfate: 2 minutes.
5. Wash in running water: 3–5 minutes.
6. Mordant in iron alum, 40°C: 15 minutes.
7. Wash in running water: 5 minutes.
8. Stain in hematoxylin, 40°C: 15 minutes.
9. Wash in running water: 5 minutes.
10. Destain in iron alum 2% (dilute stock 4% with distilled water, 1:1) until nuclei and chromatoidal bodies are sharp against colorless cytoplasm. Check under high dry objective.
11. Wash thoroughly in running water: 15–30 minutes.
12. Dehydrate, clear, and mount.

RESULTS:

nuclei, chromatoidal bodies—sharp blue black

COMMENTS:

Saturated aqueous picric acid may be used for destaining. Follow it with a rinse in dilute ammonia (2–3 drops/100 ml. water) and thorough washing in water.

Diamond (1945) added 1 drop of *Tergitol #7 (Carbide and Carbon Chemical Corporation)* to the diluted hematoxylin solution just before use (1 drop per 30–40 ml. solution). This he substituted for heat; it reduces surface tension and increases cell penetration. Reduced staining time to 5 minutes.

This method may be used for amoebae in tissue as well as in smears.

Lawless' Rapid Method (1953)

The staining method may be used for either Schaudinn's or Schaudinn-PVA fixed material.

SOLUTIONS:

Schaudinn's fixing fluid, see page 21.

Schaudinn-PVA fixative:

With stirrer going at high speed, sift 25 gm. PVA powder (*Elvanol*, grade 71–24[6]) into the vortex of a cool (20°C) solution of 312 ml. saturated aqueous mercuric chloride, 7.5 ml. glycerine, 25 ml. glacial acetic acid and 156 ml. 95% ethyl alcohol. After 10 minutes and while still stirring, heat in water bath to 75–85°C: 5–8 minutes, or until solution is complete. If solution gels during storage, warm in 56°C water bath. Some protozoa fix better in warm PVA fixative.

Stain:

chromotrope 2R, C.I. 16570	0.6 gm.
light green SF, yellowish, C.I. 42095	0.15 gm.
fast green FCF, C.I. 42053	0.15 gm.
phosphotungstic acid	0.7 gm.
glacial acetic acid	1.0 ml.
distilled water	100.0 ml.

Add acetic acid to dyes and phosphotungstic acid, let stand 15–30 minutes. Add water.

PROCEDURE:

A small portion of stool is fixed in PVA fixative (1 part stool to 3 parts fixative): 15 minutes to 1 hour or more. In this form it can be shipped in a vial. When ready to make slides, decant off excess PVA solution. Replace cap of vial and shake the emulsion. Remove cap and cover vial opening with gauze. Place 3 or 4 drops of strained material on cleansing tissue or blotter. Allow absorption of PVA for about 5 minutes. Scrape up moist residue and smear on slide or cover

[6] DuPont de Nemours and Co.

glass. Drop immediately into iodine-alcohol (page 12). If smears wash off, too much PVA was carried over; leave material for longer time on cleansing tissue.

Smears may be fixed directly on slides. Take 1 drop of fecal material to 3 drops of PVA fixative. Smear over a large area of the slide and dry in oven overnight. Immerse in iodine-alcohol.

1. Leave in iodine-alcohol: 1 minute.
2. Decolorize in 70% alcohol, 2 changes: 1–2 minutes each.
3. Stain: 5–10 minutes.
4. Differentiate in acidified 90% alcohol (1 drop glacial acetic acid/ 10 ml. alcohol): 10–20 seconds or until stain no longer runs from smear.
4. Dehydrate in absolute alcohol; rinse twice, dipping up and down.
6. Dehydrate in second change of absolute alcohol: 1 minute.
7. Clear and mount.

RESULTS:

background—predominantly green

cysts—bluish-green cytoplasm, purplish-red nuclei; green is more intense than background stain

engulfed red cells—vary, either green, red, or black

chromatoidal bodies—intense green, but may be reddish

COMMENTS:

If cysts do not stain or stain predominantly red, fixation is incomplete. Warming the fixative may help, although cold fixation yields more critical staining. A newly prepared stain is predominantly red in color and reaction; older stains show more violets and greens.

Warning: Press the cover glass in place very gently; the smear is somewhat brittle and is easily loosened. Too much pressure on the cover glass may start parts of the smear to floating around on the slide.

This stain does fade after a few years.

References: California State Department of Public Health, Bacteriology Department, Division of Laboratories, Berkeley, California; Gomori (1950) and Wheatley (1951)

Amoebae in Tissue

Meriweather (1934) Method

FIXATION: 10% formalin or a mercuric chloride fixative.

SOLUTION:

Carmine stock solution:

carmine, C.I. 75470	2.0 gm.
potassium carbonate	1.0 gm.
potassium chloride	5.0 gm.
distilled water	60.0 ml.

Boil gently for about 5 minutes, color should deepen.

Working solution:

carmine stock solution	20.0 ml.
ammonium hydroxide	30.0 ml.
methyl alcohol	30.0 ml.

PROCEDURE:

1. Hydrate slides to water, removing $HgCl_2$.
2. Stain in any preferred hematoxylin.
3. Wash in running water: 5 minutes.
4. Stain in carmine solution: 5 minutes.
5. Differentiate: 5 minutes, in:

absolute ethyl alcohol	80.0 ml.
methyl alcohol	40.0 ml.
distilled water	100.0 ml.

   Change solution if it becomes highly colored.
6. Dehydrate, clear, and mount.

RESULTS:

vegetative amoebae—highly stained with carmine, brilliant red; no cell in intestinal wall takes up carmine

COMMENTS:

Tomlinson and Grocott (1944) describe a phloxine-toluidine blue stain for malaria, *Leishmania,* microfilaria, and intestinal protozoa in tissue.

Chapter **24**

Special Procedures III

Special Mounts

Sections Mounted on Film. Pickett and Sommer (1960)

Pickett and Sommer use film in place of glass slides for supporting tissue sections. The flexibility of film and the low cost of material and time can be advantageous. Many sections mounted on a long strip of film are stained in one process by using a developing reel and then are plastic-sprayed as a unit instead of having to be individually cover-slipped. A length of film can be stored in a small space, and single sections or groups of sections can be clipped or stapled to records or reports, and filed or shipped in envelopes. Film with section also can be mounted in film holders. If desired, one section of a series can be mounted on film and a successive section mounted on glass. Sections already mounted on film can be cut out of it and mounted on glass slides in the conventional manner. Section details are clear under low and medium power. For oil-immersion or high-power examination, a cover glass should be mounted on the section with a nondrying immersion oil (cedar oil dissolves plastic). Only low-power projection can be used with this film. Pickett and Sommer include the design of a holder to keep the film flat while being scanned under the microscope.

REQUIRED MATERIALS:
35 mm. film, Cronar, P-40B leader film, E. I. DuPont
Krylon Plastic Spray, Crystal Clear Spray Coating #1302, Krylon
  Inc., Norristown, Pennsylvania
Nikor 35 mm. developing reel, stainless steel

PROCEDURE:

1. Cut strips of film of desired length; clean by dipping in acid alcohol; dry with soft cloth (not gauze).
2. Coat film with albumen fixative.
3. (*a*) Place tissue sections on water bath, maneuver film under ribbon and pick up sections. Dry in 56° oven.
   (*b*) Film can be cut in 3×1 in. strips; lay on glass slide; smear with albumen. Place section on film, pipette water under it and dry on slide warmer as usual for slides.
4. After drying, load lengths of film in reel and stain as usual. Short pieces can be handled individually. To guard against loose sections, protect with coating of 0.5% celloidin or nitrocellulose. Proceed as follows:
   (*a*) Xylene: 1–2 minutes.
   (*b*) Absolute alcohol: 1–2 minutes.
   (*c*) 0.5% celloidin: 5 minutes.
   (*d*) Air dry: 3–4 minutes.
   (*e*) 80% alcohol: 5 minutes.
   (*f*) Wash and stain.
   (*g*) Dehydrate through 95% alcohol.
   (*h*) Mixture of $\frac{1}{3}$ chloroform and $\frac{2}{3}$ absolute alcohol, 2 changes.
   (*i*) Xylene.
5. Place face up on a blotter; do not allow to dry. The film must lie flat; buckling results in uneven plastic coat. Use weights along edges. Apply spray quickly from end to end, 2–3 times until surface appears smooth. Hold can about 6 inches above film. Allow to harden: 5–10 minutes. Repeat 2–3 times. Allow to dry.
6. Label with India ink if desired.

COMMENTS:

Mylar polyester film (DuPont), 0.25 mm. thick also has been recommended for use (*Johnston, 1960*).

Burstone and Flemming (1959) recommend film for smears, touch preparations and sprayed-on suspensions. Adherence is excellent and the preparations can be floated on incubation media, staining solutions, etc. The film can be mounted in glycerine jelly, or water-soluble plastics.

Berton and Phillips (1961) use film for tissue cultures. The live cells attach and adhere firmly to film.

Cellulose Tape Mounting. Palmgren (1954)

This method has been devised for problem sections, such as tissues containing a large amount of yolk, chitinous material, hard tissue which breaks away from soft parts and falls out of sections. Cellulose tape (Scotch Tape) is pressed firmly on the section surface of the paraffin block or the tissue frozen on the freezing microtome. The sticky surface of the tape attaches to all parts of the section and prevents its wrinkling or shattering during sectioning; 1-micron to 100-micron cuts will perform equally well. Using this method Palmgren has cut whole adult mice for radiography on the freezing microtome without loss of parts. The sticky material is soluble in xylene so the paraffin cannot be dissolved while on the tape, making it preferable to transfer the sections to a glass slide or plate.

PROCEDURE:
1. Mount section and tape with section-side upwards on glass. Hold it in place with small strips of tape, but do not cover the section.
2. Spread a thin layer of 0.5% nitrocellulose over the section, but not over the tape. Let dry.
3. Immerse in xylene in a petri dish, and leave until the nitrocellulose film and section can be loosened easily from the tape. Leave in xylene a little longer to remove all sticky material.
4. Smear clean slide liberally with albumen fixative. Float section on it and press in place. Blot dry.
5. Transfer immediately to absolute alcohol-ether (1:1) and leave until nitrocellulose is dissolved. Section should be adhering to slide.
6. Transfer to 95% alcohol, hydrate to water, and stain.

COMMENTS:
Frozen section either must be dried (for radioautographs) or carried from water up to absolute alcohol before the nitrocellulose is applied for histological staining.

Serial sections can be made by adding sections in sequence to continuous tape, rolled at each end of tissue block.

Laminated Thermoplastic Mounts. LaCroix
and Preiss (1690)

LaCroix and Preiss describe a practical and simple plastic mounting method for chromosome smears, whole mounts, and cross and sagittal sections. The cellular detail is good and the plastic mounting makes these preparations practical for class study and demonstration. No danger of breakage is involved, and if the plastic gets marred, the scratches can be polished away.

APPARATUS:

Photo-Seal Kit (Therm Appliance Manufacturing Company, 608 S. First Street, St. Charles, Illinois): consists of an electric sealing press of two 4″ × 5″ aluminum platens with a 300W, 115V heater cast into the bottom platen, two 4″ × 5″ nickeloid polished plates and other necessary accessories.

PROCEDURE:

Root tip preparations:
1. Fix, hydrolyze, dehydrate and stain.
2. Arrange root tips in a drop of stain on a sheet of clear Vinylite plastic, 1″ × 3″ and 15 mils thick.
3. Cover with a second sheet of plastic.
4. Place preparation between two sheets of bibulous paper, and apply pressure.
5. When spread, remove papers and top piece of plastic; add identification label if desired, and a third clean piece of plastic.
6. Place between plates of electric press, tighten wing bolts, and heat for 3 minutes.
7. Cool under running water, and remove preparation from between plates.

Section mounts:
1. Mount on plastic in same manner as on glass slide.
2. Dissolve paraffin in carbon tetrachloride: 20 minutes.
3. Hydrate, stain, dehydrate and clear. A short stay in xylene will not dissolve the Vinylite.
4. Place second sheet on top, and laminate.

COMMENTS:

The nickeloid plates can be protected from tarnishing with aluminum foil sheets.

Autoradiography

The use of radioactive isotopes as tracers, localizing in an organ, a tissue, or individual cell, has pushed autoradiography into a position of considerable importance. The rays and particles of the isotope in tissue sections produce an image on photographic emulsion. After photographic processing, the emulsion can be studied by conventional light microscopic methods, and a comparison and correlation made with stained sections.

Only a brief summary of methods will be discussed and some references included. All kinds of material can be used. Sections of large bone can be exposed to roentgen-ray film; sections on slides, smeared and squashed material, can be exposed to a covering of stripping or fluid emulsion and tissue cultures can be placed against an emulsion to make an exposure.

As to *fixation,* formalin usually is satisfactory, but solutions containing mercuric chloride should be avoided; they produce artifacts on the emulsion (*Kaminski, 1955*). Solubilities of isotopes must be checked carefully; some leach out in water or paraffin solvents and must be prepared by freeze-drying methods (*Holt and Warren, 1953*). In some cases carbowax can be used, but it will dissolve water-soluble isotopes (*Holt et al., 1949, 1952; Holt and Warren, 1950, 1953*). Mounting must be handled with care to prevent leaching (*Gallimore et al., 1954*).

Witten and Holmstrom (1953) freeze the tissue at the microtome immediately after excision. The knife is kept cold with dry ice, keeping the section frozen after it is cut. Then the section is carried still frozen to the photographic emulsion. As the section thaws it produces a bit of moisture and thereby adheres to the emulsion.

Bone must *not* be decalcified for this process. Some of the best technics for bone use methacrylate or epoxy embedding before sectioning. (*Arnold and Jee, 1954A, 1954B; Norris and Jenkins, 1960;* and *Woodruff and Norris, 1955*)

There are various methods of assuring contact between specimen and emulsion.

PROCEDURE:

1. The specimen or slide bearing a specimen can be placed directly on the emulsion, or it may first be protected by a layer of 1% celloidin in amyl acetate and then be placed on the emulsion (*Holt and Warren, 1950*).

2. Sections can be mounted directly on the emulsion on a slide.

(a) "Stripping film" method:

"Stripping film" emulsion is removed from its glass plate. First the edges of the emulsion are cut with a razor blade and the emulsion can be peeled off and floated on distilled water with 1% Dupanol (wetting agent) added. Then the slide with the section uppermost is slipped under the emulsion and lifted out carrying the emulsion with it. To hold the emulsion in place without slipping it is folded under three sides of the slide, dried in place and the exposure made. (*Bogoroch, 1951; Pelc, 1956;* and *Simmel, 1957*)

(*b*) *Dipping in fluid emulsion:*

This is simpler than the above method. Mounted sections protected by a celloidin coat are dipped in a liquid emulsion, dried and left in the exposure box for the proper time. (*Messier and Leblon, 1957;* and *Joftes, 1959*)

COMMENTS:

In either (*a*) or (*b*) method, the film is developed, fixed, and covered or sprayed with *Krylon*.

At all times when working with photographic emulsions darkroom safety measures must be observed (*Wratten Safelight #2*).

Staining:

Sections used for autographs can be stained. *Pelc* (*1956*) has used celestin blue and hematoxylin, neutral red and carbol fuchsin, hematoxylin and eosin, carmalum, Giemsa, toluidine blue, and methyl green-pyronin. Some workers find stains confusing because the emulsion gelatine absorbs them. *Simmel et al.* (*1951*) used metanil yellow and hematoxylin with clearer results. Feulgen staining can be used. (Also see *Mérei and Gallyas, 1960*)

Most autoradiographs should be protected by glycerol jelly mounting, *Krylon* spraying or dehydration, clearing and mounting in a resin.

General Reference: Fitzgerald *et al.* (1953)

Electron Microscopy

Among the methods in use for investigators in biological and medical fields, one of the newest and fastest growing is electron microscopy. By 1940 several electron microscopes had been developed in different parts of the world. *Knoel and Ruska* in Germany had a practical marketable research scope by 1939. England began work in 1936 and *RCA* in the United States started to develop one in 1938, and had one on the market in 1941. *RCA* also has developed a desk model. In the last few years the means of cutting sections down to 1/20 micron have become reliable.

The electron microscope has a higher resolving power than the light microscope and has revealed submicroscopic structures invisible until the present time. It uses electrons as the illuminating beam, and focuses the beam on the object by the use of magnets. As the beam passes through the object under observation, some of the electrons are scattered by the object causing shadows of the scattered electrons on photographic film.

Electron beams must be handled in vacuum, therefore no wet or living tissue ordinarily can be observed. Sections must be thin to prevent appreciable electron absorption, because the image depends on the differential scattering rather than absorption.

Specimen Supports

The specimen is supported on a metal grid and is placed in the column at the electron-gun side of the object-lens aperture. This mechanical support is made of electron-opaque metal (copper, nickel or steel) permitting observation of the specimen through holes in the grid. A mesh of 200 holes per linear inch is satisfactory and provides holes small enough to support a thin film yet offers a large enough area for observation. England prepares an excellent grid with a center marker and a solid periphery (obtainable from *Ernest Fullam, Schenectady, N.Y.*).

All specimens must be placed on some supporting **film**, supported in turn on the grid. This film has to be transparent to the electron beam but strong enough to not tear when bombarded by the beam. Various materials have been used, but **celloidin** and **formvar** are favored. **Carbon** films are becoming popular, but are difficult to prepare (*Watson, 1956; Barton, 1960*).

Preparation of Film

Either celloidin, 1% in amyl acetate, or formvar, 0.2% in ethylene dichloride (1,2 dichloroethane) is flowed on a clean dry microscope slide, or the slide is dipped in the solution (slide may be previously treated with a water repellant). Evaporate film on slide and when dry float film off on surface of water. Place grids, convex side down, on film. Lower a clean slide on top of grids and sweep the slide through the water bringing out with it the grids lying between the film and the slide. Allow to dry. Grids can be left on the slide until used. The film also may be cast directly on the surface of the water, the grids placed on it and removed as above. The former method, however, forms a tougher film (*Mellors, 1959*). Formvar makes a stronger and more temperature-stable film than celloidin, but the solutions deteriorate rapidly unless kept in the refrigerator.

The grids are tiny and are most easily handled with stainless steel eye forceps. The forceps tips can be bent slightly and sharpened with fine emery paper for a delicate grip. Forceps with the bottom jaw sharpened to a knife-edge will help to lift grids from a flat surface (*Hall, 1953*).

Fixation

In order to increase the scattering of electrons, the density of the specimen must be increased—some sort of reagent must be applied to it. For these so-called "electron stains" chemicals of high atomic number have been tried, compounds of heavy metals (tungsten and osmium in particular) using phosphotungstic acid and osmic acid. *Pease and Baker (1950)* concluded that osmic acid was the "outstanding" fixative. *Luft (1956)* used potassium permanganate for membrane systems in particular.

Osmic Fixation

In this method, 1–2% osmic is buffered with either I or II below, *p*H 7.4:

SOLUTIONS:

I. *Edwards et al. (1956)*; *Palade (1952)*:

0.14M sodium acetate and sodium veronal	5.0 ml.
0.1N HCl	5.0 ml.
1–2% osmic acid	12.5 ml.
With distilled water make up to	25.0 ml.

II. *Sjostrand (1956)*:

Buffer solution *A*:

sodium acetate	9.714 gm.
sodium veronal	14.714 gm.
distilled water	500.0 ml.

Buffer solution *B*:

sodium chloride	40.25 gm.
potassium chloride	2.1 gm.
calcium chloride	0.9 gm.
distilled water	500.0 ml.

Isotonic buffered osmic acid (working solution):

solution *A*	10.0 ml.
solution *B*	3.4 ml.
0.1N HCl	11.0 ml.
distilled water	50.0 ml.

Adjust to *p*H 7.4 with 0.1N HCl

Add osmic acid	0.5 gm.

Store in brown-glass stoppered bottle in refrigerator.

METHOD:

1. Cut tissue in small fragments, 5 mm.; fix immediately. In spite of the small size only the outer cells will be well fixed. Fix 30 minutes to 4 hours minimum = maximum interval), 0–5°C.
2. Wash with Ringer's solution: 1 hour, changing every 15 minutes.
3. Dehydrate and embed.

Permanganate Fixation (LUFT, 1956)

SOLUTIONS:

Stock solution:

potassium permanganate	1.2 gm.
distilled water	100.0 ml.

Store in refrigerator in well-filled glass-stoppered bottle.

Working solution:

Equal volumes of potassium permanganate stock and Palade's veronal acetate buffer (above), *p*H 7.4–7.6, produces a final concentration of 0.6% potassium permanganate.

METHOD:

1. Cool fixative in cracked ice. Fix 1–2 mm. pieces at 0°C: 15 minutes to 12 hours.
2. Rinse several minutes in cold (0–5°C) 25% ethyl alcohol, allow to warm to room temperature in fresh 25% alcohol (15–20 minutes).
3. Dehydrate and embed.

Chromium Fixation (LOW, 1955; LOW AND FREEMAN, 1956)

Good for reticulum.

SOLUTION:

chromic acid	3.0 gm.
formalin	10.0 ml.
sodium chloride	0.85 gm.

*p*H about 3.2

METHOD:
1. Short fixation best: 0.25–0.5 hour.
2. Wash: 0.5 hour, in distilled water.
3. Dehydrate and embed.

Chromium-Osmium Fixation (DALTON, 1955)

SOLUTION:

chromic acid, 4%	10.0 ml.
sodium chloride, 3.4%	10.0 ml.
Add osmic acid, 2%	20.0 ml.

Can be used for longer period than some of others (18–24 hours) and is good for tissue of high lipid content, but produces lower contrast and increased difficulty in obtaining thin sections.

Lehmann and Mancuso's Fixative (1957)

SOLUTIONS:
Solution I:

20% formalin	80.0 ml.
acetone	16.0 ml.
glacial acetic acid	0.5 ml.

Solution II:

2.5% osmic acid, aqueous

METHOD:
1. Mix equal parts of solutions I and II. Fix for 30 minutes. This is recommended for preservation of fibrous cytoplasmic structures; penetrates rapidly and partially dehydrates.
2. A subsequent treatment with chromic acid improves preservation of some lipid and fibrous structures. After 20 minutes in original fixative, add 10% chromic acid (2 ml. for every 5 ml. of above). Leave for additional 20 minutes.
3. Rinse in tap water: 15 minutes, dehydrate and embed.

Embedding

Only plastic embedding permits sections of 0.01 to 0.05 microns to be cut. *Glauert and Glauert (1958)* recommend the epoxy resin *Araldite,* saying that there is greater stability of resin, less shrinkage of tissue, greater degree of variation possible in viscosity of mixture, less tendency to form bubbles and greater hardness and uniformity of block than is true of other plastics. The required solutions can be obtained as a *Cargille (Nysem) Epoxy Embedding Kit* from *Cargille Sons, Little Falls, N.J.* Full directions for use are enclosed with the kit. (Also see *Richardson et al., 1960*)

Pease (1960) disagrees with the above, saying that the epoxy resin forms brittle blocks, causing cutting artifacts and producing poor contrast in some specimens. Biological systems should be "stained" when embedded in it. "Epon" epoxy resins are being developed; at the present he prefers methacrylate embedding, although the methacrylate decomposes under electron bombardment.

Butyl Methacrylate Embedding (NEWMAN, BORYSKO, AND SWERDLOW, 1949)

METHOD:

1. From fixative, quick rinse in salt solution or veronal buffer such as fixative ions prepared in.
2. Dehydrate in 50, 75, and 95% alcohol: 3–5 minutes each. Several changes of absolute alcohol, at least 2 changes: 5–10 minutes; 1 change: 15–20 minutes.
3. Transfer to equal volumes of absolute ethyl alcohol and n-butyl methacrylate monomer[7]: about 1 hour.
4. Transfer to monomer (no catalyst) 3 changes: 1 hour each.
5. Set body of #00 gelatine capsule upright in wooden block or other base. Fill with monomer plus 1% (by weight) of catalyst (2,4-dichlorobenzoyl peroxide[8]). Orient tissue in it and slip on lid.
6. Place in oven, 45–50°C. Important that capsule be heated evenly over entire surface. Suspend with cellophane tape from rod or other support inside oven. Within 6–8 hours a solid matrix of polymerized monomer has formed. Additional period of several hours insures complete polymerization.
7. Soak in water and peel off capsule.

COMMENTS:

The n-butyl methacrylate contains an inhibitor which must be removed by repeated washings in a separatory funnel with dilute aqueous sodium carbonate until no color is visible in the washings. Follow with calcium chloride to remove the water. Keep in the refrigerator to inhibit polymerization. Do not use rubber or plastic container for storing.

[7] Rohm and Haas Co., Philadelphia.
[8] Lucidol Division, Novadel-Agene Corporation, Buffalo.

Pease (1960) makes the following suggestions: make solution changes, fixation, dehydration, etc. in small wide-mouthed weighing bottles. He considers the blocks formed by pure butyl methacrylate as too soft and adds anywhere from 10 to 30% of ethyl methacrylate to his solution. The catalyst dissolves slowly and must be complete before the solution is placed in the capsules. He recommends polymerization by ultraviolet light, saying that it forms a block superior to that formed by heat. It is more uniform and has fewer bubbles. Use a *Westinghouse Fluorescent Sun Lamp bulb, #5TT12* about 1 inch from the capsules.

Ultrathin Sectioning

Conventional-type microtomes have been modified for ultrathin sections. *Pease and Baker (1948); Newman, Borysko and Swerdlow (1949); Newman (1950); Geren and McCullock (1951); Nylen and Holland (1957)*. Three good specially designed microtomes are available:

1. *Porter and Blum (1953)* utilizes a cantilever action, is manufactured and distributed by *Ivan Sorvall, Inc., Norwalk, Conn.*
2. *Sjostrand* utilizes a thermal expansion feed and is motor driven, is manufactured by *LKB Produkter in Stockholm*, is handled by *Sorvall*.
3. *Reichert of Austria* also manufactures one.

KNIVES

Steel knives must be exceedingly sharp, but are dulled rapidly by plastic cutting.

Glass knives are popular and cheap. They can be made from 3/16 inch or ¼ inch plate glass, shaped as rhomboidal equilateral parallelograms with a cutting edge of 45° *(Porter and Blum, 1953)*, and fitted in a specially designed holder *(Cameron, 1956 and Sheldon, 1957)*. They dull rapidly but are easily replaceable; they can be made in the laboratory or purchased from *Acme Glass Company, Cambridge, Massachusetts*. *Gavin and Lloyd (1959)* recommend a *vycor brand* glass for less scratching in the sections. The angle between front side of the knife and the plane of the passing section should not exceed 10°, preferably 3–50. *Sjostrand* uses a hand-sharpened Schick razor blade in a special holder.

Diamond knives (Fernandez-Moran, 1953, 1956; Crandall, 1961) are more durable but are expensive. *Sorvall* carries them.

SECTIONING

Recovery of sections was difficult until *Hillier and Gettner (1950)* developed a water trough attached to the knife, thereby permitting the sections to float directly onto a fluid surface as soon as they were cut. The trough is filled with 10–40% acetone or ethyl alcohol in water to facilitate the flattening (also see *Solelo, 1957*). The sections are picked up from the solution onto the coated grids, or, if somewhat compressed, are transferred first to 50% alcohol and then to grids.

For serial sections see *Gay and Anderson (1954), Williams and Kallman (1954),* and *Westfall (1961).*

The thickness of the sections can be determined by the color analysis of *Porter and Blum (1953).* While the sections float on the bath, they display interference colors depending on their thickness. Silver indicates a thickness of 20–50 millimicra; gold, 50–80 millimicra; purple, 80–130 millimicra. Silver and gold sections are best for electron microscopy, but as they begin to appear blue or green they are getting too thick for efficient observation.

Three-dimensional images may be obtained by metal shadowing and this is finding favor with many researchers. Metals, such as silver, chromium, palladium, platinum and others are evaporated on the specimen at a small angle. A thin film of the metal covers the specimen except for a "shadow" caused by the specimen being in the way of passage of the metal. From the shape and dimension of the shadow, height and contour of the specimen can be observed. (*Williams and Wyckoff, 1944; Williams and Backus, 1949; de Harven, 1958*)

Plastic sections can be used for *optical examination.* The sections (1–2 microns) are dried on a slide, immersed (12–24 hours) in xylene to remove the plastic and then can be stained for *light microscopy,* or mounted for *phase microscopy.* (*Borysko and Sapranauskas, 1954; Farquhar and Rinehart, 1954;* and *Houcks and Dempsey, 1954*)

See also *Fernandez-Moron (1960)* for the application of *low temperature techniques* for electron microscopy utilizing HELIUM II. In addition, this source describes the use of a *liquid nitrogen stage* for cooling specimens during observation in the electron microscope.

References: Farquhar (1956), Hall (1953), Mellors (1959), and Pease (1960).

PART IV

SOLUTION PREPARATION AND GENERAL LABORATORY AIDS

Section **1**

Solution Preparation

Abbreviations and Terms

Abbreviations

ml. (cc)—milliliter, cubic centimeter
gm.—gram
mg.—milligram
aq.—aqueous
M—molecular solution, see below
N—normal solution, see below

Molecular Solutions (COWDRY, 1952)

A **molecular** solution contains the molecular weight in grams of the substance made up to 1 liter with distilled water. For example: **M** oxalic acid $(COOH)_2 \cdot 2H_2O$ is 126 grams (molecular weight) in 1 liter of water.

Molecular weight expressed in grams is called the **gram-molecular** weight or **mole**. A **millimole** is 1/1000 of a mole.

Normal Solutions

A **normal** solution contains 1 gram-molecular weight of dissolved substance divided by the hydrogen equivalent of the substance (that is, 1 gram equivalent) per liter of solution. **N** oxalic acid is half the concentration of the **M** solution above.

Percentage Solutions

In the case of percentage solutions, it should be indicated in some way as to whether the percentage is determined by weight or volume: either written out in grams and milliliters or expressed thus:

w/v means weight in grams in a 100 ml. volume of solution
v/v means volume in milliliters in 100 ml. total volume of solution

Although it is erroneous, a long-established habit of technicians is maintained. Percentage solutions of liquids are diluted as though the reagent solution is 100% concentration. That is, a 1% solution of acetic acid is 1 ml. of glacial acetic acid in 99 ml. of distilled water. In most procedures the dilution is indicated in parentheses following the percentage desired.

Dilutions for 1N Solutions.*

	Molecular weight	Percentage assay	Specific gravity	gm per liter	ml per liter
acetic	60.05	99.7–*100*†	1.0498	1050	57.2
acid		99.0	1.0524	1042	57.6
CH₃COOH		98.0	1.0549	1034	58.0
ammonium	17.03	26	0.904	235	72.4
hydroxide		28†	0.8980	251.4	67.7
NH₄OH		30	0.8920	267.6	63.63
formic	46.03	96	1.217	1180	39.3
acid		98†	1.2183	1194	38.4
HCOOH		99	1.2202	1208	38.0
		100	1.2212	1221	37.6
hydrochloric	36.46	36	1.1789	424.4	85.9
acid		37–*38*†	1.188–1.192	451.6 *	80.4
HCl		40	1.1980	479.2	76.0
nitric	63.02	69	1.4091	972.3	64.8
acid		70†	1.4134	989.4	63.6
HNO₃		71	1.4176	1006	62.6
		72	1.4218	1024	61.5
sulfuric	98.075	95	1.8337	1742	28.1
acid		96†	1.8355	1762	27.8
H₂SO₄		97	1.8364	1781	27.5

* Calculated from Norbert Adolph Lange, 1956, Handbook of Chemistry, Handbook Publishers Inc., Sandusky, Ohio. *Italicized* numbers indicate figures used in calculations.
† Indicate most common form of the reagent. In addition, a calculation has been made for the nearest lower and higher percentages as well.

To make a normal solution, add to the ml. in the right-hand column enough distilled water to make a combined total of 1 liter. This will be accurate enough for histological preparations.

Stock Solutions

The solutions included under this title are probably found (with a few exceptions) on most histology laboratory shelves.

Three physiological solutions are included to offer a choice, depending on the particular need of the type of research in progress. The use of physiological solutions can be imperative at times. A *normal* solution (**isotonic**) contains the proper amount of salts to maintain tissues in a normal condition. For instance, red blood cells will remain unaltered in form and will not experience a loss of hemoglobin if isotonic fluids are used with the cells. The osmotic pressure and salt content of the physiological solution and of the blood fluid is the same. If the solution is **hypotonic,** the osmotic pressure and salt content is less than that of the body fluids and the cells will swell. If the solution is **hypertonic,** the osmotic pressure and salt content is greater than that of the body fluids, and the cells will shrink. Plain distilled water will be hypotonic until the proper quantity of salt has been added.

Just as physiological solutions are useful for land vertebrates, so are environmental solutions convenient for some invertebrates. In the case of marine invertebrates, such solutions can become necessary for successful preparations and sometimes are recommended as the basic fluid for fixing solutions. Among the physical properties of sea water, the salt content has to be considered. It varies and is complex, but an arbitrary definition of salt content (**salinity**) has been calculated. Salinity (S 0/00) equals the weight in grams (*in vacuo*) of solids in 1 kilogram of sea water. The major constituent, which is easily determined, is silver-precipitating halides. **Chlorinity** (Cl 0/00) is defined as the weight in grams (*in vacuo*) of chlorides in 1 kilogram of sea water. Standard sea water is about 19.4 0/00 chlorinity and 34.3243 0/00 salinity. (*Barnes, 1954*)

Not all of the adhesive or buffer solutions will be found or required in every laboratory: however, a listing of the more widely used ones seems practical. Then if a need should arise, the information is at hand.

Stain solubilities are only occasionally useful, but they are definitely needed when a saturated solution must be made.

ACID ALCOHOL.

    70% ethyl alcohol .... 100.0 ml.

    hydrochloric acid, concentrated .... 1.0 ml.

ALKALINE ALCOHOL.

    70% ethyl alcohol .... 100.0 ml.

    ammonia, concentrated .... 1.0 ml.

(or saturated aqueous sodium or lithium bicarbonate)

CARBOL-XYLOL.

    phenol (carbolic acid) melted .... 1 part

    xylene .... 3 parts

During use, keep covered to reduce evaporation of xylene.
For *creosote-xylol* use beechwood creosote in place of phenol. For
aniline-xylol use aniline.

GOLD CHLORIDE STOCK SOLUTION.

    gold chloride .... 1.0 gm.

    distilled water .... 100.0 ml.

LUGOL'S SOLUTION. There are various formulas to which this name has
been applied.

a. The strongest concentration is:

    iodine crystals .... 1.0 gm.

    potassium iodide .... 2.0 gm.

    distilled water .... 12.0 ml.

b. Weigert's variation:

    iodine .... 1.0 gm.

    potassium iodide .... 2.0 gm.

    distilled water .... 100.0 ml.

c. Gram's variation:

    iodine .... 1.0 gm.

    potassium iodide .... 2.0 gm.

    distilled water .... 300.0 ml.

In all cases, first dissolve the potassium iodide, then the iodine will
go into solution readily.

PHYSIOLOGICAL SOLUTIONS

Physiological Saline—NaCl in distilled water

    mammals, 0.9% (9 gm./1000 ml. water)

    birds, 0.75% (7.5 gm./1000 ml. water)

salamander, 0.8% (8 gm./1000 ml. water)

frogs, 0.64% (6.4 gm./1000 ml. water)

Locke's Solution

sodium chloride	0.85 gm.
(for cold-bloods, 0.65 gm.)	
potassium chloride	0.042 gm.
sodium bicarbonate	0.02 gm.
calcium chloride	0.024 gm.
distilled water	100.0 ml.

Ringer's Solution

sodium chloride	0.9 gm.
(for cold-bloods, 0.65 gm.)	
potassium chloride	0.042 gm.
calcium chloride	0.025 gm.
distilled water	100.0 ml.

Best prepared fresh.

ARTIFICIAL SEA WATER, HALE (1958).

chlorinity, 19 0/00

salinity, 34.33 0/00

$NaCl$		23.991 gm.
KCl		0.742 gm.
$CaCl_2$		1.135 gm.
($CaCl_2 \cdot 6H_2O$	2.240 gm.)	
$MgCl_2$		5.102 gm.
($MgCl_2 \cdot 6H_2O$	10.893 gm.)	
Na_2SO_4		4.012 gm.
($Na_2SO_4 \cdot 10H_2O$	9.1 gm.)	
$NaHCO_3$		0.197 gm.
$NaBr$		0.085 gm.
($NaBr \cdot 2H_2O$	0.115 gm.)	
$SrCl_2$		0.011 gm.
($SrCl_2 \cdot 6H_2O$	0.018 gm.)	
H_3BO_3		0.027 gm.

Dissolve in distilled water and make up to 1 liter.

Note: The weights in the right-hand column are for the anhydrous form of the salt; those in parentheses have water of crystallization present, as indicated on the reagent bottle.

SCOTT's SOLUTION.

sodium bicarbonate	2.0 gm.
magnesium sulfate	20.0 gm.
distilled water	100.0 ml.

Add a pinch of thymol to retard molds.

SODIUM THIOSULFATE SOLUTION (hypo), 5%

sodium thiosulfate $Na_2S_2O_3$	5.0 gm.
distilled water	100.0 ml.

CLEANING SOLUTION FOR GLASSWARE.

Strong:

potassium dichromate	20.0 gm.
water	200.0 ml.

Dissolve dichromate in water; when cool add very slowly:

sulfuric acid, concentrated	20.0 ml.

Weak:

potassium dichromate, 2% aqueous	9 parts
sulfuric acid	1 part

Sufficiently strong for most purposes.

Adhesive Solutions

Mayer's Albumen Fixative

Beat white of an egg (only until well broken up, but not stiff) with egg beater and pour into tall cylinder. Let stand until the air brings suspended material to the top (overnight). Pour off liquid from bottom and to it add an equal volume of glycerol. A bit of sodium salicylate, thymol, merthiolate, or formalin (1:100) will prevent growth of molds. Many technicians filter their solution through glass wool, but the author has found this of no advantage.

Faulkner and Lillie (1945B) substitute dried egg white. A 5% solution of dried egg white in 0.5% NaCl is shaken at intervals for one day. Do not allow it to froth. Filter in a small Buchner funnel with vacuum. Add an equal amount of glycerol and 0.5 ml. of 1:10,000 merthiolate to each 100 ml. of solution.

Masson's Gelatine Fixative

gelatine	50.0 gm. mg
distilled water	25.0 ml.

Recommended by many for *alkaline silver techniques,* when sections tend to float off during or after impregnation. Float sections on solution on slide, and place on warm plate. When sections have spread, drain off excess gelatine and blot dry with filter paper. Place in formalin vapor, 40–50°C overnight.

Haupt's Gelatine Fixative (1930)

gelatine	1.0 gm.
distilled water	100.0 ml.

Dissolve at 30°C (not above) in water bath or oven. Add:

phenol (carbolic acid) crystals	2.0 gm.
glycerol	15.0 ml.

Stir well, and filter.

Use 2% formalin when mounting sections. This hardens the gelatine; water is not adequate. Some may find the formalin fumes to be irritating to the eyes and nostrils.

Haupt suggests that if sections tend to loosen, place a small uncovered dish of concentrated formalin in an oven with the slides while drying them. The formalin tends to make the gelatine insoluble and helps to hold the sections in place.

Weaver's Gelatine Fixative (1955)

SOLUTION A:

gelatine	1.0 gm.
calcium propionate[1]	1.0 gm.
Roccal (1% benzalkonium chloride)	1.0 ml.
distilled water	100.0 ml.

SOLUTION B:

chrome alum ($Cr_2K_2(SO_4)_4 \cdot 24H_2O$)	1.0 gm.
distilled water	90.0 ml.
formalin	10.0 ml.

Mix in proportions of 1 part of A to 9 parts of B. Flood slide with adhesive mixture, add paraffin ribbons, and allow to stretch as usual. Drain off excess adhesive and blot. Wipe edges close to paraffin. Deposits of adhesive should be removed because it does pick up stain. Good for sections which are difficult to affix.

[1] Mycoba, manufactured by E. I. DuPont de Nemours and Co., Inc.

Blood Serum Fixative (PRIMAN 1954)

fresh human blood serum (only from negative
Wasserman's) .... 15.0 ml.
distilled water .... 10.0 ml.
formalin, 5% .... 6.0 ml.

Filter through filter paper and use same as albumen fixative. Does
not stain and sections do not loosen.

Buffer Solutions

Molecular Weights of Buffer Ingredients

acetic acid, CH_3COOH	60.05
borax, $Na_2B_4O_7 \cdot 10H_2O$	381.43
boric acid, $B(OH)_3$	61.84
citric acid (anhydrous), $C_3H_4(OH)(COOH)_3$	192.12
citric acid crystals, $C_3H_4(OH)(COOH)_3 \cdot H_2O$	210.14
formic acid, $HCOOH$	46.03
hydrochloric acid, HCl	36.465
maleic acid, $HOOCCH\text{-}CHOOH$	116.07
potassium acid phosphate, KH_2PO_4	136.09
sodium acetate, CH_3COONa	82.04
sodium acetate, crystals, $CH_3COONa \cdot 3H_2O$	136.09
sodium barbital, $C_8H_{11}O_3N_2Na$	206.18
sodium citrate, crystals, $C_3H_4OH(COONa)_3 \cdot 5\frac{1}{2}H_2O$	357.18
sodium citrate, granular, $C_3H_4OH(COONa)_3 \cdot 2H_2O$	294.12
sodium hydroxide, $NaOH$	40.005
sodium phosphate, monobasic, $NaH_2PO_4 \cdot H_2O$	138.01
sodium phosphate, dibasic, $Na_2HPO_4 \cdot 7H_2O$	141.98
sulfuric acid, H_2SO_4	98.082
tris (hydroxymethyl) aminomethane $C_4H_{11}NO_3$	121.14

These are a few of the more commonly used chemicals for buffer solutions; for others consult a chemical handbook. Nine buffer tables follow, and will be adequate for most histological preparations.

0.2M Acetate Buffer (GOMORI) (*p*H 3.8–5.6)

STOCK SOLUTIONS:

acetic acid: 12.0 ml. made up to 1000 ml. with distilled water
sodium acetate: 27.0 gm. made up to 1000 ml. with distilled water
Add a few crystals of *camphor* to both solutions.

For desired *p*H mix correct amounts as indicated below:

pH	acetic acid	sodium acetate
	milliliters	milliliters
3.8	87.0	13.0
4.0	80.0	20.0
4.2	73.0	27.0
4.4	62.0	38.0
4.6	51.0	49.0
4.8	40.0	60.0
5.0	30.0	70.0
5.2	21.0	79.0
5.4	14.5	85.5
5.6	11.0	89.0

Acetate-Acetic Acid Buffer (WALPOLE) (*p*H 2.7–6.5)

STOCK SOLUTIONS:

M/5 *acetic acid*: 11.5 ml. (99% assay) and 988.5 ml. distilled water

M/5 *sodium acetate*: 2.72 gm. made up to 1000 ml. with distilled water

For desired *p*H mix correct amounts as indicated below:

pH	M/5 acetic acid	M/5 sodium acetate
	milliliters	milliliters
2.70	200.0	0.0
2.80	199.0	1.0
2.91	198.0	2.0
3.08	196.0	4.0
3.14	195.0	5.0
3.20	194.0	6.0
3.31	192.0	8.0
3.41	190.0	10.0
3.59	185.0	15.0
3.72	180.0	20.0
3.90	170.0	30.0
4.04	160.0	40.0
4.16	150.0	50.0
4.27	140.0	60.0
4.36	130.0	70.0
4.45	120.0	80.0

pH	M/5 acetic acid	M/5 sodium acetate
	milliliters	milliliters
4.53	110.0	90.0
4.62	100.0	100.0
4.71	90.0	110.0
4.80	80.0	120.0
4.90	70.0	130.0
4.99	60.0	140.0
5.11	50.0	150.0
5.22	40.0	160.0
5.38	30.0	170.0
5.57	20.0	180.0
5.89	10.0	190.0
6.21	5.0	195.0
6.50	0.0	200.0

0.05M Barbital Buffer (GOMORI) (pH 8.7–6.9)

STOCK SOLUTIONS:

sodium barbital: 1.03 gm. in 50 ml. distilled water

Add *0.1N HCl* according to table below and dilute to total of 100 ml.:

pH	0.1N HCl
	milliliters
8.7	5.0
8.5	7.5
8.3	11.0
8.1	15.0
7.9	19.0
7.65	26.0
7.45	31.0
7.3	36.0
7.15	41.0
6.9	43.5

Boric Acid-borax Buffer (HOLMES) (pH 7.4–9.0)

STOCK SOLUTIONS:

M/5 boric acid: 12.368 gm. made up to 1000 ml. with distilled water
M/20 borax: 19.071 gm. made up to 1000 ml. with distilled water
For desired pH mix correct amounts as indicated below:

pH	M/5 boric acid	M/20 borax
	milliliters	milliliters
7.4	90.0	10.0
7.6	85.0	15.0
7.8	80.0	20.0
8.0	70.0	30.0
8.2	65.0	35.0
8.4	55.0	45.0
8.7	40.0	60.0
9.0	20.0	80.0

0.2M Phosphate Buffer (GOMORI) (pH 5.9–7.7)

STOCK SOLUTIONS:

monobasic sodium phosphate: 27.6 gm. made up to 1000 ml. with distilled water

dibasic sodium phosphate: 53.6 gm. made up to 1000 ml. with distilled water

For desired pH mix correct amounts as indicated below:

pH	monobasic sodium phosphate	dibasic sodium phosphate
	milliliters	milliliters
5.9	90.0	10.0
6.1	85.0	15.0
6.3	77.0	23.0
6.5	68.0	32.0
6.7	57.0	43.0
6.9	45.0	55.0
7.1	33.0	67.0
7.3	23.0	77.0
7.4	19.0	81.0
7.5	16.0	84.0
7.7	10.0	90.0

Phosphate Buffer (SORENSEN) (pH 5.29–8.04)

STOCK SOLUTIONS:

M/15 dibasic sodium phosphate: 9.465 gm. made up to 1000 ml. with distilled water

M/15 potassium acid phosphate: 9.07 gm. made up to 1000 ml. with distilled water

For desired pH mix correct amounts as indicated below: (Some technics will require dilution up to 1000 ml.)

*p*H	M/15 dibasic sodium phosphate	M/15 potassium acid phosphate
	milliliters	milliliters
5.29	2.5	97.5
5.59	5.0	95.0
5.91	10.0	90.0
6.24	20.0	80.0
6.47	30.0	70.0
6.64	40.0	60.0
6.81	50.0	50.0
6.98	60.0	40.0
7.17	70.0	30.0
7.38	80.0	20.0
7.73	90.0	10.0
8.04	95.0	5.0

Standard Buffer (MCILVAINE) (*p*H 2.2–8.0)

STOCK SOLUTIONS:

0.1M citric acid (anhydrous): 19.212 gm. made up to 1000 ml. with distilled water

0.2M disodium phosphate: 28.396 gm. made up to 1000 ml. with distilled water

For desired *p*H mix correct amounts as indicated below:

*p*H	citric acid	disodium phosphate
	milliliters	milliliters
2.2	19.6	0.4
2.4	17.76	1.24
2.6	17.82	2.18
2.8	16.83	3.17
3.0	15.89	4.11
3.2	15.06	4.94
3.4	14.3	5.7
3.6	13.56	6.44
3.8	12.9	7.1
4.0	12.29	7.71
4.2	11.72	8.28
4.4	11.18	8.82
4.6	10.65	9.35
4.8	10.14	9.86
5.0	9.7	10.3
5.2	9.28	10.72
5.4	8.85	11.15
5.6	8.4	11.6

pH	citric acid	disodium phosphate
	milliliters	milliliters
5.8	7.91	12.09
6.0	7.37	12.63
6.2	6.78	13.22
6.4	6.15	13.85
6.6	5.45	14.55
6.8	4.55	15.45
7.0	3.53	16.47
7.2	2.61	17.39
7.4	1.83	18.17
7.6	1.27	18.73
7.8	0.85	19.15
8.0	0.55	19.45

0.2M Tris Buffer (HALE) (pH 7.19–9.1)

STOCK SOLUTIONS:

0.2M tris (hydroxymethyl) aminomethane: 24.228 gm. made up to 1000 ml. with distilled water

0.1N HCl (38% assay): 8.04 ml. made up to 1000 ml. with distilled water

To 25 ml. 0.2M tris add 0.1N HCl as indicated in table below and dilute to 100 ml.

pH	0.1N HCl
	milliliters
7.19	45.0
7.36	42.5
7.54	40.0
7.66	37.5
7.77	35.0
7.87	32.5
7.96	30.0
8.05	27.5
8.14	25.0
8.23	22.5
8.32	20.0
8.41	17.5
8.51	15.0
8.62	12.5
8.74	10.0
8.92	7.5
9.1	5.0

Tris Maleate Buffer (GOMORI) (*p*H 5.8–8.2)

STOCK SOLUTIONS:

maleic acid......................... 29.0 gm.

tris (hydroxymethyl) aminomethane.... 30.3 gm.

distilled water..................... 500.0 ml.

Add 2 gm. charcoal, shake, let stand 10 minutes and filter. To 40 ml. of stock solution add *N NaOH* (*4%*) as indicated below and dilute to 100 ml.

*p*H	sodium hydroxide
	milliliters
5.8	9.0
6.0	10.5
6.2	13.0
6.4	15.0
6.6	16.5
6.8	18.0
7.0	19.0
7.2	20.0
7.6	22.5
7.8	24.2
8.0	26.0
8.2	29.0

Stain Solubilities

	in water *per cent*		in absolute ethyl alcohol *per cent*	
	(*from* Conn, 1953)	(*from* Gurr, 1960)	(*from* Conn, 1953)	(*from* Gurr, 1960)
	26°C	15°C	26°C	15°C
acid alizarine blue	—	1.0	—	0.75
acid fuchsin	—	45.0	—	3.0
acridine orange	—	5.0	—	0.75
acridine yellow	—	0.5	—	0.75
acriflavine	—	15.0	—	1.0
alcian blue	—	9.5	—	6.0
alizarine red *S*	7.69	6.5	0.15	0.15
aniline blue *ws*	—	50.0	—	0.0
auramin *O*	0.74	1.0	4.49	4.0

	in water per cent		in absolute ethyl alcohol per cent	
	(from Conn, 1953)	*(from Gurr, 1960)*	*(from Conn, 1953)*	*(from Gurr, 1960)*
	26°C	15°C	26°C	15°C
aurantia	0.0	0.1	0.33	0.55
azocarmine *G*	—	1.0	—	0.1
basic fuchsin	0.26–0.39	1.0	5.93–8.16	8.0
biebrich scarlet	—	5.0	0.5	0.25
bismark brown	1.36	1.5	1.08	3.0
brilliant cresyl blue	—	3.0	—	2.0
celestin blue *B*	—	2.0	—	1.5
chlorantine fast red	—	1.0	—	0.45
chlorazol black *E*	—	6.0	—	0.1
chromotrope *2R*	19.3	19.0	0.17	0.15
chrysoidin *Y*	0.86	5.5	2.21	4.75
congo red	—	5.0	0.19	0.75
coriphosphine *O*	—	4.75	—	0.6
cresyl violet (cresylecht violet)	0.38	9.5	0.25	6.0
crystal violet (methyl violet *10B*)	1.68	9.0	13.87	8.75
eosin *B*	39.11	10.0	0.75	3.0
eosin *(S) alc. sol.* (ethyl eosin)	0.03	0.0	1.13	1.0
eosin *Y, ws*	44.20	44.0	2.18	2.0
erythrosin *B*	11.10	10.0	1.87	5.0
erythrosin *Y*	—	8.5	—	4.5
fast green *FCF*	16.04	4.0	0.35	9.0
fluorescein (uranin)	50.02	50.0	7.19	7.0
gallocyanin (bisulfite)	—	3.0	—	0.5
gallocyanin (hypochlorite)	—	0.5	—	1.25
hematein	—	1.5	—	7.5
hematoxylin	1.75	10.0	60.0	10.0
janus green *B*	5.18	5.0	1.12	1.0
light green *SF* yellowish	20.35	20.0	0.82	4.0
luxol fast blue	—	0.0	—	3.0
malachite green	—	10.0	—	8.5
martius yellow	4.57	1.0	0.16	0.0
metanil yellow	5.36	5.0	1.45	1.5
methyl violet *2B*	2.93	—	15.21	—
methyl violet *6B*	—	4.7	—	9.5
methylene blue	3.55	9.5	1.48	6.0
naphthol yellow *S*	—	12.5	—	0.65

	in water per cent		in absolute ethyl alcohol per cent	
	(from Conn, 1953)	*(from Gurr, 1960)*	*(from Conn, 1953)*	*(from Gurr, 1960)*
	26°C	15°C	26°C	15°C
neutral red	5.64	4.0	2.45	1.8
new fuchsin	1.13	1.0	3.2	8.0
nigrosin, *alc. sol.*	—	0.0	—	2.5
nigrosin *ws*	—	10.0	—	0.0
nile blue sulfate	—	6.0	—	5.0
oil red *O*	—	0.0	—	0.5
orange *G*	10.86	8.0	0.22	0.22
orcein	—	2.0	—	4.2
phloxine *B*	—	10.5	—	5.0
picric acid	1.18	1.2	8.96	9.0
ponceau *2R*	—	5.0	—	0.1
ponceau *S*	—	1.35	—	1.2
ponceau de xylidine	—	5.0	—	0.1
primilin	—	0.25	—	0.03
pyronin *B*	—	10.0	—	0.5
pyronin *Y*	8.96	9.0	0.6	0.5
quinoline yellow	—	0.5	—	0.0
rhodamin *B*	0.78	2.0	1.47	1.75
rhodamin *6G*	—	1.5	—	6.5
safranin *O*	5.45	4.5	3.41	3.5
sudan black *B*	—	0.0	—	0.25
sudan III	0.0	0.0	0.15	0.25
sudan IV	0.0	0.0	0.09	0.5
thioflavine *S*	—	1.0	—	0.4
thioflavine *T*	—	2.0	—	1.0
thionin	0.25	1.0	0.25	1.0
titian yellow	—	1.0	—	0.02
toluidine blue *O*	3.82	3.25	0.57	1.75
trypan blue	—	1.0	—	0.02
victoria blue *B*	—	4.3	—	8.25
victoria blue *4R*	3.23	3.0	20.49	20.0

Solubilities of different batches of dyes can vary, but the above table can be consulted when preparing saturated solutions. Certain dyes whose solubilities were not available are not included, such as pinacyanole and saffron. For greater detail concerning dyes see: Conn (1953); Gurr (1960).

Section **2**

General Laboratory Aids

Labeling and Cleaning Slides

If using ordinary slide labels, which must be glued on with moisture, processed slides should be cleaned; otherwise the labels will eventually loosen from the glass. Dip the slides (when mountant is thoroughly hardened) in water to which has been added a small amount of ammonia and cleanser, such as *Bon Ami* (glass cleaner may be substituted). Wipe dry, and paste on label.

A simpler method for labeling is provided by the *Professional Tape Company, Inc., 355 Burlington, Riverside, Illinois.* Their labels are called "Time Microscopic Slide Labels" and are applied by pressure only. They are manufactured in a standard thickness, size $\frac{7}{8} \times \frac{7}{8}$ inch, and a so-called "tissue-high" thickness, size $\frac{7}{8} \times \frac{7}{8}$ and $\frac{3}{8} \times \frac{7}{8}$ inch. The latter is used as an end label protecting the cover glass from sticking to any object laid upon it.

All slide labels should contain complete information, name or number of tissue, section thickness, stain and date, and possibly fixative.

Mounting can be untidy, and some of the resin may ooze over the cover glass. If this happens, when completely dry, scrape off excess resin with a razor blade, taking care not to chip or break the cover. It is not practical, however, to clean away the resin too close to the cover glass; in fact, a small band of it may be left to protect the cover from chipping or being caught against an object.

423

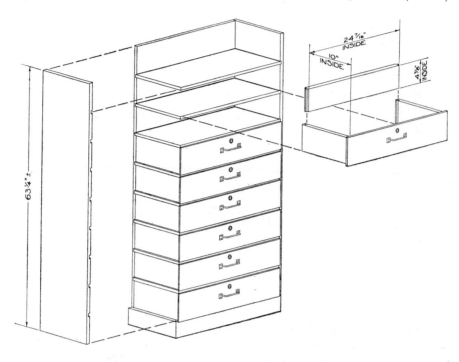

Figure 28. *A cabinet of drawers designed for use in microtechnic classes at the University of California at Los Angeles. The cabinets are not a part of the working table, but are arranged along a wall of the classroom. The drawers are designed to hold coplin jars, mountant jars, and similar items. The student can carry the drawer to the work table, turn it around with back-side facing forward, remove the back panel, and carry on the staining right in the drawer. This relieves work table of staining equipment when the space is required for other purposes, and the student can carry all the staining jars in one "basket" rather than trot back and forth several times with only as many jars as his hands will hold. If locking the drawers is unnecessary, the front panel can be removable; this eliminates having to turn the drawer around. Locking a removable front panel has been found impractical. Drawers may be left out of the upper compartment, or upper two compartments, to make convenient storage nooks for student books, lunches, sweaters, etc. These cabinets are custom made. Standard cabinets can be adapted to this purpose, but do not have a removable panel. [Kewanee Manufacturing Company, Adrian, Michigan (Technical Furniture Inc., Statesville, North Carolina), Unit #P3, drawers: inside dimensions, $20^{15}/_{16}$" length, $5^{1}/_{8}$" height and $12^{1}/_{2}$" wide.]*

Restaining Faded Slides

McCormick (1959A) Method

Slides on long standing or if exposed to bright light frequently will fade. If they must be recovered, McCormick offers the following method to bleach them for restaining.

PROCEDURE:
1. Remove cover glass by soaking slides in xylene until cover glass slips off. Do not force it off; the sections might get torn.
2. Soak longer in xylene to make certain that all of the resin is removed.
3. Hydrate to water.
4. Treat with 0.5% potassium permanganate (0.5 gm./100 ml. water): 5 minutes.
5. Wash in running water: 5 minutes.
6. Bleach with 0.5% oxalic acid (0.5 gm./100 ml. water) until colorless: 1–2 minutes. If old stain still remains, repeat steps 4, 5 and 6.
7. Wash thoroughly in running water: 5 or more minutes.
8. Restain, using more-dilute stains or for a shorter time. Potassium permanganate and oxalic acid make tissues especially sensitive to hematoxylin and aniline nuclear stains.

Two Different Stains on One Slide

Feder and Sidman (1957) Method

This method can be used advantageously when it expedites a quick checking of a tissue against two stains, side by side.

PROCEDURE:
1. Hydrate sections to water.
2. Blot carefully and while still moist coat alternate sections with silicone grease. A soft brush may be used, or more efficiently use a 1 ml. syringe and #15 needle clipped off and flattened.
3. Apply first staining procedure.
4. Dehydrate and leave in xylene 15–30 minutes to remove coating. (After 5 minutes in xylene, blotting with filter paper helps to remove grease)
5. Rehydrate; apply coating to stained sections.
6. Apply second staining procedure.

7. Repeat step 4.

8. Rinse briefly in absolute alcohol, and clear in fresh xylene. Mount.

Reclaiming and Storing Specimens

Graves (1943) Method

If biopsy material has dried, do not try to process it before first softening and rehydrating it. Place it in physiological saline solution for 1 hour, then fix, dehydrate, clear, and embed as usual.

Dried Gross Specimens[1]

Tissues which have been stored in alcohol or formalin often become completely or partially desiccated. If a major catastrophe arises and tissue must be reclaimed, partial recovery can be undertaken with fair returns for microscopic identification. *Van Cleave and Ross (1947)* restored desiccated helminths and invertebrates to normal size by soaking them in a 0.5% aqueous solution of trisodium phosphate. Trial runs of this nature were made on dried formalin-fixed specimens for from 4 hours to 30 days, depending on hardness and size of tissue. Occasional changing of the fluid seemed to help in cases of exceptionally dry pieces, also warming in a 40°C± oven. Increasing the concentration of the phosphate did not speed recovery. Finally the tissues were washed for from 30 minutes to 2–3 hours, again depending on size.

If the specimen was fixed in a mercuric chloride fixative, the trisodium phosphate was found to be ineffective until the tissue had been pretreated as follows: (1) soaked in water with enough Lugol's solution added to color the solution a deep brown: 1–2 days (if the solution became colorless, it was renewed); (2) washed in running waters: 2 hours; (3) treated with 5% sodium thiosulfate: $\frac{1}{2}$–1 hour; (4) washed: 2 hours; (5) treated with 0.5% trisodium phosphate until soft.

Only fair results were obtained by the above methods. Considerable shrinkage remained in the cells, and the nuclei stained lightly. The latter condition improved somewhat after mordanting in mercuric chloride or potassium dichromate.

Since recovery was based on the detergent action of trisodium phosphate, the inevitable question occurred, why not try one of the modern household detergents? A 1% solution of *Trend* in water was added to dried tissues and kept overnight in a paraffin oven at approximately

[1] Special acknowledgment is made to Robert Ingersoll Howes, Jr., for hours of effort in developing a recovery process for the Los Alamos Medical Center, summer of 1959.

58°C. This was followed by 6–8 hours washing and then processing overnight in the Technicon for embedding the next morning. The results were creditable, good enough for tissue identification and some pathological reading. The tissues in this run averaged 10–25 cm. in size and were fixed in either formalin or a mercuric chloride fixative. A longer stay in detergent might be required for larger pieces. No pretense is being made that results are exceptional: considerable shrinkage remains in the cells, and staining is not brilliant, but it is better than after trisodium phosphate. If, however, it is essential to check back on a tissue concerning its identity, a malignancy, or some other "matter of life or death," the author suggests trying this method of recovery of otherwise irretrievable tissue. It might save the day.

Storing Gross Specimens

Sealing tissues for storage has been a serious problem. Bottled storage has risks; any seal can spring a leak, and resulting evaporation culminates in desiccated tissue. Storing in plastic bags can be a more reliable system than the use of bottles. A heavy quality of polyethylene plastic is recommended. Lighter grades can split or unseal, whereas the heavy grade, once well sealed, almost supports itself without collapsing. The plastic can be cut to any size and sealed on all four edges, if necessary, with the "Pack Rite Poly Jaw Sealer" of *Pack-Rite Machines, 407 E. Michigan St., Milwaukee, Wisconsin.* A small amount of formalin included in the bag will keep the tissue moist so long as the bag remains sealed. A quantity of small containers can be sealed together in a large bag, affording additional protection against drying. Plastic tags with data can be enclosed or attached to the outside. Storing in bags also saves storage space, preservative and containers.[2]

See also: Lieb (1959); Gordon (1953); and Broadway and Koelle (1960).

Preserving Gross Specimens in a Pliable Condition

Palkowski (1960) Method

Sometimes it is economical to preserve gross specimens, pathological ones in particular, for future teaching or demonstration purposes. Fix as soon as possible in modified *Kaiserling Solution:* 3–4 hours.

---

[2] Polyethylene plastic bags may be purchased from a number of companies, in addition to the one listed here: Falcon Plastics Company, 6020 W. Washington Blvd., Culver City, California. Available are 9 sizes of bags, from 4″ × 6″ to 10″ × 15″ in 2 thicknesses—0.002 in. and 0.004 in.; units of 100 in a package, 500 to 200 in a case, depending on size of bag.

chlorate hydrate	300.0 gm
potassium sulfate	6.0 gm.
potassium nitrate	114.0 gm.
sodium sulfate	54.0 gm.
sodium chloride	66.0 gm.
sodium bicarbonate	60.0 gm.
formalin	300.0 ml.
distilled water	10,000.0 ml.

Because of contained air, lungs will float on the fixative. Submerge them under cotton soaked with fixative.

Drain off excess Kaiserling and place specimens in four times their volume of 80% alcohol: 18–24 hours.

Deep freeze at $-29°C\pm$, sealed in air-tight polyethylene bags not much larger than the specimen.

The specimens will keep indefinitely this way, retain their color, and become pliable after thawing. After use, they can be returned to deep freeze with little deterioration.

Removing Laboratory Stains from Hands and Glassware

STAIN   TREATMENT

basic fuchsin—difficult to remove; try strong acetic acid in 95% alcohol, or dilute HCl.

carmine—strong ammonia water or weak HCl; if stain resists, use them alternately.

chromic acid—dilute sulfurous acid in water, or concentrated sodium thiosulfate and a few drops of sulfuric acid added.

fast green and other similar acid stains—ammonia water.

hematoxylin—weak acid or lemon juice.

hemoglobin—fresh stains: lukewarm to cool water (never hot); older stains: soften with borax solution, dilute ammonia or tincture of green soap, finally treat with 2% aqueous oxalic acid.

iodine—sodium thiosulfate.

iron alum stains on glassware—(1) strong NaOH (sticks) in water, followed by (2) strong HCl.

methylene blue—acid alcohol or tincture of green soap.

most dyes—tincture of green soap.

osmic acid on glassware—3% H_2O_2 (*Carr and Bacsich, 1958*).

picric acid—lithium iodide or carbonate, aqueous.

potassium permanganate—dilute sulfurous acid, HCl, oxalic acid or hyposulfite.

safranin and gentian violet—difficult to remove; try acid alcohol.

silver—Lugol's or tincture of iodine, followed by sodium thiosulfate.

Verhoeff's—4% aqueous citric acid (*Hull and Wegner, 1952*).

Teaching Films

Motion pictures can be of considerable value to instructors of laboratory methods. See especially: "Pathology Film Reviews" in *Laboratory Investigation* (Vol. 9, No. 5, Part II, September-October, 1960). This lists motion pictures for education, research and recruitment, reviewing the content of the films, type of audience, where distributed or loaned. Samples are: "Autopsy Technique," "Compound Microscope," "Cytotechnologist's Role," and "Career: Medical Technologist."

References

ACKERMAN, G. ADOLPH. "A combined alkaline phosphatase-PAS staining method." *Stain Technology, 33* (1958), 269–271.

ADAMSTONE, F. B. and TAYLOR, A. B. "The rapid preparation of frozen tissue sections." *Stain Technology, 23* (1948), 109.

ADEY, W. R., RUDOLPH, ALICE F., HINE, I. F. and HARRITT, NANCY J. "Glees staining of monkey hypothalamus: a critical appraisal of normal and experimental material." *Journal of Anatomy, 92* (1958), 219–235.

AGRELL, IVAR P. S. "Whole mounts of small embryos attached directly to glass slides." *Stain Technology, 33* (1958), 265–267.

ALBRECHT, MILDRED. "Mounting frozen sections with gelatin." *Stain Technology, 29* (1954), 89–90.

———. "A simple mechanical aid in staining frozen sections in quantity." *Stain Technology, 31* (1956), 231–233.

ALLEN, ANTON M. "Two methods for coloring mast cells of mammalian tissues." *American Journal of Clinical Pathology, 33* (1960), 461–469.

AMERICAN PUBLIC HEALTH ASSOCIATION. *Diagnostic Procedures for Virus and Rickettsial Diseases.* Publication Office, 1790 Broadway, N.Y. (1956).

AMMERMAN, FRANK. "A chrome-alum preparation for delicate and difficult fixations." *Stain Technology, 25* (1950), 197–199.

ANDERSON, F. D. "Dichromate-chlorate perfusion prior to staining degeneration in brain and spinal cord." *Stain Technology, 34* (1959), 65–67.

ANTHONY, ADAM and CLATER, MERLIN. "Alcohol-xylene versus Dioxane in the shrinkage of tissue." *Stain Technology, 34* (1959) 9–13.

ARENSBURGER, KONSTANTIN E. and MARKELL, EDWARD K. "A simple combination direct smear and fecal concentrate for permanent stained preparations." *American Journal of Clinical Pathology, 34* (1960), 50–51.

ARMSTRONG, J. A. "Histochemical differentiation of nucleic acids by means of induced fluorescence." *Experimental Cell Research, 11* (1956), 640–643.

ARNOLD, JAMES S. and JEE, WEBSTER S. S. "Preparing bone sections for radioautography." *Stain Technology, 29* (1954 A), 49–54.

——— and ———. "Embedding and sectioning undecalcified bone and its application to radioautography." *Stain Technology, 29* (1954 B), 225–239.

ARNOLD, ZACH M. "A rapid method for concentrating small organisms for sectioning." *Stain Technology, 27* (1952), 199–200.

ARZAC, J. P. "A simple histochemical reaction for aldehydes." *Stain Technology, 25* (1950), 187–194.

ATKINSON, WILLIAM B. "Studies on the preparation and recoloration of fuchsin sulfurous acid." *Stain Technology, 27* (1952), 153–160.

AUSTIN, A. P. "Iron alum aceto-carmine staining for chromosomes and other anatomical features of Rhodophyceae." *Stain Technology, 34* (1959), 69–75.

BAKER, J. R. "A new method for mitochondria." *Nature, 30* (1932), 134.

———. "The structure and chemical composition of the Golgi element." *Quarterly*

431

Journal of Microscopical Science, 85 (1944), 1–72.

――――. *Cytological Technique.* Methuen's Monographs on Biological Subjects. London, Methuen and Company, Ltd. (1945).

――――. *Principles of Biological Technique.* London, Methuen and Company, Ltd., or, New York, John Wiley and Co. (1958).

BANGLE, RAYMOND. "Gomori's paraldehyde fuchsin stain." *Journal of Histochemistry and Cytochemistry, 2* (1954), 291–299.

BANNY, THERESA M. and CLARK, GEORGE. "A simplified method for the double embedding of tissue." *Stain Technology, 24* (1949), 223–224.

―――― and ――――. "New domestic cresyl echt violet." *Stain Technology, 25* (1950), 195–196.

BARER, R. "Phase contrast and interference microscopy in cytology." *Physical Techniques in Biological Research*, ed., Gerald Oster and Arthur W. Pollister, Vol. III, N.Y., *Academic Press* (1956).

――――. "Interference and Polarizing Microscopy." *Analytical Cytology*, ed., Robert C. Mellors. N.Y., *Blakiston* (1959).

BARNARD, JOHN W., ROBERTS, J. O. and BROWN, JOSEPH G. "A simple macroscopic staining and mounting procedure for wet sections from cadaver brains." *Anatomical Record, 105* (1949), 11–17.

BARNES, H. "Some tables for the ionic composition of sea water." *Journal Experimental Biology, 31* (1954), 582–588.

BARR, MURRAY L., BERTRAM, FRASER and LINDSAY, HUGH A. "The morphology of the nerve cell nucleus, according to sex." *Anatomical Record, 107* (1950), 283–292.

BARRETT, A. M. "On the removal of formaldehyde-produced precipitate from sections." *Journal of Pathology and Bacteriology, 56* (1944), 135–136.

BARTHOLOMEW, J. W. and MITTWER, TOD. "The mechanism of the Gram reaction. 1. The specificity of the primary dye." *Stain Technology, 25* (1950), 103–110.

―――― and ――――. "The mechanism of the Gram reaction. 3. Solubilities of dye-iodine precipitates, and further studies of primary dye substitutes." *Stain Technology, 26* (1951), 231–240.

――――, ―――― and FINKLESTEIN, HAROLD. "The phenomenon of Gram-positivity; its definition and some negative evidence on the causative role of sulfhydryl groups." *Stain Technology, 34* (1959), 147–154.

BARTON, A. A. "The examination of ultrathin sections with a light microscope after electron microscopy." *Stain Technology, 34* (1959), 348–349.

――――. "Carbon coated grids for electron microscopy." *Stain Technology, 35* (1960), 287–289.

BAYLEY, JOHN. "'Cracking' and 'chatter' in paraffin sections." *Journal Pathology and Bacteriology, 70* (1955), 548–549.

BEAMER, PARKER R. and FIRMINGER, HARLAN I. "Improved methods for demonstrating acid-fast and spirochaetal organisms in histological sections." *Laboratory Investigation, 4* (1955), 9–17.

BECK, CONRAD. *The Microscope. Theory and Practice.* London, R. J. Beck, Ltd. (1938).

BECKER, E. R. and ROUDABUSH, R. L. *Brief Directions in Histological Technique.* Ames, Iowa, Collegiate Press, Inc. (1935).

BEECH, R. H. and DAVENPORT, H. A. "The Bielschowsky staining technic. A study of the factors influencing its specificity for nerve fibers." *Stain Technology, 8* (1933), 11–30.

BELANGER, LEONARD F. "A method for routine detection of radio-phosphates and other radioactive compounds in tissues. The inverted autograph." *Anatomical Record, 107* (1950), 149–156.

――――. "Improvements in the melted emulsion technique of autoradiography." *Nature, 170* (1952), 165.

―――― and HARTNETT, ANNA. "Persistent toluidine blue metachromasia." *Journal Histochemistry and Cytochemistry, 8* (1960), 75.

BELL, J. THOMAS. "Polyoxyethylene Sorbitan monopalmitate (Tween 40) as a vehicle for oil red O fat stain." *Stain Technology, 34* (1959), 219–221.

BELLING, JOHN. "The iron-aceto-carmine method of fixing and staining chromosomes." *Biological Bulletin, Woods Hole, 50* (1926), 160–162.

――――. *The Use of the Microscope.* N.Y., McGraw-Hill Book Co. (1930).

BENCOSME, SERGIE, STONE, ROBERT S., LATTA, HARRISON and MADDEN, SIDNEY C. "A rapid method for localization of tissue structures or lesions for electron microscopy." *Journal Biophysical and Biochemical Cytology, 5* (1959), 508–509.

BENGE, W. P. J. "Staining autoradiographs at low temperatures." *Stain Technology, 35* (1960), 106–108.

BENNETT, H. STANLEY. "The microscopical investigation of biological materials with polarized light." *Handbook of Micro-*

scopical Technique, ed., Ruth McClung Jones, 3rd ed., N.Y., Hoeber (1950).

BENSLEY, R. R. and BENSLEY, S. H. *Handbook of Histological and Cytological Technique.* Chicago, University of Chicago Press (1938).

BENSLEY, SYLVIA H. "Pinacyanol erythrosinate as a stain for mast cells." *Stain Technology,* 27 (1952), 269–273.

———. "The scope and limitations of histochemistry." *American Journal Medical Technology,* 25 (1959), 15–32.

BERGERON, JOHN A. and SINGER, MARCUS. "Metachromasy: an experimental and theoretical re-evaluation." *Journal Biophysical and Biochemical Cytology,* 4 (1958), 433–457.

BERTON, WILLIAM M. and PHILLIPS, W. R. "A film leader technic for the study of cells in culture." *Laboratory Investigation,* 10, #2, Part II (1961), 373–380.

BERTRAM, E. G. "A non-sticking coverglass weight." *Stain Technology,* 33 (1958), 143–144.

BHARADWAJ, T. P. and LOVE, ROBERT. "Staining mitochondria with hematoxylin after formalin-sublimate fixation; a rapid method." *Stain Technology,* 34 (1959), 331–334.

BIELSCHOWSKY, M. "Die Silber impragnation der Axencylinder." *Neurologisches Centralblatt,* 21 (1902), 579–584.

BLANDAU, R. J. "A method of eliminating the electrification of paraffin ribbons." *Stain Technology,* 13 (1938), 139–141.

BLANK, HARVEY and MCCARTHY, PHILIP L. "A general method for preparing histologic sections with a water-soluble wax." *Journal Laboratory and Clinical Medicine,* 36 (1950), 776.

———, ———, and DELAMATER, EDWARD D. "A non-vacuum freezing-dehydrating technic for histology, autoradiography, and microbial cytology." *Stain Technology,* 26 (1951), 193–197.

BLOCK, M., SMALLER, VICTORIA and BROWN, JESSIE. "An adaptation of the Maximow technique for preparation of sections of hematopoietic tissue." *Journal Laboratory and Clinical Medicine,* 42 (1953), 145–151.

BODIAN, DAVID. "A new method for staining nerve fibers and nerve endings in mounted paraffin sections." *Anatomical Record,* 65 (1936), 89–97.

———. "The staining of paraffin sections of nervous tissues with activated Protargol. The role of fixatives." *Anatomical Record,* 69 (1937), 153–162.

BOGEN, EMIL. "Detection of tubercle bacilli by fluorescence microscopy." *American Review of Tuberculosis,* 44 (1941), 267–271.

BOGOROCH, RITA. "Detection of radio-elements in histological slides by coating with stripping emulsion—the strip-coating technic." *Stain Technology,* 26 (1951), 43–50.

BORYSKO, EMIL. "Recent developments in methacrylate embedding. 1. A study of the polymerization damage phenomenon by phase contrast microscopy." *Journal Biophysical and Biochemical Cytology,* 2, Part 2, Supplement (1956), 3–14.

——— and SAPRANAUSKAS, P. "A technique for comparison phase-contrast and electron microscope studies of cells grown in tissue culture with evaluation of time-lapse cinemicrographs." *Bulletin, Johns Hopkins Hospital,* 95 (1954), 68–80.

BOYD, G. A. *Autoradiography in Biology and Medicine.* N.Y., Academic Press (1955).

BRADLEY, MURIEL V. "An aceto-carmine squash technic for mature embryo sacs." *Stain Technology,* 23 (1948 A), 29–40.

———. "A method for making aceto-carmine squashes permanent without removal of the cover slip." *Stain Technology,* 23 (1948 B), 41–44.

———. "Sudan black B and aceto-carmine as a combination stain." *Stain Technology,* 32, (1957), 85–86.

BRIDGES, C. B. "The vapour method of changing reagents and of dehydration." *Stain Technology,* 12 (1937), 51–52.

BRIDGES, CHARLES H. and LUNA, LEE. "Kerr's improved Warthin-Starry technic. Study of permissible variations." *Laboratory Investigation,* 6 (1957), 357–367.

BRIGGS, NORMAN L. "A double embedding technic for fibrous connective tissue." *Stain Technology,* 33 (1958), 299.

BROADWAY, CHARLES B. and KOELLE, DONALD G. "Use of polyethylene plastic bags for storage of pathologic tissue." *Technical Bulletin, Registry of Medical Technologists,* 30 (1960), 17–21.

BROOKE, M. M. and DONALDSON, A. W. "Use of a surface active agent to prevent transfer of malarial parasites between blood films during mass staining procedures." *Journal of Parasitology,* 36 (1950), 84.

BROWN, J. H. and BRENN, L. "A method for differential staining of gram positive and gram negative bacteria in tissue sections." *Bulletin, Johns Hopkins Hospital, 48* (1931), 69–73.

BROWN, JAMES O. "A simplified and convenient method for the double embedding of tissues." *Stain Technology, 23* (1948), 83–89.

BUCK, R. C. and JARVIC, C. E. "A simple automatic ultramicrotome." *Stain Technology, 34* (1959), 109–111.

BUCKLEY, SONJA M., WHITNEY, ELINOR and RAPP, FRED. "Identification by fluorescent antibody of developmental forms of psittacosis virus in tissue culture." *Proceedings, Society Experimental Biology and Medicine, 90* (1955), 226–230.

BULLIVANT, S. and HOTCHIN, J. "Chromyl chloride, a new stain for electron microscopy." *Experimental Cell Research, 21* (1960), 211–214.

BURRELL, P. C. "Root tip smear method for difficult material." *Stain Technology, 14* (1939), 147–149.

BURROWS, WILLIAM. "Textbook of Microbiology." Philadelphia, W. B. Saunders Co. (1954).

BURSTONE, M. S. "Polyvinyl acetate as a mounting medium for azo-dye procedures." *Journal Histochemistry and Cytochemistry, 5* (1957 A), 196.

————. "Polyvinyl pyrrolidone as a mounting medium for stains for fat and for azo-dye procedures." *American Journal Clinical Pathology, 28* (1957 B), 429–430.

————. "The relationship between fixation and techniques for the histochemical localization of hydrolytic enzymes." *Journal Histochemistry and Cytochemistry, 6* (1958), 322–339.

————. "New histochemical techniques for the demonstration of tissue oxidase (cytochrome oxidase)." *Journal Histochemistry and Cytochemistry, 7* (1959 A), 112–121.

————. "Acid phosphatase activity of calcifying bone and dentin matrices." *Journal Histochemistry and Cytochemistry, 7* (1959 B), 147–148.

————. "Histochemical demonstration of cytochrome oxidase with new amine reagents." *Journal Histochemistry and Cytochemistry, 8* (1960 A), 63–70.

————. "Postcoupling, noncoupling and fluorescence techniques for the demonstration of alkaline phosphatase." *Journal National Cancer Institute, 24* (1960 B), 1199–1218.

———— and FLEMMING, T. J. "A new technique for the histochemical study of smears." *Journal Histochemistry and Cytochemistry, 7* (1959), 203.

———— and FOLK, J. E. "Histochemical demonstration of aminopeptidase." *Journal Histochemistry and Cytochemistry, 4* (1956), 217–226.

BURTON, J. F. "Histochemical demonstration of acid phosphatase by an improved azo-dye method." *Journal Histochemistry and Cytochemistry, 2* (1954), 88–94.

BUSH, VANNEVAR and HEWITT, RICHARD E., "Frozen sectioning, A new and rapid method." *American Journal of Pathology, 28* (1952), 863–867.

CAMERON, D. A. "A note on breaking glass knives." *Journal Histochemistry and Cytochemistry, 2* (1956), 57–59.

CAMERON, M. L. and STEELE, J. E. "Simplified aldehyde-fuchsin staining of neurosecretory cells." *Stain Technology, 34* (1959), 265–266.

CARES, A. "A note on stored formaldehyde and its easy reconditioning." *Journal Technical Methods, 25* (1945), 67–70.

CAREY, EBEN J. "Experimental pleomorphism of motor nerve plates as a mode of functional protoplasmic movement." *Anatomical Record, 81* (1941), 393–413.

CARLETON, H. M. and LEACH, E. H. "Histological Technique." N.Y., Oxford University Press (1947).

CARR, L. A. and BACSICH, P. "Removal of osmic acid stains." *Nature, 182* (1958), 1108.

CARSON, RUTH H. "Staining of cytologic smears without ethyl alcohol." *American Journal Clinical Pathology, 32* (1959), 370.

CARTER, JERRY J., BARZILAI, GEMMA and OPPENHEIM, ABRAHAM. "Orcein-acetic squashing in Cancer detection." *American Journal Clinical Pathology, 32* (1959), 533–535.

CASE, NORMAN M. "The use of a cation exchange in decalcification." *Stain Technology, 28* (1953), 155–158.

CASON, JANE E. "A rapid one-step Mallory-Heidenhain stain for connective tissue." *Stain Technology, 25* (1950), 225–226.

CASSELMAN, W. B. BRUCE. *Histochemical Technique.* London, Methuen and Co., Ltd.; N.Y., John Wiley and Sons (1959).

CASTAÑEDA, M. RUIZ. "Experimental pneumonia produced by typhus Rickettsia." *American Journal Pathology, 15* (1939), 467–475.

CELARIER, ROBERT P. "Tertiary butyl alcohol dehydration of chromosome smears." *Stain Technology, 31* (1956), 155–157.

CHEN, TZE-TUAN. "Staining nuclei and

chromosomes in protozoa." *Stain Technology, 19* (1944 A), 83–90.
———. "The nuclei in Avian parasites. I. The structure of nuclei in *Plasmodium elongatum* with some considerations on technique." *American Journal Hygiene, 40* (1944 B), 26–34.

CHESSICK, RICHARD D. "Histochemical study of the distribution of Esterases." *Journal Histochemistry and Cytochemistry, 1* (1953), 471–485.

CHESTERMAN, W. and LEACH, E. H. "A bleaching method for melanin and two staining methods." *Quarterly Journal Microscopical Society, 99* (1958), 65–66.

CHIFFELLE, THOMAS L. and PUTT, FREDERICK A. "Propylene and ethylene glycol as solvents for Sudan IV and Suda.1 Black B." *Stain Technology, 26* (1951), 51–56.

CHIPPS, A. D. and DUFF, G. L. "Glycogen infiltration of the liver cell nuclei." *American Journal Pathology, 18* (1942), 645–660.

CHURG, JACOB and PRADO, ARTIE. "A rapid Mallory trichrome stain (chromotrope-aniline blue)." Am. Med. Assoc., *Archives of Pathology, 62* (1956), 505–506.

CLARKE, GEORGE. "A simplified method for embedding cellular contents of body fluids in paraffin." *American Journal Clinical Pathology, 17* (1947), 256.
——— and SPERRY, MARGARET. "A simplified Nissl stain with thionin." *Stain Technology, 20* (1945), 23–24.

CLAYDEN, E. C. "A discussion on the preparation of bone sections by the paraffin wax method with special reference to the control of decalcification." *Journal Medical Laboratory Technologists, 10* (1952), 103.

COCKE, E. C. "A method for fixing and staining earthworms." *Science, 87* (1938), 443–444.

COHEN, SOPHIA M.; GORDON, IRVING; RAPP, FRED; MACAULAY, JOHN C. and BUCKLEY, SONJA M. "Fluorescent antibody and complement-fixation tests of agents isolated in tissue culture from measles patients." *Proceedings, Society Experimental Biology and Medicine, 90* (1955), 118–122.

COLE, E. C. "Ferric chloride as a mordant for phosphate ripened hematoxylin." Mimeographed copy received from author (1933).
———. "Studies on hematoxylin stains." *Stain Technology, 18* (1943), 125–142.

COLE, WILBUR V. A gold chloride method for motor-end plates." *Stain Technology, 21* (1946), 23–24.

CONGER, ALAN D. "Dentist's Sticky wax: a cover sealing compound for temporary slides." *Stain Technology, 35* (1960), 225.
——— and FAIRCHILD, LUCILE M. "A quick-freeze method for making smear slides permanent." *Stain Technology, 28* (1953), 281–283.

CONN, H. J. "Cautions in the use of Dioxane." *Stain Technology, 14* (1939), 152.
———. "The development of histological staining." *Ciba Symposia, 7* (1946).
———. *History of Staining.* Geneva, N.Y., Biotech Publications (1948).
———. *Biological Stains.* Geneva, N.Y., Biotech Publications (1953).
———, ———, and EMMEL, VICTOR M. *Staining Procedures.* Baltimore, Williams and Wilkins Co. (1960).

COONS, ALBERT H. "Histochemistry with labeled antibody." *International Review of Cytology,* ed., G. H. Bourne and J. F. Danielli. N.Y., Academic Press (1956), *V:* 1–23.
———. "Fluorescent antibody methods," in *General Cytochemical Methods,* ed., J. F. Danielli. N.Y., Academic Press (1958), I: 399–422.
———, CREECH, H. J., JONES, NORMAN and BERLINER, ERNEST. "The demonstration of pneumococcal antigen in tissues by the use of fluorescent antibody." *Journal Immunology, 45* (1942), 159–170.
——— and KAPLAN, MELVIN H. "Localization of antigen in tissue cells. II. Improvements in a method for the detection of antigen by means of fluorescent antibody." *Journal Experimental Medicine, 91* (1950), 1–13.
———, LEDUC, ELIZABETH H. and CONNOLLY, JEANNE M. "Studies on antibody production. I. A method for the histochemical demonstration of specific antibody and its application to a study of the hyperimmune rabbit." *Journal Experimental Medicine, 102* (1955), 49–60.
———, ———, and KAPLAN, MELVIN H. "Localization of antigen in tissue cells. VI. The fate of injected foreign proteins in the mouse." *Journal Experimental Medicine, 93* (1951), 173–188.
———, SNYDER, JOHN C.; CHEEVER, F. SARGENT and MURRAY, EDWARD S. "Localization of antigen in tissue cells. IV. Antigens of rickettsiae and mumps virus." *Journal Experimental Medicine, 91* (1950), 31–37.

CORLISS, JOHN O. "Silver impregnation of ciliated Protozoa by the Chatton-Lwoff technic." *Stain Technology, 28* (1953), 97–100.

CossLETT, V. E. *The Electron Microscope.* N.Y., Interscience Publishers (1947).

Cowdry, E. V. *Laboratory Technique in Biology and Medicine,* 3rd Ed. Baltimore, Williams and Wilkins Co. (1952).

CRANDALL, FRANK B. "An improved diamond knife holder for ultra-microtomy." *Stain Technology, 36* (1961), 34–36.

CULLING, C. E. A. *Handbook of Histopathological Technique.* London, Butterworth and Co. (1957).

CULLING, CHARLES and VASSER, PHILIP. "Desoxyribose nucleic acid. A fluorescent histochemical technique." *Archives Pathology, 71* (1961), 88/76–92/80.

CUMLEY, R. W., CROW, J. F. and GRIFFIN, A. B. "Clearing specimens for demonstration of bone." *Stain Technology, 14* (1939), 7–11.

DALTON, A. J. "A chrome-osmium fixative for electron microscopy." *Anatomical Record, 121* (1955), 281.

DANIELLI, J. F. *Cytochemistry.* N.Y., John Wiley and Sons (1953).

DARROW, MARY A. "Synthetic orcein as an elastic tissue stain." *Stain Technology, 27* (1952), 329–332.

DART, LEROY H. and TURNER, THOMAS R. "Fluorescence microscopy in exfoliative cytology." *Laboratory Investigation, 8,* Part II (1959), 1513–1522.

DAVENPORT, H. A. "Block staining of nervous tissue with silver. III. Pericellular end-bulbs or boutons." *Stain Technology, 8* (1933), 143–147.

———. "Protargol: old and new." *Stain Technology, 23* (1948), 219–220.

———. *Histological and Histochemical Technics.* Philadelphia, W. B. Saunders and Co. (1960).

——— and COMBS, C. M. "Golgi's dichromate silver method. 3. Chromating fluids." *Stain Technology, 29* (1954), 165–173.

———, WINDLE, W. F., and BUCH, R. H. "Block staining of nervous tissue. IV. Embryos." *Stain Technology, 9* (1934), 5–10.

DAVIDSON, WILLIAM M. and SMITH, D. ROBERTSON. "A morphological sex difference in the polymorphonuclear neutrophil leucocytes." *British Medical Journal,* July 3 (1954), 6–7.

DAVIES, HOWARD G. "The determination of mass and concentration by microscopic interferometry." *General Cytochemical Methods,* Vol. I, ed., J. F. Danielli, N.Y., Academic Press (1958).

DAVIS, HELEN and HARMON, PINKNEY J. "A

suggestion for prevention of loose sections in the Bodian protargol method." *Stain Technology, 24* (1949), 249.

DAWSON, A. B. "A note on the staining of the skeleton of cleared specimens with alizarin red S." *Stain Technology, 1* (1926), 123–124.

DEBRUYN, P. P. H., FARR, R. S., BANKS, HILDA and MORTHLAND, F. W. "*In vivo* and *in vitro* affinity of diaminoacridine for nucleoproteins." *Experimental Cell Research, 4* (1953), 174–180.

———, ROBERTSON, ROBERT C., and FARR, RICHARD S. "*In vivo* affinity of diaminoacridines for nuclei." *Anatomical Record, 108* (1950), 279–307.

DECK, J. DAVID and DESOUZA, G. "A disrupting factor in silver staining techniques." *Stain Technology, 34* (1959), 287.

DEHARVEN, ETIENNE. "A new technique for carbon films." *Journal Biophysical and Biochemical Cytology, 4* (1958), 133–134.

DELAMETER, EDWARD D. "Basic fuchsin as a nuclear stain." *Stain Technology, 23* (1948), 161–176.

———. "A staining and dehydrating procedure for handling of micro-organisms." *Stain Technology, 26* (1951), 199–204.

DELEZ, ARTHUR L. and DAVIS, OLIVE STULL. "The use of oxalic acid in staining with phloxine and hematoxylin." *Stain Technology, 25* (1950), 111–112.

DEL VECCHIO, P. R., DEWITT, S. H., BORELLI, J. I., WARD, J. B., WOOD, T. A. JR. and MALMGREN, R. A. "Application of millipore fixation technique to cytologic material." *Journal National Cancer Institute, 22* (1959), 427–432.

DEMKE, DONALD D. "Staining and mounting helminths." *Stain Technology, 27* (1952), 135–139.

DEMPSTER, WILFRED TAYLOR. "Principles of microscopic illumination and the problem of glare." *Journal Optical Society of America, 34* (1944 A), 695–710.

———. "Visual factors in microscopy." *Journal Optical Society of America, 34* (1944 B), 711–717.

———. "Properties of paraffin relating to microtechnique." *Michigan Academy of Science, Arts, and Letters, 29* (1944 C), 251–264.

DEWITT, S. H., DELVECCHIO, P. R., BORELLI, J. I. and HILBERG, A. W. "A method for preparing wound washings and bloody fluids for cytologic evaluation." *Journal National Cancer Institute, 19* (1957), 115–122.

DIAMOND, L. S. "A new rapid stain technic

for intestinal Protozoa, using Tergitol-hematoxylin." *American Journal Clinical Pathology, 15* (1945), 68–69.

DOTTI, LOUIS B., PAPARO, GARY P. and CLARKE, EARLE. "The use of ion-exchange resin in decalcification of bone." *American Journal Clinical Pathology,* Technical Section, *21* (1951), 475–479.

DOWDING, GRACE L. "Plastic embedding of undecalcified bone." *American Journal Clinical Pathology, 32* (1959), 245–249.

DUNN, R. C. "A hemoglobin stain for histologic use based on the cyanol-hemoglobin reaction." *Archives Pathology, 41* (1946), 676–677.

DuPont Vinyl Products Bulletin. " 'Elvanol' polyvinyl alcohol for adhesives and binders." *V 2-254, E. I. DuPont de Nemours and Co.,* Wilmington, Del.

DZIABIS, MARVIN DEAN. "Luxol Fast Blue MBS, a stain for gross brain sections." *Stain Technology, 33* (1958), 96–97.

EAPEN, J. "The effect of alcohol-acetic formalin, Zenker's fluid, and gelatin on the activity of lipase." *Stain Technology, 35* (1960), 227–228.

EARLE, W. R. "Iron hematoxylin stain containing high concentration of ferrous iron." *Science, 89* (1939), 323–324.

EAYRS, J. T. "An apparatus for fixation and supravital staining of tissues by perfusion method." *Stain Technology, 25* (1950), 137–142.

EHRENRICH, THEODORE and KERPE, STASE. "A new rapid method of obtaining dry fixed cytological smears." *Journal American Medical Association, 170* (1959), 94–95.

EINARSON, L. "On the theory of gallocyanin-chromalum staining and its application for quantitative estimation of basophilia. A selective staining of exquisite progressivity." *Acta Pathologica et Microbiologica Scandinavica, 28* (1951), 82–102.

ELFTMAN, HERBERT. "A direct silver method for the Golgi apparatus." *Stain Technology, 27* (1952), 47–52.

———. "Controlled chromation." *Journal Histochemistry and Cytochemistry, 2* (1954), 1–8.

———. "Response of the anterior pituitary to dichromate oxidation." *Journal Histochemistry and Cytochemistry, 4* (1956), 410.

———. "A chrome-alum fixative for the pituitary." *Stain Technology, 32* (1957 A), 25–28.

———. "Phospholipid fixation by dichro-mate-sublimate." *Stain Technology, 32* (1957 B), 29–31.

———. "Effects of fixation in lipoid histochemistry." *Journal Histochemistry and Cytochemistry, 6* (1958), 317–321.

———. "Combined aldehyde-fuchsin and PAS staining of the pituitary." *Stain Technology, 34* (1959 A), 77–80.

———. "Aldehyde-fuchsin for pituitary cytochemistry," *Journal Histochemistry and Cytochemistry, 7* (1959 B), 98–100.

———. "A Schiff reagent of calibrated sensitivity." *Journal Histochemistry and Cytochemistry, 7* (1959 C), 93–97.

———. "Hematoxylin as a pituitary stain." *Stain Technology, 35* (1960), 97–101.

——— and ELFTMAN, ALICE G. "Histological methods for the demonstration of gold in tissues." *Stain Technology, 20* (1945), 59–62.

ELLINGER, P. "Fluorescence microscopy in Biology." *Biological Reviews, 15* (1940), 323–350.

EMIG, WILLIAM H. *Microtechnique; Text and Laboratory Exercises.* William H. Emig, 2621 E. Wilamette Ave., Colorado Springs, Colorado (1959).

ENDICOTT, K. M. "Plasma or serum as a diluting fluid for thin smears of bone marrow." *Stain Technology, 20* (1945), 25–26.

ENGSTRÖM, ARNE. *Historadiography. Physical Techniques in Biological Research,* Vol. III, eds., Gerald Oster and Arthur W. Pollister, N.Y., Academic Press (1956).

———. *X-ray microscopy. Analytical Cytology,* ed., Robert C. Mellors, N.Y., Blakiston (1959).

ENLOW, DONALD H. "A plastic seal method for mounting sections of ground bones." *Stain Technology, 29* (1954), 21–22.

EVANS, T. C. "Radioautographs in which tissue is mounted directly on photographic plate." *Proceedings, Society Experimental Biology and Medicine, 64* (1947), 313–315.

FAIRLEY, A., LINTON, E. C. and FORD-MOORE, A. H. "Toxicity to animals of some oxidation products of 1:4 Dioxan." *Journal of Hygiene, 36* (1936), 341–347.

FALCK, BENGT and HILLARP, NILS-AKE. "A note on the chromaffin reaction." *Journal Histochemistry and Cytochemistry, 7* (1959), 149.

FARBER, EMMANUEL and LOUVRIERE, CONNIE D. "Histochemical localization of specific oxidative enzymes. IV. Soluble oxidation —reduction dyes as aids in histochemical localization of oxidative enzymes with tetrazolium salts." *Journal Histochemistry and Cytochemistry, 4* (1956), 347–356.

———— and BUELING, ERNEST. "Histochemical localization of specific oxidative enzymes. V. The dissociation of succinic dehydrogenase from carriers by lipase and the specific histochemical localization of the dehydrogenase with phenazine methosulfate and tetrazolium salts." *Journal Histochemistry and Cytochemistry, 4* (1956), 357–362.

FARNSWORTH, MARJORIE. "Rapid embedding of minute objects in paraffin." *Stain Technology, 31* (1956), 295–296.

FARQUHAR, MARILYN G. "Preparation of ultrathin tissue sections for electron microscopy." *Laboratory Investigation, 5* (1956), 317–337.

———— and RINEHART, J. F. "Electron microscopic studies on the anterior pituitary glands of castrate rats." *Endocrinology, 54* (1954), 516–541.

FAULKNER, R. R. and LILLIE, R. D. "A buffer modification of the Warthin-Starry silver method for spirochetes in single paraffin sections." *Stain Technology, 20* (1945 A), 81–82.

———— and LILLIE, R. D. "Dried egg white for Mayer's albumin fixative." *Stain Technology, 20* (1945 B), 99–100.

FAVORSKY, B. A. "Eine modifikation des silber impregnations-verfahrens Rámon y Cajal für das periphere nervensystem." *Anatomischer Anzeiger, 70* (1930), 376–378.

FEDER, NED and SIDMAN, RICHARD. "A method for applying different stains to alternate serial sections on a single microscope slide." *Stain Technology, 32* (1957), 271–273.

———— and ————. "Methods and principles of fixation by freeze-substitution." *Journal Biophysical and Biochemical Cytology, 4* (1958), 593–600.

FENTON, J. C. B. and INNES, JAMES. "A staining method for malaria parasites in thick blood films." *Transactions Royal Society of Tropical Medicine and Hygiene, 39* (1945), 87–90.

FÉRNANDEZ-MORAN, H. "A diamond knife for ultrathin sectioning." *Experimental Cell Research, 5* (1953), 255.

————. "Application of a diamond knife for ultrathin sectioning to the study of the fine structure of biological tissues and metals." *Journal Biophysical and Biochemical Cytology,* Supplement 2 (1956), 29–31.

————. "Low temperature preparation techniques for electron microscopy of biological specimens based on rapid freezing with liquid Helium II. Freezing and drying of biological materials. Part III." *Annals of N.Y. Academy of Sciences, 85* (1960), 689–713.

FERREIRA, ALBERTO VAZ and COMBS, C. MURPHY. "Deterioration of nitrocellulose solutions caused by light." *Stain Technology, 26* (1951), 81–84.

FIRMINGER, HARLAN I. "Carbowax embedding for obtaining thin tissue sections and study of intracellular lipids." *Stain Technology, 25* (1950), 121–123.

FISCHER, H. W. "A technic for radiography of lymph nodes and vessels." *Laboratory Investigation, 6* (1957), 522–527.

FISHER, E. R. and HASKELL, A. E. "Combined Gomori methods for demonstration of pancreatic alpha and beta cells." *American Journal Clinical Pathology, 24* (1954), 1433–1434.

FITZGERALD, PATRICK J., SIMMEL, EVA, WINSTEIN, JERRY and MARTIN, CYNTHIA. "Radioautography: Theory, Technic and Applications." *Laboratory Investigation, 2* (1953), 181–222.

FITZ-WILLIAM, WILLIAM G., JONES, GEORGEANNA SEEGAR and GOLDBERG, BENJAMIN. "Cryostat techniques: Methods for improving conservation and sectioning of tissues." *Stain Technology, 35* (1960), 195–204.

FLAX, MARTIN and POLLISTER, ARTHUR W. "Staining of nucleic acids by Azure A." *Anatomical Record, 105* (1949), 536–537.

FOLEY, JAMES O. "A protargol method for staining nerve fibers in frozen or celloidin sections." *Stain Technology, 18* (1943), 27–33.

FOOT, NATHAN CHANDLER. "Comments on the impregnation of neuroglia with ammoniacal silver salts." *American Journal Pathology, 51* (1929), 223–238.

FREED, JEROME J. "Freeze-drying technics in cytology and cytochemistry." *Laboratory Investigation, 4* (1955), 106–121.

FREEMAN, BARBARA L., MOYER, ELIZABETH K. and LASSEK, ARTHUR M., "The pH of fixing fluids during fixation of tissues." *Anatomical Record, 121* (1955), 593–600.

FRIEDE, RICHARD. "Improved technique for the histochemical demonstration of succinic dehydrogenase in brain tissue." *Journal Histochemistry and Cytochemistry, 6* (1958), 347–351.

FRIEDLAND, LESTER M. "A note on frozen section technic." *American Journal Clinical Pathology, 21* (1951), 797.

FROST, H. M. "Staining of fresh, undecalcified thin bone sections." *Stain Technology, 34* (1959), 135–146.

FULLMER, HAROLD M. and LILLIE, R. D. "A selective stain for elastic tissue (orcinol-new fuchsin)." *Stain Technology, 31* (1956), 27–29.

—— and ——. "The peracetic acid-aldehyde fuchsin stain." *Journal Histochemistry and Cytochemistry, 6* (1958), 391.

GABOR, D. *The Electron Microscope.* N.Y., Chemical Publishing Co., Inc. (1948).

GAGE, SIMON HENRY. *The Microscope.* Ithaca, N.Y., Comstock Publishing Assoc. (1943).

GALIGHER, A. E. "The Essentials of Practical Microtechnique." Privately published (1934).

GALLIMORE, JOHN C., BAUER, E. C. and BOYD, GEORGE A. "A non-leaching technic for autoradiography." *Stain Technology, 29* (1954), 95–98.

GALTSOFF, PAUL S. "Simple method of making frozen sections." *Stain Technology, 31* (1956), 231.

GARDNER, D. L. "Preparation of bone marrow sections." *Stain Technology, 33* (1958), 295–297.

GATENBY, J. BRONTÉ and BEAMS, H. W. *The Microtomist's Vade-Mecum.* London, J. and A. Churchill (1950).

GAVIN, MARY ANN and LLOYD, BOLIVAR J. JR. "Knives of high silica content glass for thin sectioning." *Journal Biophysical and Biochemical Cytology, 5* (1959), 507.

GAVIN, THELMA. "Spirochetal stain on paraffin sections." *American Journal Clinical Pathology, Technical Supplement, 2* (1938), 144–145.

GAY, H. and ANDERSON, T. F. "Serial sections for electron microscopy." *Science, 120* (1954), 1071–1073.

GEORGE, J. C. and SYPE, P. THOMAS. "Improved histochemical demonstration of lipase activity." *Stain Technology, 35* (1960), 151–152.

GEREN, B. B. and McCULLOCK, D. "Development and use of the Minot Rotary microtome for thin sectioning." *Experimental Cell Research, 2* (1951), 97–102.

GERSH, ISIDORE. "The Altman technique for fixation by drying while freezing." *Anatomical Record, 53* (1932), 309–337.

——. "The preparation of frozen-dried tissue for electron microscopy." *Journal Biophysical and Biochemical Cytology, 2, Suppl.* (1956), 37–43.

GETTNER, I. R. and ORNSTEIN, L. *Physical Techniques in Biological Research.* N.Y., Academic Press, Inc. (1956).

GIOVACCHINI, RUBERT P. "Affixing Carbowax sections to slides for routine staining." *Stain Technology, 33* (1958), 274–278.

GLAUERT, AUDREY M. and GLAUERT, R. H. "Araldite as an embedding medium for electron microscopy." *Journal Biophysical and Biochemical Cytology, 4* (1958), 191–194.

GLEGG, R. E., CLERMONT, Y., and LEBLOND, C. P. "The use of lead tetra-acetate, benzidine, O-dianisidine, and a "Film Test" in investigating the periodic-acid-Schiff technic." *Stain Technology, 27* (1952), 277–305.

GLENNER, G. G. and LILLIE, R. D. "A Rhodocyan technic for staining anterior pituitary." *Stain Technology, 32* (1957), 187–190.

—— and ——. "The histochemical demonstration of indole derivatives by the post-coupled *p*-dimethylaminobenzylidene reaction." *Journal of Histochemistry and Cytochemistry, 5* (1957), 279–296.

GLICK, DAVID. *Techniques of Histo- and Cytochemistry.* N.Y., Interscience Publishers (1949).

—— and MALSTROM, B. G. "Studies in histochemistry. XXIII. A simple and efficient freezing-drying apparatus for the preparation of embedded tissue." *Experimental Cell Research, 3* (1952), 125–235.

GLYNN, J. H. "The application of the Gram stain to paraffin sections." *Archives Pathology, 20* (1935), 896–899.

GOETSCH, JOHN B. and REYNOLDS, PATRICIA M. "Obtaining uniform results in the histochemical technic for acid phosphatase." *Stain Technology, 26* (1951), 145–151.

GOLAND, PHILIP P., JASON, ROBERT S. and BERRY, KATHRYN P. "Combined Carbowax-paraffin technic for microsectioning fixed tissues." *Stain Technology, 29* (1954), 5–8.

GOLDMAN, MORRIS. "A single solution iron-hematoxylin stain for intestinal protozoa." *Stain Technology, 24* (1949), 57–60.

GOMORI, GEORGE. "Microtechnical demonstration of iron." *American Journal Pathology, 12* (1936), 655–663.

——. "The distribution of phosphatase in normal organs and tissues." *Journal Cellular and Comparative Physiology, 17* (1941 A), 71–84.

——. "Observations with differential stains on human islets of Langerhans." *American Journal Pathology, 17* (1941 B), 395–406.

———. "The study of enzymes in tissue sections." *American Journal Clinical Pathology, 16* (1946), 347–352.

———. "Chemical Character of enterochromaffin cells." *Archives Pathology, 45* (1948), 48–55.

———. "An improved histochemical technic for acid phosphatase." *Stain Technology, 25* (1950 A), 81–85.

———. "A rapid one-step trichrome stain." *American Journal Clinical Pathology, 20* (1950 B), 662–664.

———. "Aldehyde-fuchsin; a new stain for elastic tissue." *American Journal Clinical Pathology, 20* (1950 C), 665–666.

———. "Sources of error in enzymatic histochemistry." *Journal Laboratory and Clinical Medicine, 35* (1950 D), 802–809.

——— (ENGLE, EARL T. Ed.) "Menstruation and its Disorders." Springfield, Ill., Charles C. Thomas (1950 E).

———. "Alkaline phosphatase of cell nuclei." *Journal Laboratory and Clinical Medicine, 37* (1951), 526–531.

———. *Microscopic Histochemistry.* Chicago, University of Chicago Press (1952).

———. "Human Esterases." *Journal Laboratory and Clinical Medicine, 42* (1953), 445–453.

———. "The histochemistry of mucopolysaccharides." *British Journal Experimental Pathology, 35* (1954 A), 377–380.

———. "Histochemistry of the enterochromaffin substance." *Journal Histochemistry and Cytochemistry, 2* (1954 B), 50–53.

———. "Histochemistry of human esterases." *Journal Histochemistry and Cytochemistry, 3* (1955), 479–484.

———. "Histochemical methods for acid phosphatase." *Journal Histochemistry and Cytochemistry, 4* (1956), 453–361.

GONZALEZ, ROMEO. "The removal of mercury after fixation in sublimate-containing mixtures." *Stain Technology, 34* (1959 A), 111–112.

———. "Differentiation of mastocyte granules by tartrazine counterstaining after PAS procedure." *Stain Technology, 34* (1959 B), 173–174.

GORDON, HAROLD. "Method for storing wet histologic accessions and disposing of autopsy material." *Laboratory Investigation, 2* (1953), 152–153.

GOUGH, J. and FULTON, J. D. "A new fixative for mitochondria." *Journal Pathology and Bacteriology, 32* (1929), 765–769.

GOWER, W. CARL. "A modified stain and procedure for trematods." *Stain Technology, 14* (1939), 31–32.

GRADWOHL, R. B. H. *Clinical Laboratory Methods and Diagnosis.* Vol. II. St. Louis, C. V. Mosby (1956).

GRAUPNER, HEINZ and WEISSBERGER, ARNOLD. "Über der Verwendung des Dioxanes beim Einbetten mikroskopischer Objekte. Mitteilungen zur mikroskopischen Technik I." *Zoologischer Anzeiger, 96* (1931), 204–206.

——— and ———. "Die Verwendung von Lösungen in Dioxan als Fixierungsmittel für Gefrierschnitte." *Zoologischer Anzeiger, 102* (1933), 39–44.

GRAVES, K. D. "Restoration of dried biopsy tissue." *American Journal Clinical Pathology,* Technical Section, 7 (1943), 111.

GRAY, PETER. *Handbook of Basic Microtechnique.* N.Y., The Blakiston Co. (1952).

———. "The Microtomist's Formulary and Guide." N.Y., The Blakiston Co. (1954).

GREEN, JAMES A. "Luxol Fast Blue MBS: a stain for phase contrast microscopy." *Stain Technology, 31* (1956), 219–221.

GREENBLATT, ROBERT A. "Method for preparation of blood smear for chromosomal sex determination." *Endocrinology and Metabolism,* Eighth Annual Postgraduate Assembly of the Endocrine Society, Texas Medical Center, Houston (1956), 133.

——— and MANAUTOU, JORGE MARTINEZ. "A simplified staining technique for the study of chromosomal sex in oral mucosal and peripheral blood smears." *American Journal Obstetrics and Gynecology, 74* (1957), 629–634.

GREGG, V. R. and PUCKETT, W. O. "A corrosive sublimate fixing solution for yolk-laden Amphibian eggs." *Stain Technology, 18* (1943), 179–180.

GRIDLEY, MARY FRANCES. "A modification of the silver impregnation method of staining reticular fibers." *American Journal Clinical Pathology, 21* (1951), 897–899.

———. "A stain for fungi in tissue sections." *American Journal Clinical Pathology, 23* (1953), 303–307.

———. *Manual of Histologic and Special Staining Technics.* Armed Forces Institute of Pathology, Washington, D.C. (1957).

GRIFFIN, LAWRENCE E. and McQUARRIE, AGNES M. "Iron hematoxylin staining of salivary gland chromosomes in *Drosophila.*" *Stain Technology, 17* (1942), 41–42.

GROAT, RICHARD A. "Initial and persisting staining power of solutions of iron hematoxylin lake." *Stain Technology, 24* (1949), 157–163.

GROCOTT, R. G. "A stain for fungi in tissue

sections and smears, using Gomori's methenamine-silver nitrate method." *American Journal Clinical Pathology, 25* (1955), 975–979.

GRUNBAUM, BENJAMIN, GEARY, JOHN R. JR. and GLICK, DAVID. "Studies in Histochemistry: the design and use of improved apparatus for the preparation and freezing-drying of fresh-frozen sections of tissue." *Journal Histochemistry and Cytochemistry, 4* (1956), 555–560.

GUARD, HORMEZ, R. "A new technic for differential staining of the sex chromatin and the determination of its incidence in exfoliated vaginal epithelial cells." *American Journal Clinical Pathology, 32* (1959), 145–151.

GUDE, W. D. and ODELL, T. T. "Vinisil as a diluent in making bone marrow smears." *Stain Technology, 30* (1955), 27–28.

GUILLERY, R. W., SHIRRA, B. and WEBSTER, K. E. "Differential impregnation of degenerating nerve fibers in paraffin-embedded material." *Stain Technology, 36* (1961), 9–13.

GURR, EDWARD. *A Practical Manual of Medical and Biological Staining Techniques.* N.Y., Interscience Publishers, Inc. (1956).

———. *Methods of Analytical Histology and Histochemistry.* London, Leonard Hill Ltd. (1958).

———. *Encyclopaedia of Microscopic Stains.* London, Edward Gurr, or Baltimore, William and Wilkins (1960).

GURR, G. T. *Biological Staining Methods.* London, G. T. Gurr, Ltd. (1953).

GUYER, M. F. *Animal Micrology.* Chicago, University of Chicago Press (1953).

HALE, ARTHUR J. "The effect of temperature and of relative humidity on sectioning of tissues embedded in polyethylene glycol wax." *Stain Technology, 27* (1952), 189–192.

———. "The effect of formalin on the periodic acid Schiff staining of certain types of mucus." *Journal Histochemistry and Cytochemistry, 3* (1955), 421–429.

HALE, C. W. "Histochemical demonstration of acid polysaccharides in animal tissue." *Nature, 157* (1946), 802.

HALE, L. J. *Biological Laboratory Data.* Methuen's Monographs, London, Methuen and Co., or N.Y., John Wiley and Sons, Inc. (1958).

HALL, C. E. *Introduction to Electron Microscopy.* N.Y., McGraw-Hill Book Co. (1953).

HALMI, NICHOLAS S. "Two types of basophils in the anterior pituitary of the rat and their respective cytophysiological significance." *Endocrinology, 47* (1950), 289–299.

———. "Differentiation of two types of basophils in the adenohypophysis of the rat and the mouse." *Stain Technology, 27* (1952), 61–64.

HAM, ARTHUR WORTH. *Histology.* 3rd ed. Philadelphia, J. B. Lippincott Co. (1957).

HAMLYN, J. H. "Application of the Nauta-Gygax technic for degenerating axons to mounted sections." *Stain Technology, 32* (1957), 123–126.

HANCE, ROBERT T. and GREEN, FLOYD J. "Rapid ripening of hematoxylin solutions." *Stain Technology, 34* (1959), 237–238.

HANCOX, N. M. "Experiments on the fundamental effects of freeze substitution." *Experimental Cell Research, 13* (1957), 263–275.

HANSON, A. A. and OLDEMEYER, D. L. "Staining root tip smears with aceto-carmine." *Stain Technology, 26* (1951), 241–242.

HARADA, KIYOSHI. "Selective staining of mast cell granules with chrysoidin stain." *Stain Technology, 32* (1957), 183–186.

HARMON, JOHN W. "The selective staining of mitochondria." *Stain Technology, 25* (1950), 69–72.

HARNDEN, D. G. "A human skin culture technique used for cytological examinations." *British Journal Experimental Pathology, 41* (1959), 31–37.

Hartman-Leddon Company. "Informative Bulletin, #306-2." Philadelphia (1952).

HARTROFT, W. S. "Fluorchromy as an aid in the resolution of the specific granules of the islets of Langerhans." *Nature, 168* (1951), 1000.

HARTZ, P. H. "Frozen sections from Bouin-fixed material in histopathology." *Stain Technology, 20* (1945), 113–114.

———. "Simultaneous histologic fixation and gross demonstration of calcification." *American Journal Clinical Pathology, 17* (1947), 750.

HAUPT, A. W. "A gelatin fixative for paraffin sections." *Stain Technology, 5* (1930), 97.

HAUSE, WELLAND A. "Saw for preparation of blocks of bone." *Technical Bulletin, Registry of Medical Technicians, 29* (1959), 101.

HAUST, M. DARIA. "Tetrahydrofuran (THF) for dehydration and infiltration." *Laboratory Investigation, 7* (1958), 58–67.

———. "Tetrahydrofuran (THF) for routine dehydration clearing and infiltration." *Technical Bulletin, Registry of Medical Technicians, 29* (1959), 33–37.

HEGNER, ROBERT W., CORT, WILLIAM W. and ROOT, FRANCIS M. *Outlines of Medical Zoology.* N.Y., Macmillan (1927).

HETHERINGTON, DUNCAN C. "Pinacyanol as a supravital stain for blood." *Stain Technology, 11* (1936), 153–154.

HICKS, J. D. and MATTHAEI, E. "Fluorescence in Histology." *Journal Pathology and Bacteriology, 70* (1955), 1–12.

—— and ——. "A selective fluorescence stain for mucin." *Journal Pathology and Bacteriology, 75* (1958), 473–476.

HILLARY, B. B. "Permanent preparations from rapid cytological technics." *Stain Technology, 13* (1938), 161–167.

HILLEMAN, HOWARD H. and LEE, C. H. "Organic chelating agents for decalcification of bones and teeth." *Stain Technology, 28* (1953), 285–286.

HILLIER, J. and GETTNER, M. E. "Sectioning of tissue for electron microscopy." *Science, 112* (1950), 520–523.

HIMES, MARION and MORIBER, LOUIS. "A triple stain for desoxyribonucleic acid, polysaccharides, and proteins." *Stain Technology, 31* (1956), 67–70.

HODGE, ALAN J., HUXLEY, HUGH E. and SPIRO, DAVID. "A simple new microtome for ultrathin sectioning." *Journal Histochemistry and Cytochemistry, 2* (1954), 54–61.

HODGMAN, CHARLES D. *Handbook of Chemistry and Physics.* Cleveland, Chemical Rubber Publishing Co. (1957).

HOERR, N. L. "Cytological studies by the Altmann-Gersch freezing-drying method. I. Recent advances in the technique." *Anatomical Record, 65* (1936), 293–317.

HOLDE, P. and ISLER, H. "The effect of phosphomolybdic acid on the stainability of connective tissue by various dyes." *Journal Histochemistry and Cytochemistry, 6* (1958), 265–270.

HOLLISTER, GLORIA. "Clearing and dyeing fish for bone study." *Zoologica, 12* (1934), 89–101.

HOLMES, W. C. "The mechanism of staining. The case for the physical theories." *Stain Technology, 4* (1929), 75–80.

HOLT, MARGARET and WARREN, SHIELDS. "A radioautograph method for detailed localization of radioactive isotopes in tissues without isotope loss." *Proceedings Society Experimental Biology and Medicine, 73* (1950), 545.

—— and ——. "Freeze-drying tissues for autoradiography." *Laboratory Investigation, 2* (1953), 1–14.

——, COWING, R. F. and WARREN, S. "Preparation of radioautographs of tissues without loss of water soluble P^{32}." *Science, 110* (1949), 328–329.

——, SOMMERS, S. C. and WARREN, S. "Preparation of tissue sections for quantitative histochemical studies." *Anatomical Record, 112* (1952), 177–186.

HOOD, R. C. W. S. and NEILL, W. M. "A modification of alizarine red S technic for demonstrating bone formation." *Stain Technology, 23* (1948), 209–218.

HOTCHKISS, R. D. "A microchemical reaction resulting in the staining of polysaccharide structures in fixed tissues." *Archives of Biochemistry, 16* (1948), 131–141.

HOUCKS, C. E. and DEMPSEY, E. W. "Cytological staining procedures applicable to methacrylate embedded tissues." *Stain Technology, 29* (1954), 207–212.

HUBER, WILLIAM M. and CAPLIN, SAMUEL M. "Simple plastic mount for preservation of fungi and small arthropods." *Archives Dermatology and Syphilology, 56* (1947), 763–765.

HULL, SUSAN and WEGNER, SALLY. "Removal of stains." *Stain Technology, 27* (1952), 224.

HUMASON, GRETCHEN L. and LUSHBAUGH, C. C. "Selective demonstration of elastin, reticulum, and collagen by silver, orcein, and aniline blue." *Stain Technology, 35* (1960), 209–214.

—— and ——. "Pinacyanol stain for frozen sections and smears." in press (1961).

HUMPHREY, A. A. "Di-nitrosoresorcinol— a new specific for iron in tissue." *Archives Pathology, 20* (1935), 256–258.

——. "A new rapid method for frozen section diagnosis." *Journal Laboratory and Clinical Medicine, 22* (1936), 198–199.

HUTCHISON, H. E. "The significance of stainable iron in sternal marrow sections." *Blood, 8* (1953), 236–248.

HUTNER, S. H. "Destaining agents for iron alum hematoxylin." *Stain Technology, 9* (1934), 57–59.

HUTTON, W. E. "Ninhydrin staining of tissue sections." *Stain Technology, 28* (1953), 173–175.

IBANEZ, MICHAEL L., RUSSELL, WILLIAM O., CHANG, JEFFREY P. and SPEECE, ARTHUR J. "Cold chamber frozen sections for operating room diagnosis and routine surgical pathology. *Laboratory Investigation, 9* (1960), 98–109.

IRUGALBANDARA, Z. E. "Simplified differentiation of Nissl granules stained by toluidine blue in paraffin sections." *Stain Technology, 35* (1960), 47–48.

JENNINGS, ROBERT B. "A simple apparatus for dehydration of frozen tissues." *Archives Pathology, 52* (1951), 195–197.

JOFTES, DAVID L. "Liquid emulsion autoradiography with Tritium." *Laboratory Investigation, 8* (1959), 131–148.

———, and WARREN, S. "Simplified liquid emulsion radioautography." *Journal Biological Photographic Association, 23* (1955), 145.

JOHANSON, DONALD. Plant Microtechnique. N.Y., McGraw-Hill Book Co. (1940).

JOHNSON, PERCY L. and KELIN, MORRIS N. "Application of the Papanicolaou stain to paraffin sections." *Stain Technology, 31* (1956), 223–225.

JOHNSTON, MURIEL E. "Film as a histological tissue support." *Journal Histochemistry and Cytochemistry, 8* (1960), 139.

JONES, ROSE M., THOMAS, WILBUR A. and O'NEAL, ROBERT M. "Embedding of tissues in Carbowax." *Technical Bulletin, Registry of Medical Technologists, 29* (1959), 49–52.

KABAT, ELVIN A. and FURTH, JACOB. "A histochemical study of the distribution of alkaline phosphatase in various normal and neoplastic tissues." *American Journal Pathology, 17* (1941), 303–318.

KAMINSKI, E. J. "Histological processing in autoradiography; loss of radioactivity." *Stain Technology, 30* (1955), 139–145.

KAPLAN, MELVIN H., COONS, ALBERT H. and DEANE, HELEN WENDLER. "Localization of antigen in tissue cells. III. Cellular distribution of pneumococcal polysaccharides, types II and III, in the mouse." *Journal Experimental Medicine, 91* (1950), 15–29.

KASSEL, ROBERT and MELNITSKY, IDA. "Embedding and staining ameboid forms." *Stain Technology, 26* (1951), 167–171.

KASTEN, FREDERICK and BURTON, VIVIAN. "A modified Schiff's solution." *Stain Technology, 34* (1959), 289.

KELLER, G. J. "A reliable Nissl stain." *Journal Technical Methods, 25* (1945), 77–78.

KERBAUGH, MILDRED A. "Identification of Beta hemolytic streptococci, group A, by the fluorescent method." *Official Journal American Medical Technologists, 22* (1960), 13–16.

KERENYI, N. "Congo red as a simple stain for the beta cells of the hypophysis." *Stain Technology, 34* (1959), 343–346.

KERR, DONALD A. "Improved Warthin-Starry method of staining spirochetes in tissue sections." *American Journal Clinical Pathology, Technical Supplement, 2* (1938), 63–67.

KESSEL, J. F. "The distinguishing characteristics of the intestinal protozoa of man." *China Medical Journal, Feb.* (1925), 1–57.

KLINGER, H. P. "The fine structure of the sex chromatin body." *Experimental Cell Research, 14* (1958), 207–211.

——— and LUDWIG, KURT S. "A universal stain for the sex chromatin body." *Stain Technology, 32* (1957), 235–244.

KLIONSKY, B. and MARCOUX, L. "Frozen storage of incubation media for enzyme histochemistry." *Journal Histochemistry and Cytochemistry, 8* (1960), 329.

KLOECK, JOHN M. and SWEANEY, HENRY C. "Binocular fluorescent microscopy." *American Journal Clinical Pathology, Technical Section, 7* (1943), 96–98.

KLUVER, H. and BARRERA, E. "A method for the combined staining of cells and fibers in the nervous system." *Journal Neuropathology and Experimental Neurology, 12* (1953), 400–403.

KOENIG, HAROLD, GROAT, RICHARD A. and WINDLE, WILLIAM F. "A physiological approach to perfusion-fixation of tissues with formalin." *Stain Technology, 20* (1945), 13–22.

KONEFF, ALEXEI A. "An iron hematoxylin-aniline blue staining method for routine laboratory use." *Anatomical Record, 66* (1936), 173.

———. "Adaptation of the Mallory-Azan staining method to the anterior pituitary of the rat." *Stain Technology, 13* (1938), 49–52.

——— and LYONS, W. R. "Rapid embedding with hot low-viscosity nitrocellulose." *Stain Technology, 12* (1937), 57–59.

KORNHAUSER, S. I. "Hematein. Its advantages for general laboratory usage." *Stain Technology, 5* (1930), 13–15.

———. "A quadruple stain for strong color contrasts." *Stain Technology, 18* (1943), 95–97.

———. "A revised method for the 'Quad' stain." *Stain Technology, 20* (1945), 33–35.

———. "Orcein and elastic fibers." *Stain Technology, 27* (1952), 131–134.

KRAJIAN, ARAM A. and GRADWOHL, R. B. H.

Histopathological Technic. St. Louis, C. V. Mosby Co. (1952).

KRICHESKY, BORIS. "A modification of Mallory's triple stain." *Stain Technology, 6* (1931), 97–98.

KRISTENSEN, HAROLD K. "An improved method of decalcification." *Stain Technology, 23* (1948), 151–154.

KROPP, B. "Grinding thin sections of plastic embedded bone." *Stain Technology, 29* (1954), 77–80.

KRUSZYNSKI, J. "Selective demonstration of the Golgi structure and of mitochondria." *Stain Technology, 29* (1954), 151–155.

KUBIE, LAWRENCE S. and DAVIDSON, DAVID. "The ammoniacal silver solution as used in neuropathology." *Archives Neurology and Psychiatry, 19* (1928), 888–903.

KUHN, GERALDINE D. and LUTZ, EARNEST L. "A modified polyester embedding medium for sectioning." *Stain Technology, 33* (1958), 1–7.

KURNICK, N. B. "Histological staining with methyl green-pyronin." *Stain Technology, 27* (1952), 233–242.

———. "Pyronin Y in the methyl green-pyronin histological stain." *Stain Technology, 30* (1955), 213–230.

KUYPER, CH. M. A. "Identification of mucopolysaccharides by means of fluorescent basic dyes." *Experimental Cell Research, 13* (1957), 198–200.

LACEY, PAULE E. and DAVIES, J. "Demonstration of insulin in mammalian pancrease by the fluorescent antibody method." *Stain Technology, 34* (1959), 85–89.

LACOUR, L. "Technic for studying chromosome structure." *Stain Technology, 10* (1935), 57–60.

———. "Acetic-orcein: a new stain-fixative for chromosomes." *Stain Technology, 16* (1941), 169–174.

LACROIX, J. DONALD and PREISS, SISTER ROSE FREDERICK. "Lamination of thermoplastic sheets as a means of mounting histological material." *Stain Technology, 35* (1960), 331–337.

LAIDLOW, G. F. "Silver staining of the skin and its tumors." *American Journal Pathology, 5* (1929), 239–248.

LANDING, BENJAMIN H. "Histological study of the anterior pituitary." *Laboratory Investigation, 3* (1954), 348–368.

——— and HALL, HAZEL E. "Differentiation of human anterior pituitary cells by combined metal-mordant and mucoprotein stains." *Laboratory Investigation, 4* (1955), 275–278.

LANGE, NORBERT ADOLPH. *Handbook of Chemistry.* Sandusky, O., Handbook Publishers, Inc. (1956).

LASCANO, EDUARDO F. "A new silver method for the Golgi apparatus." *Archives Pathology, 68* (1959), 499–500.

LASKY, A. and GRECO, J. "Argentaffin cells of the human appendix." *Archives of Pathology, 46* (1948), 83–84.

LAWLESS, D. K. "A rapid permanent mount stain technic for the diagnosis of the intestinal protozoa." *American Journal Tropical Medicine and Hygiene, 2* (1953), 1137.

LAZARUS, SIDNEY S. "A combined periodic acid-Schiff trichrome stain." *American Medical Association, Archives Pathology, 66* (1958), 767–772.

LEACH, E. H. "Curtis' substitute for van Gieson stain." *Stain Technology, 21* (1946), 107–109.

LEDUC, ELIZABETH H., COONS, ALBERT H. and CONNOLLY, JEANNE M. "Studies on antibody production. II. The primary and secondary responses in the popliteal lymph node of the rabbit." *Journal Experimental Medicine, 102* (1955), 61–71.

LEHMANN, F. E. and MANCUSO, V. "Improved fixative for astral rays and nuclear membrane of *Tubifex* embryos." *Experimental Cell Research, 13* (1957), 161–164.

LENDRUM, ALAN C. "On the cutting of tough and hard tissues embedded in paraffin." *Stain Technology, 19* (1944), 143–144.

——— and McFARLANE, DAVID. "A controllable modification of Mallory's trichrome staining method." *Journal Pathology and Bacteriology, 50* (1940), 38–40.

LENNOX, BERNARD. "A ribonuclease-gallocyanin stain for sexing skin biopsies." *Stain Technology, 31* (1956), 167–172.

LEV, MAURICE and THOMAS, JOHN T. "An improved method for fixing and staining frozen sections." *American Journal Clinical Pathology, 25* (1955), 465.

LEVINE, M. "A method for staining connective tissue mast cells." *Journal Laboratory and Clinical Medicine, 14* (1928), 172.

LEWIS, LOUIS W. "Method for affixing celloidin sections." *Stain Technology, 20* (1945), 138.

LHOTKA, J. F. and DAVENPORT, H. A. "Differential staining of tissue in the block with picric acid and the Feulgen reaction." *Stain Technology, 22* (1947), 139–144.

——— and ———. "Deterioration of Schiff's

reagent." *Stain Technology* 24 (1949), 237–239.

——— and ———. "Aldehyde reactions in tissues in relation to the Fculgen technic." *Stain Technology*, 26 (1951), 35–41.

——— and MYHRE, BYRON A. "Periodic acid-Foot stain for connective tissue." *Stain Technology*, 28 (1953), 129–133.

——— and VAZ FERREIRA, ALBERTO. "A comparison of deformalinizing technics." *Stain Technology*, 25 (1950), 27–32.

LIEB, ETHEL. "Permanent stain for amyloid." *American Journal Clinical Pathology*, 17 (1947), 413–414.

———. "A modified phosphotungstic acid-hematoxylin." *Archives Pathology*, 45 (1948), 559–560.

———. "The plastic (mylar) sack as an aid in the teaching of pathology." *American Journal Clinical Pathology*, 32 (1959), 385–392.

LIEBMAN, EMIL. "Permanent preparations with the Thomas arginine histochemical test." *Stain Technology*, 26 (1951), 261–263.

LILLIE, R. D. "Gram stain. A quick method for staining Gram positive bacteria in tissues." *Archives Pathology*, 5 (1928), 828.

———. "A brief method for the demonstration of mucin." *Journal of Technical Methods and Bulletin, International Association of Medical Museums*, 12 (1929), 120–121.

———. "Further experiments with the Masson trichrome modifications of the Mallory connective tissue stain." *Stain Technology*, 15 (1940), 17–22.

———. "Acetic methylene blue counterstain in staining tissues for acid fast bacilli." *Stain Technology*, 18 (1944), 45.

———. "A simplified method of preparation of di-ammine-silver hydroxide for reticulum impregnation; comments on the nature of the so-called sensitization before impregnation." *Stain Technology*, 21 (1946), 69–72.

———. "Studies on the histochemistry of normal and pathologic mucin in man and laboratory animals." *Bulletin, International Association Medical Museums*, 29 (1949), 1–53.

———. "Histochemical comparison of the Casella, Bauer, and peric⁀ᵈᶜ acid oxidation Schiff leucofuchsin technics." *Stain Technology*, 26 (1951 A), 123–136.

———. "Simplification of the manufacture of Schiff reagent for use in histochemical procedures." *Stain Technology*, 26 (1951 B), 163–165.

———. "The allochrome procedure. A differential method segregating the connective tissues, collagen, reticulum, and basement membranes into two groups." *American Journal Clinical Pathology*, 21 (1951 C), 484–488.

———. "Factors influencing periodic-Schiff reaction of collagen fibers." *Journal Histochemistry and Cytcohemistry*, 1 (1953), 353–361.

———. "Argentaffin and Schiff reactions after periodic acid oxidation and aldehyde blocking reactions." *Journal Histochemistry and Cytochemistry*, 2 (1954 A), 127–136.

———. *Histopathologic Technic and Practical Histochemistry.* N.Y., The Blakiston Co. (1954 B).

———. "The basophilia of melanins." *Journal Histochemistry and Cytochemistry*, 3 (1955), 453–454.

———. "Nile blue staining technic of the differentiation of melanin and lipofuchsins." *Stain Technology*, 31 (1956 A), 151–153.

———. "The mechanism of nile blue staining of lipofuchsins." *Journal Histochemistry and Cytochemistry*, 4 (1956 B), 377–381.

———. "The p-dimethylaminobenzaldehyde reaction for pyrroles in histochemistry: melanins, enterochromaffin, zymogen granules, lens." *Journal Histochemistry and Cytochemistry*, 4 (1956 C), 118–129.

———. "Ferrous ion uptake." *Archives of Pathology*, 64 (1957 A) 100–103.

———. "The xanthydrol reaction for pyrroles and indoles in histochemistry: zymogen granules, lens, enterochromaffin, and melanins." *Journal Histochemistry and Cytochemistry*, 5 (1957 B), 188–195.

———. "Metal reduction reactions in melanins." *Journal Histochemistry and Cytochemistry*, 5 (1957 C), 325–333.

———. "Metal chelate reaction of enterochromaffin." *Journal Histochemistry and Cytochemistry*, 9 (1960), 44–48.

———. "Investigations on the structure of the enterochromaffin substance." *Journal Histochemistry and Cytochemistry*, 9 (1961), 184–189.

——— and BURTNER, H. J. "The ferric ferricyanide reduction test in histochemistry." *Journal Histochemistry and Cytochemistry*, 1 (1953), 87–92.

———, ———, GRECO, J., and HENSON, P. "Diazo-safranin for staining enterochromaffin." *Journal Histochemistry and Cytochemistry*, 1 (1953), 154–159.

—— and EARLE, W. R. "The use of Janssen's iron hematoxylin in place of the Weigert acid iron chloride hematoxylin." *Stain Technology, 14* (1939 A), 53–54.

—— and ——. "Iron hematoxylins containing ferric and ferrous iron." *American Journal Pathology, 15* (1939 B), 765–770.

——, and GLENNER, G. G. "Histochemical aldehyde blockade by aniline in glacial acetic acid." *Journal Histochemistry and Cytochemistry, 5* (1957), 167–169.

——, HENSON, JACQUELIN P., GRECO, J. and BURTNER, HELEN C. J. "Metal reduction reactions of melanins: silver and ferric ferricyanide reduction by various reagents *in vitro.*" *Journal Histochemistry and Cytochemistry, 5* (1957), 311–324.

——, ——, ——, and CARSON, JOSEPH C. "Azo-coupling rate of enterochromaffin with various diazonium salts." *Journal Histochemistry and Cytochemistry, 9* (1960), 11–21.

——, LASKY, A., GRECO, J., BURTNER, H. JACQUIER and JONES, P. "Decalcification of bone in relation to staining and phosphatase technics." *American Journal Clinical Pathology, 21* (1951), 711–722.

——, WINDLE, W. F. and ZIRKLE, CONWAY. "Interim report of the committee on histologic mounting media: resinous media." *Stain Technology, 25* (1950), 1–9.

——, ZIRKLE, CONWAY, DEMPSEY, EDWARD and GRECO, JACQUELINE F. "Final report of the committee on histological mounting media." *Stain Technology, 28* (1953), 57–80.

LISON, LUCIEN. "Alcian blue 8G with Chlorantine fast red 5B. A technic for selective staining of mucopolysaccharides." *Stain Technology, 29* (1954), 131–138.

LIU, WINIFRED. *An Introduction to Gynecological Exfoliative Cytology. A Working Manual for Cytotechnicians.* Springfield, Ill., Charles C. Thomas (1960).

LONG, MARGARET E. "Differentiation of myofibrillae, reticular and collagenous fibrillae in vertebrates." *Stain Technology, 23* (1948), 69–75.

LOUIS, C. J. "Cutting unfixed frozen sections for fluorescence antibody studies." *Stain Technology, 32* (1957), 279–282.

LOW, FRANK N. "A fixation method for the electron microscopy of endoplasmic reticulum. *Anatomical Record, 121* (1955), 332–333.

—— and FREEMAN, JAMES A. "Some experiments with chromium compounds as fixers for electron microscopy." *Journal Biophysical and Biochemical Cytology, 2* (1956), 629–631.

LUCAS, R. B. "Observations on the electrolysis method of decalcification." *Journal Pathology and Bacteriology, 64* (1952), 654–657.

LUFT, JOHN H. "Permanganate—a new fixative for electron microscopy." *Journal Biophysical and Biochemical Cytology, 2* (1956), 799–601.

LUNA, L. G. and BALLOU, E. F., "Better paraffin sections with the aid of vacuum." *American Journal Medical Technologists, 25* (1959), 411–413.

McCLINTOCK, BARBARA. "A method for making aceto-carmine smears permanent." *Stain Technology, 4* (1929), 53.

McCLUNG, C. E. *Handbook of Microscopical Technique.* N.Y., Paul B. Hoeber and Co. (1939).

McCORMICK, JAMES B. "Technic for restaining faded histopathologic slides." *Technical Bulletin, Registry of Medical Technologists, 29* (1959 A), 13–14.

——. "One hour paraffin processing technic for biopsy of bone marrow and other tissues, and specimens of fluid sediment." *American Journal Clinical Pathology, 31* (1959 B), 278–279.

McGEE-RUSSELL, S. M. "Histochemical methods for calcium." *Journal Histochemistry and Cytochemistry, 6* (1958), 22–42.

MACLEAN, KENNETH S. "Automation in staining of cytologic specimens." *Stain Technology, 35* (1960), 31–34.

McMANUS, J. F. A. "The histological demonstration of mucin after periodic acid." *Nature, 158* (1946), 202.

——. "Histological and histochemical uses of periodic acid." *Stain Technology, 23* (1948), 99–108.

—— and MOWRY, ROBERT W. "Effects of fixation on carbohydrate histochemistry." *Journal Histochemistry and Cytochemistry, 6* (1958), 309–316.

—— and ——. "Staining Methods: Histologic and Histochemical." N.Y., *Paul B. Hoeber and Co.* (1960).

McNAMARA, W. L., MURPHY, BERTA and GORE, W. A. "Method for simultaneous fixation and decalcification of bone." *Journal Laboratory and Clinical Medicine, 25* (1940), 874–875.

MAHON, GEORGE S. "Stain for myelin sheaths in tissue embedded in paraffin." *Archives Neurology and Psychiatry, 38* (1937), 103.

MAKOWSKI, E. L., PREM, K. A. and KAISER,

I. H. "Detection of sex of fetuses by the incidence of sex chromatin body in nuclei of cells in amniotic fluid." *Science, 123* (1956), 542–543.

MALLORY, FRANK B. *Pathological Technique.* Philadelphia, W. B. Saunders Co. (1944).

MANHEIMER, LEON H. and SELIGMAN, ARNOLD. "Improvement in the method for histochemical demonstration of alkaline phosphatase and its use in a study of normal and neoplastic tissues." *Journal National Cancer Institute, 9* (1949), 181–199.

MANIKAS, S. G. and UMIKER, W. O. "An improved rapid method for mounting cytologic smears." *American Journal Clinical Pathology, 31* (1959), 414.

Manufacturing Chemists' Association. Technical Data on Plastics. Manufacturing Chemists' Association, Inc., Washington 6, D.C. (1957).

MANWELL, REGINALD D. "The JSB stain for blood parasites." *Journal Laboratory and Clinical Medicine, 30* (1945), 1078–1082.

MARBERGER, EVE, BOCCABELLA, RITA A. and NELSON, WARREN O. "Oral smear as a method of chromosomal sex detection." *Proceedings Society Experimental Biology and Medicine, 89* (1955), 488–489.

MARGOLIS, G. and PICKETT, J. P. "New applications of the luxol fast blue myelin stain." *Laboratory Investigation, 5* (1956) 459–474.

MARKERT, CLEMENT L. and HUNTER, ROBERT L. "The distribution of esterases in mouse tissues." *Journal Histochemistry and Cytochemistry, 7* (1959), 42–49.

MARTI, WALTER J. and JOHNSON, BERKLEY H. "Acid fast staining technic for histological sections." *American Journal Clinical Pathology, 21* (1951), 793.

MARWAH, A. S. and WEINMANN, J. P. "A sex difference in epithelial cells of human gingiva." *Journal Periodontology, 26* (1955), 11–13.

MASSIGNANI, ADRIANA and MALFERRARI, ROSELLA. "Phosphotungstic acid-eosin combined with hematoxylin as a stain for Negri bodies in paraffin sections." *Stain Technology, 36* (1961), 5–8.

———— and REFINETTI, ELOISA MISASI. "The Papanicolaou stain for Negri bodies in paraffin sections." *Stain Technology, 33* (1958), 197–199.

MASSON, P. "Carcinoids (argentaffin cell tumors) and nerve hyperplasia of the appendicular mucosa." *American Journal of Pathology, 4* (1928), 181–211.

MELANDER, YNGVE and WINGSTRAND, KARL

GEORG. "Gomori's hematoxylin as a chromosome stain." *Stain Technology, 28* (1953), 217–223.

MELLORS, ROBERT C. *Analytical Cytology.* New York, McGraw-Hill Book Co., Blakiston Division (1959).

————, SIEGEL, MALCOLM and PRESSMAN, DAVID. "Analytic Pathology. Histochemical demonstration of antibody localization in tissues with special reference to the antigenic components of kidney and lung." *Laboratory Investigation, 4* (1955), 69–89.

MELVIN, DOROTHY M. and BROOKE, M. M. "Triton X-100 in Giemsa staining of blood parasites." *Stain Technology, 30* (1955), 269–275.

MENDELOW, HARVEY and HAMILTON, JAMES B. "A new technique for rapid freezing and dehydration of tissues for histology and histochemistry." *Anatomical Record, 107* (1950), 443–451.

MENZIES, D. W. "Picro-Gomori method." *Stain Technology, 34* (1959), 294–295.

MEREI, F. T. and GALLYAS, F. "A simple method for staining histologic sections in autoradiography." *Journal Histochemistry and Cytochemistry, 8* (1960), 444–445.

MERIWETHER, L. S. "Proceedings of Staff Meetings of Mayo Clinic," Mayo Foundation, *9* (1934), 95–96.

MERYMAN, H. T. "Sublimation freeze-drying without vacuum." *Science, 130* (1959), 628–629.

————. "Freezing and drying of biological materials. Part III. Principles of freeze-drying." *Annals of N.Y. Academy of Sciences, 85* (1960), 501–734.

MESSIER, B. and LEBLOND, C. P. "Preparation of coated radioautographs by dipping sections in fluid emulsion." *Proceedings Society of Experimental Biology and Medicine, 96* (1957), 7–10.

METCALF, R. L. and PATTON, R. L. "Fluorescence microscopy applied to Entomology and allied fields." *Stain Technology, 19* (1944), 11–27.

METTLER, FRED A. "The Marchi method for demonstrating degenerated fiber connections within the central nervous system." *Stain Technology, 7* (1932), 95–106.

———— and HANADA, RUTH E. "The Marchi method." *Stain Technology, 17* (1942), 111–116.

———— METTLER, CECELIA C., and STRONG, F. C. "The cellosolve-nitrocellulose technic." *Stain Technology, 11* (1936), 165–166.

METTLER, SIDNEY and BARTHA, ALEXANDER

S. "Brilliant cresyl blue as a stain for chromosome smear preparations." *Stain Technology, 23* (1948), 27–28.

MEYER, JAMES R. "Colchicine-Feulgen leaf smears." *Stain Technology, 18* (1943), 53–56.

———. "Prefixing with paradichlorobenzene to facilitate chromosome study." *Stain Technology, 20* (1945), 121–125.

MEYER-ARENDT, JURGEN R. "Mylar film as carrier material for microradiography." *Journal Histochemistry and Cytochemistry, 7* (1959), 351–352.

MILLER, BERNARD JOSEPH. "The use of Dioxane in the preparation of histological sections." *The Mendel Bulletin*, December (1937), 5–9.

MITTWER, TOD, BARTHOLOMEW, T. W. and KALLMAN, BURTON J. "The mechanism of the Gram reaction. 2. The function of iodine in the Gram stain." *Stain Technology, 25* (1950), 169–179.

MOFFAT, D. B. "Demonstration of alkaline phosphatase and periodic acid-Schiff positive material in the same section." *Stain Technology, 33* (1958), 225–228.

MOHR, J. L. and WEHRLE, WILLIAM. "Notes on mounting media." *Stain Technology, 17* (1942), 157–160.

MOLINER, ENRIQUE RAMON. "A chlorate-formaldehyde modification of the Golgi method." *Stain Technology, 32* (1957), 105–116.

MOORE, KEITH L. and BARR, MURRAY L. "Smears from the oral mucosa in the detection of chromosomal sex." *The Lancet, 269*, Vol. 2 (1955), 57–58.

———, GRAHAM, MARGARET A. and BARR, MURRAY L. "The detection of chromosomal sex in hermaphrodites from a skin biopsy." *Surgery, Gynecology and Obstetrics, 96* (1953), 641–648.

MONK, CECIL R. "An aqueous media for mounting small objects." *Science, 88* (1938), 174.

MORAN, THOMAS J., RADCLIFFE, MERLE L. and TEVAULT, ISABELLE H. "Rapid method of staining tubercle bacilli with Tergitol." *American Journal Clinical Pathology, 17* (1947), 75–77.

MOREE, R. "Control of the ferric ion concentration in iron-acetocarmine staining." *Stain Technology, 19* (1944), 103–108.

MORRIS, RUSSELL E. and BENTON, ROBERT S. "Studies on demineralization of bone. IV. Evaluation of morphology and staining characteristics of tissues after demineralization." *American Journal Clinical Pathology, 26* (1956), 882–898.

MORRISON, MAURICE and SAMWISK, A. A. "Restoration of overstained Wright films and a new method of staining blood smears." *American Journal Clinical Pathology, Technical Supplement, 4* (1940), 92–93.

MORTON, ALPERT, JACOBOWITZ, DAVID, and MARKS, BERNARD H. "A simple method for the demonstration of lipofuchsin pigment." *Journal Histochemistry and Cytochemistry, 8* (1960), 153–158.

MOSSMAN, H. W. "The Dioxan technic." *Stain Technology, 12* (1937), 147–156.

MOVAT, HENRY Z. "Demonstration of all connective tissue elements in a single section." *Archives of Pathology, 60* (1955), 289–295.

MOWRY, ROBERT W. "Alcian blue technique for histochemical study of acidic carbohydrates." *Journal Histochemistry and Cytochemistry, 4* (1956), 407.

———. "Improved procedure for the staining of acidic polysaccharides by Müller's colloidal (hydrous) ferric oxide and its combination with the Feulgen and P.A.S. reactions." *Laboratory Investigation, 7* (1958), 566–576.

———. "Effect of periodic acid used prior to chromic acid on the staining of polysaccharides by Gomori's methenamine silver." *Proceedings Histochemical Society, Journal Histochemistry and Cytochemistry, 7* (1959), 288.

———. "Revised method producing improved coloration of acidic mucopolysaccharides with alcian blue 8GX supplied currently." *Journal Histochemistry and Cytochemistry, 8* (1960), 323.

——— and WINKLER, C. H. "The coloration acidic carbohydrates of bacteria and fungi in tissue sections with special reference to capsules of *Crytococcus neoformans, Pneumococcus* and *Stapylococcus*." *American Journal Pathology, 32* (1956), 628–629.

MULLEN, JOHN P. and McCARTER, JOHN C. "A mordant preparing formaldehyde-fixed neuraxis tissue for phosphotungstic acid hematoxylin staining." *American Journal Pathology, 17* (1941), 289–291.

MUNOZ, FRANK and CHARIPPER, HARRY A. *The Microscope and its Use.* Brooklyn, N.Y., Chemical Publishing Co. (1943).

MURDOCK, S. E. "A method for the removal of precipitate from tissues fixed in formaldehyde." *Journal Technical Methods, 25* (1945), 71–72.

NACHLAS, MARVIN and SELIGMAN, ARNOLD

M. "The histochemical demonstration of esterase." *Journal National Cancer Institute, 9* (1949), 415–435.

————, TSOU, KWAN-CHUNG, DESOUZA, EUSTACE, CHENG, CHAO-SHING and SELIGMAN, ARNOLD M. "Cytochemical demonstration of succinic dehydrogenase by the use of a new *p*-nitrophenyl substituted ditetrazole." *Journal Histochemistry and Cytochemistry, 5* (1957), 420–436.

NASSAR, TAMIR K. and SHANKLIN, WILLIAM M. "Staining neuroglia with silver diamminohydroxide after sensitizing with sodium sulfite and embedding in paraffin." *Stain Technology, 26* (1951), 13–18.

NAUTA, W. J. H. and GYGAX, P. A. "Silver impregnation of degenerating axon terminals in the central nervous system. 1. Technic. Chemical Notes." *Stain Technology, 26* (1951), 5–11.

———— and ————. "Silver impregnation of degenerating axons in the central nervous system: a modified technic." *Stain Technology, 29* (1954), 91–93.

———— and RYAN, LLOYD F. "Selective silver impregnation of degenerating axons in the central nervous system." *Stain Technology, 27* (1952), 175–179.

NAVASQUEZ, S. D. "Experimental tubular necrosis of the kidneys accompanied by liver changes due to dioxane poisoning." *Journal of Hygiene, 35* (1935), 540–548.

NEEDHAM, GEORGE HERBERT. *The Practical Use of the Microscope.* Springfield, Ill., Charles C. Thomas (1958).

NEWCOMER, EARL A. "An osmic impregnation method for mitochondria in plant cells." *Stain Technology, 15* (1940), 89–90.

————. "Feulgen staining of tissues prior to embedding and sectioning." *Stain Technology, 34* (1959), 349–350.

NEWMAN, SANFORD B. "A new technique for cutting very thin sections and its application for the electron microscopy of fibers." *ASTM Bulletin, 163* (1950), 57–60.

————, BORYSKO, EMIL and SWERDLOW, MAX. "Ultra microtomy by a new method." *Journal of Research, National Bureau of Standards, 43* (1949 A), 183–199.

————, ————, and ————. "New sectioning techniques for light and electron microscopy." *Science, 110* (1949 B), 66–68.

New York Society of Electron Microtomists. Bibliography of Electron Microscopy. 2 E. 63rd Street, N.Y.

NICKERSON, MARK. "A dry ice freezing unit for rotary microtomes." *Science, 100* (1944), 177–178.

NITO, YUICHI and STOKES, J. R. "An improved colloidal iron staining reagent." *Stain Technology, 35* (1960), 103.

NOBLE, GLENN A. "A five-minutes method for staining fecal smears." *Science, 100* (1944), 37–38.

NOLTE, D. J. "A modified technic for salivary gland chromosomes." *Stain Technology, 23* (1948), 21–25.

NONIDEZ, JOSÉ F. "Studies on the innervation of the heart. I. distribution of the cardiac nerves, with special reference to the identification of the sympathetic and parasympathetic postganglionics." *American Journal of Anatomy, 65* (1939), 361–413.

NORRIS, WILLIAM P. and JENKINS, PHYLLIS. "Epoxy resin embedding in contrast radioautography of bones and teeth." *Stain Technology, 35* (1960), 253–260.

NOVIKOFF, ALEX B., SHIN, WOO-YUNG and DRUCKER, JOAN. "Cold acetone fixation for enzyme localization in frozen sections." *Journal Histochemistry and Cytochemistry, 8* (1960), 37–40.

NOYES, WILBUR FISKE. "Visualization of Egypt 101 virus in the mouse's brain and in cultured human carcinoma cells by means of fluorescent antibody." *Journal Experimental Medicine, 102* (1955), 243–247.

———— and WATSON, BARBARA K. "Studies on the increase of vaccine virus in cultured human cells by means of fluorescent antibody technique." *Journal Experimental Medicine, 102* (1955), 237–242.

NURNBERGER, JOHN J. "Ultraviolet microscopy and microspectroscopy," *Analytical Cytology,* ed., Robert C. Mellors. N.Y., Blakiston (1955).

NYLEN, MARIE USSING and HOLAND, W. J. "A modified Spencer microtome for thin sectioning." *Experimental Cell Research, 13* (1957), 88–95.

O'MARA, G. G. "Observations on the immediate effects of colchicine." *Journal Heredity, 30* (1939), 35–37.

ORA, ARVID, I. "Rapid stain for myelin sheaths, using formalin-fixed paraffin sections." *American Journal Clinical Pathology, Technical Section, 29* (1958), 510.

OSTER, GERALD. "X-ray diffraction techniques and their application to the study of biomolecular structures." *Analytical*

Cytology, ed., Robert C. Mellors. N.Y., Blakiston (1955).

PACKER, D. M. and SCOTT, GORDON H. "A cryostat of new design for low temperature dehydration." *Journal of Technical Methods,* 22 (1942), 85–96.

PADAWAR, JACQUES. "A stain for mast cells and its application in various vertebrates and in a Mastocytoma." *Journal Histochemistry and Cytochemistry,* 7 (1959), 352–353.

PAGET, G. E. and ECCLESTON, ENID. "Aldehyde-thionin: a stain having similar properties to aldehyde-fuchsin." *Stain Technology,* 34 (1959), 223–226.

—— and ——. "Simultaneous specific demonstration of thyrotroph, gonadotroph and acidophil cells in the anterior hypophysis." *Stain Technology,* 35 (1960), 119–122.

PALADE, G. E. "A study of fixation for electron microscopy." *Journal Experimental Medicine,* 95 (1952), 285–297.

PALKOWSKI, WALTER. "A new method of deep freezing pathologic specimens in a pliable state." *Technical Bulletin of Registry of Medical Technologists,* 30 (1960), 187.

PALMGREN, AXEL. "Tape for microsectioning of very large, hard, or brittle specimens." *Nature,* 174 (1954), 46.

PANTIN, C. F. A. *"Notes on Microscopical Technique for Zoologists."* Cambridge University Press (1946).

PAPAMILTIADES, M. "Sur la composition de deus hematoxylines pour les colorations cytologiques." *Acta Anatomica,* 19 (1953), 25.

PAPANICOLAOU, GEORGE N. "A new procedure for staining vaginal smears." *Science,* 95 (1942), 438–439.

——. "The cytology of the gastric fluid of carcinoma of the stomach." *Journal National Cancer Institute,* 7 (1947), 357–360.

——. *Atlas of Exfoliative Cytology.* Cambridge, Mass., *Harvard University Press* (1954).

——. "The cancer diagnostic potential of uterine exfoliative cytology." *CA, Bulletin of Cancer Progress,* 7 (1957), 125–135.

PATTEN, BRADLEY M. "Early Embryology of the Chick." 4th ed. N.Y., Blakiston (1952).

PATTEN, STANLEY F. and BROWN, KENNETH A. "Freeze-solvent substitution technic. A review with application to fluorescence

microscopy." *Laboratory Investigation,* 7 (1958), 209–223.

PEARSE, A. G. EVERSON. "The cytochemical demonstration of gonadotropic hormone in the human anterior hypophysis." *Journal Pathology and Bacteriology,* 61 (1949), 195–202.

——. "Differential stain for human and animal anterior hypophysis." *Stain Technology,* 25 (1950), 95–102.

——. "Copper phthalocyanins as phospholipid stains." *Journal Pathology and Bacteriology,* 70 (1955), 554–557.

——. *Histochemistry, Theoretical and Applied.* Boston, Little Brown and Co. (1960).

PEARSON, BJARNE. "Improvement in the histochemical localization of succinic dehydrogenase by the use of nitroneotetrazolium chloride." *Journal Histochemistry and Cytochemistry,* 6 (1958), 112–121.

PEARY, JOSEPH IGOR. "Freeze dehydration for permanent mounts after aceto-orcein stain." *Stain Technology,* 30 (1955), 213–230.

PEASE, DANIEL C. *"Histological Techniques for Electron Microscopy."* N.Y., Academic Press (1960).

—— and BAKER, R. F. "Sectioning techniques for electron microscopy using conventional microtome." *Proceedings, Society Experimental Biology and Medicine,* 67 (1948), 470–474.

—— and ——. "Electron microscopy of the kidney." *American Journal Anatomy,* 87 (1950), 349–390.

PELC, S. R. "A stripping film technique for autoradiography." *International Journal Applied Radiation and Isotopes,* 1 (1956), 172–177.

PELTIER, LEONARD F. "The demonstration of fat emboli in tissue sections using phosphin 3R, a water-soluble fluorochrome." *Journal Laboratory and Clinical Medicine,* 43 (1954), 321–323.

PEQUENO, RUBENS ALVES. "A simple pen method for preparing linear blood films for accurate differential leukocyte counts." *Technical Bulletin, Registry of Medical Technologists,* 30 (1960), 193–196.

PERSIDSKY, MAXIM D. "Restoration of deteriorated temporary aceto-carmine preparations." *Stain Technology,* 29 (1954), 278.

PICKETT, JOHN PHILLIP, BISHOP, CARL M., CHICK, ERNEST W. and BAKER, ROGER D. "A simple fluorescent stain for fungi." *American Journal Clinical Pathology,* 34 (1960), 197–202.

—— and SOMMER, JOACHIM R. "Thirty-five mm. film as mounting base, and plastic spray as cover glass, for histologic sections." *American Medical Association, Archives Pathology, 69* (1960), *13*/239–21/247.

POIRIER, LOUIS J., AYOTTE, ROBERT A., and GAUTHIER, CLAUDE. "Modification of the Marchi technic." *Stain Technology, 29* (1954), 71–75.

POLLAK, O. J. "A rapid trichrome stain." *Archives Pathology, 37* (1944), 294.

POPPER, HANS and SZANTO, PAUL B. "Fluorescence Microscopy." *Handbook of Microscopical Technique,* ed., Ruth McClung Jones. N.Y., Hoeber (1950).

PORTER, KEITH R. and BLUM, J. "A study in microtomy for electron microscopy." *Anatomical Record, 117* (1953), 685–710.

POWERS, MARGARET M., CLARK, GEORGE, DARROW, MARY, and EMMEL, VICTOR M. "Darrow red, a new basic dye." *Stain Technology, 35* (1960), 19–22.

PREECE, ANN. *A Manual for Histologic Technicians.* Boston, Little, Brown and Co. (1959).

PRIMAN, JACOB. "Blood serum as an adhesive for paraffin sections." *Stain Technology, 29* (1954), 105–107.

Proceedings of the Electron Microscopy Society of America, Journal Applied Physiology, 24 (1953).

PROESCHER, FREDERICK. "Pinacyanol as a histological stain." *Proceedings Society Experimental Biology and Medicine, 31* (1933), 79–81.

——. "Contribution to the staining of neuroglia." *Stain Technology, 9* (1934), 33–38.

—— and ARKUSH, A. S. "Metallic lakes of the oxazines (gallamin blue, gallocyanin, and coelestin blue) as nuclear stain substitutes for hematoxylin." *Stain Technology, 2* (1928), 28–38.

PUGH, M. H. and SAVCHUCK, W. B. "Suggestions on the preparation of undecalcified bone for microradiography." *Stain Technology, 33* (1958), 287–293.

PUTT, F. A. "Modified eosin counterstain for formaldehyde-fixed tissues." *Archives Pathology, 45* (1948), 72.

——. "A modified Ziehl-Neelsen method." *American Journal Clinical Pathology, 21* (1951), 92–95.

——. "Flaming red as a dye for the demonstration of lipids." *Laboratory Investigation, 5* (1956), 377–379.

QUAY, W. B. "Experimental cyanine red, a new stain for nucleic acid and mucopolysaccharides." *Stain Technology, 32* (1957), 175–182.

RAE, C. A. "Masson's trichrome stain after Petrunkewitsch or Susa fixation." *Stain Technology, 30* (1955), 147–148.

RAFALKO, STANLEY. "A modified Feulgen technic for small and diffuse chromatin elements." *Stain Technology, 21* (1946), 91–94.

RALPH, P. H. "The histochemical demonstration of hemoglobin in blood cells and tissue smears." *Stain Technology, 16* (1941), 105–106.

RÁMON y CAJAL, S. "Un sencillo metodo de coloracion selectiva del reticulo protoplasmico y sus effectos en los diversos organos nerviosos." *Trabajos del Laboratorio Investigaciones Biologica,* University of Madrid, *2* (1903), 129–221.

——. "Las formulas del proceder del nitrato de plata reducido." *Trabajos del Laboratorio Investigaciones Biologica,* University of Madrid, *8* (1910), 1–26.

—— and DE CASTRO, F. "Elementos de tecnica micrografica del sistema nerviosa." Madrid, *Tipografia Artistica* (1933).

RANDOLPH, L. F. "A new fixing fluid and a revised schedule for the paraffin method in plant cytology." *Stain Technology, 10* (1935), 95–96.

RAWLINS, T. E. and TAKAHASHI, WILLIAM. "Elimination of distortion and poor staining in paraffin sections of plant tissues." *Stain Technology, 22* (1947), 99–102.

REINER, LEOPOLD. "Principles of rapid frozen sectioning." *Laboratory Investigation, 2* (1953), 336–348.

RENAUD, SERGE. "Superiority of alcoholic over aqueous fixation in the histochemical detection of calcium." *Stain Technology, 34* (1959), 267–271.

RICHARDS, OSCAR W. "An efficient method for the identification of *M. tuberculosis* with a simple fluorescence microscope." *American Journal Clinical Pathology, Technical Section, 5* (1941), 1–8.

——. *The Effective Use and Proper Care of the Microtome.* American Optical Company (1949).

——. *The Effective Use and Proper Care of the Microscope.* American Optical Company (1954).

——, KLINE, EDMUND K. and LEACH, RAYMOND E. "Demonstration of tubercle bacilli by fluorescence microscopy." *American Review of Tuberculosis, 44* (1941), 255–266.

RICHARDSON, HOWARD L. "The advantages of a glycol fixative for the preparation of Papanicolaou smears." *Technical Bulletin, Registry of Medical Technologists, 30* (1960), 15.

RICHARDSON, K. C., JARETT, L. and FINKE, E.H. "Embedding in epoxy resins for ultrathin sectioning in electron microscopy." *Stain Technology, 35* (1960), 313–323.

RICHMOND, GORDON W. and BENNETT, LESLIE. "Clearing and staining of embryos for demonstration of ossification." *Stain Technology, 13* (1938), 77–79.

RIGGS, J. L., SEIWALD, R. J., BURKHALTER, J. H., DOWNS, C. M. and METCALF, T. G. "Isothiocyanate compounds as fluorescent labeling agents for immune serum." *American Journal Pathology, 34* (1958), 1081–1092.

RINEHART, J. F. and ABUL-HAJ, S. K. "An improved method for histologic demonstration of acid mucopolysaccharides in tissues." *Archives Pathology, 52* (1951), 189–194.

RITTER, H. R. and OLESON, J. J. "Combined histochemical staining of acid mucopolysaccharides and 1,2 glycol groupings in paraffin sections." *American Journal Pathology, 26* (1950), 639–645.

RODRIQUEZ, JOSE and DEINHARDT, FRIEDRICH. "Preparation of a semipermanent medium for fluorescent antibody studies." *Virology, 12* (1960), 316–317.

ROMEIS, B. "Mikroskopischen Technick." Leibniz Verlag, München (1948).

ROSA, CHARLES G. "Preparation and use of aldehyde fuchsin stain in the dry form." *Stain Technology, 28* (1953), 299–302.

——— and VELARDO, JOSEPH. "Histochemical demonstration of succinic dehydrogenase activity in tissue sections by a modified technique." *Journal Histochemistry and Cytochemistry, 2* (1954), 110–114.

ROTHFELS, K. H. and SIMINOVITCH, L. "An air drying technique for flattening chromosomes in mammalian cells grown *in vitro*." *Stain Technology, 33* (1958), 73–77.

RUBIN, ROBERT. "A rapid method for making permanent mounts of nematodes." *Stain Technology, 26* (1951), 257–260.

RUCH, FRITZ. "Birefringence and dichroism of cells and tissues." *Physical Techniques in Biological Research*, Vol. I, eds., Gerald Oster and Arthur W. Pollister. N.Y., Academic Press (1955).

RUDDLE, FRANK H., BERMAN, LAWRENCE and

STULBERG, CYRIL S. "Chromosome analysis of five long-term cell culture populations derived from nonleukemic human peripheral blood (Detroit strains)." *Cancer Research, 18* (1958), 1048–1059.

RUTENBERG, ALEXANDER M. and SELIGMAN, ARNOLD M. "The histochemical demonstration of acid phosphatase by a postincubation coupling technique." *Journal Histochemistry and Cytochemistry, 3* (1955), 455–470.

———, GOFSTEIN, RALPH and SELIGMAN, ARNOLD M. "Preparation of a new tetrazolium salt which yields a blue pigment on reduction and its use in the demonstration of enzymes in normal and neoplastic tissues." *Cancer Research, 10* (1950), 113–121.

———, WOLMAN, MOSHI and SELIGMAN, ARNOLD M. "Comparative distribution of succinic dehydrogenase in six mammals and modification in the histochemical technic." *Journal Histochemistry and Cytochemistry, 1* (1953), 66–81.

RUTH, E. B. "Demonstration of the ground substance of cartilage, bone, and teeth." *Stain Technology, 21* (1946), 27–30.

SACHS, LEO. "Simple methods for mammalian chromosomes." *Stain Technology, 28* (1953), 169–172.

ST. AMAND, GEORGIA SIMS and ST. AMAND, W. "Shortening maceration time for Alizarine red S preparations." *Stain Technology, 26* (1951), 271.

SANDBERG, AVERY A., CROSSWHITE, LOIS H. and GORDY, EDWIN. "Trisomy of a large chromosome." *Journal American Medical Association, 174* (1960), 221–225.

SCHAJOWICZ, F. and CABRINI, R. L. "The effect of acids (decalcifying solutions) and enzymes on the histochemical behavior of bone and cartilage." *Journal Histochemistry and Cytochemistry, 3* (1955), 122–129.

——— and ———. "Chelating agents as histological and histochemical decalcifiers." *Stain Technology, 31* (1956), 129–133.

——— and ———. "Histochemical demonstration of acid phosphatase in hard tissues." *Stain Technology, 34* (1959), 59–63.

SCHLEGEL, JORGEN ULRIK. "Demonstration of blood vessels and lymphatics with a fluorescent dye in ultraviolet light." *Anatomical Record, 105* (1949), 433–443.

SCHLEICHER, EMIL MARO. "Floating solutions

for mounting paraffin sections." *American Journal Clinical Pathology, 21* (1951), 900.

SCHLEIFSTEIN, J. "A rapid method for demonstrating Negri bodies in tissue sections." *American Journal Public Health, 27* (1937), 1283–1285.

SCHMIDT, ROBERT W. "Simultaneous fixation and decalcification of tissue." *Laboratory Investigation, 5* (1956), 306–307.

SCHUBERT, MAXWELL and HAMERMAN, DAVID. "Metachromasia: chemical theory and histochemical use." *Journal Histochemistry and Cytochemistry, 4* (1956), 159–189.

SCOTT, H. R. and CLAYTON, B. P. "A comparison of the staining affinities of aldehyde-fuchsin and the Schiff reagent." *Journal Histochemistry and Cytochemistry, 1* (1953), 336–352.

SCOTT, JESSE F. "Ultraviolet absorption spectrophotometry." *Physical Techniques in Biological Research*, Vol. I, eds., Gerald Oster and Arthur W. Pollister. N.Y., Academic Press (1955).

SEAL, S. H. "A method for concentrating cancer cells suspended in large quantities of fluid." *Cancer, 9* (1956), 866–868.

SERRA, J. A. "Histochemical tests for proteins and amino acids; the characterization of basic proteins." *Stain Technology, 21* (1946), 5–18.

SHANKLIN, W. M. and NASSAR, T. K. "Luxol fast blue combined with periodic acid Schiff procedure for cytological staining of kidney." *Stain Technology, 34* (1959), 257–260.

———, ———, and ISSIDORIDES, M. "Luxol fast blue as a selective stain for alpha cells in the human pituitary." *Stain Technology, 34* (1959), 55–58.

SHEEHAN, DEZNA. "A comparative study of the histologic techniques for demonstrating chromaffin cells." *American Journal Medical Technologists, 26* (1960), 237–240.

SHELDON, H. "A method for evaluating glass knives." *Journal Biophysical and Biochemical Cytology, 3* (1957), 615–621.

SHILLABER, CHARLES PATTEN. *Photomicrography, in Theory and Practice*. N.Y., John Wiley and Sons, Inc. (1944).

SIERACKI, JOSEPH, MICHAEL, JAMES E. and CLARK, DAISY A. "The demonstration of beta cells in pancreatic islets and their tumors." *Stain Technology, 35* (1960), 67–69.

SILLS, BERNARD and MARSH, WALTON H. "A simple technic for staining fat with oil-soluble azo dyes." *Laboratory Investigation, 8* (1959), 1006–1009.

SILVER, MAURICE L. "Colloidal factors controlling silver staining." *Anatomical Record, 82* (1942), 507–529.

SILVERSTEIN, ARTHUR M. "Contrasting fluorescent labels for two antibodies. "*Journal Histochemistry and Cytochemistry, 5* (1957), 94–95.

SIMMEL, EVA B. "The use of a fast, coarse grain stripping film for radioautography." *Stain Technology, 32* (1957), 299–300.

———, FITZGERALD, P. J. and GODWIN, J. T. "Staining of radioautography with metanil yellow and iron hematoxylin." *Stain Technology, 26* (1951), 25–28.

SIMONDS, HERBERT R., WEITH, ARCHIE J. and BIGELOW, M. H. *Handbook of Plastics*. N.Y., D. Van Nostrand Co., Inc. (1949).

SIMPSON, WILLIAM L. "An experimental analysis of the Altmann technic of freezing-drying." *Anatomical Record, 80* (1941), 173–189.

SINGER, MARCUS. "Factors which control the staining of tissues with acid and basic dyes." *International Review of Cytology* (1952), 211–255.

SINHA, RANENDRA NATH. "Sectioning insects with sclerotized cuticle." *Stain Technology, 28* (1953), 249–253.

SJOSTRAND, F. S. "Electron microscopy of cells and tissues." *Physical Techniques in Biological Research, 3* (1956), 241–298.

SLIDDERS, W., FRASER, D. S., SMITH, R. and LENDRUM, A. C. "On staining the nucleus red." *Journal Pathology and Bacteriology, 75* (1958), 466–468.

SMITH, LUTHER. "The acetocarmine technique." *Stain Technology, 22* (1947), 17–31.

SMITH, G. STEWART. "A danger attending the use of ammoniacal solutions of silver." *Journal Pathology and Bacteriology, 55* (1943), 227–228.

SMYTH, J. D. "A technic for mounting free-living protozoa." *Science, 100* (1944), 62.

SOLELO, J. R. "Technical improvements in specimen preparation for electron microscopy." *Experimental Cell Research, 13* (1957), 599–601.

SOUTHGATE, H. W. "Note on preparing mucicarmine." *Journal Pathology and Bacteriology, 30* (1927), 729.

SPATZ, MARIA. "Bismarck brown as a selective stain for mast cells." *American Journal Clinical Pathology, 34* (1960), 285–287.

SPICER, S. S. "A correlative study of the histochemical properties of Rodent acid mucopolysaccharides." *Journal Histochemistry and Cytochemistry, 8* (1960), 18–33.

—— and MEYER, D. B. "Histochemical differentiation of acid mucopolysaccharides by means of combined aldehyde fuchsin-alcian blue staining." *American Journal Clinical Pathology, Technical Section, 33* (1960), 453–456.

STAFFORD, E. S. "An eosin-methylene blue technique for rapid tissue diagnosis." *Bulletin, Johns Hopkins Hospital, 55* (1934), 229.

STAFFORD, MARVIN W. "An improved method for labelling frosted-end microslides used in exfoliative cytology." *Technical Bulletin, Registry of Medical Technologists, 30* (1960), 26–27.

STAPP, PAUL and CUMLEY, RUSSELL W. "A technic for clearing large insects." *Stain Technology, 11* (1936), 105–106.

STEARN, ALLEN E. and STEARN, ESTHER. "The mechanism of staining explained on a chemical basis. I. The reaction between dyes, proteins, and nucleic acid." *Stain Technology, 4* (1929), 111–119.

—— and ——. "The mechanism of staining explained on a chemical basis. II. General considerations." *Stain Technology, 5* (1930), 17–24.

STEEDMAN, H. F. "Alcian blue 8G: a new stain for mucin." *Quarterly Journal Microscopical Society, 91* (1950), 477–479.

STEIL, W. "Modified Wright's method for staining blood smears." *Stain Technology, 11* (1936), 99–100.

STOWELL, ROBERT E. "Effect on tissue volume of various methods of fixation, dehydration, and embedding." *Stain Technology, 16* (1941), 67–83.

——. "Feulgen reaction for thymonucleic acid." *Stain Technology, 20* (1945), 45–58.

——. "The specificity of the Feulgen reaction for thymonucleic acid." *Stain Technology, 21* (1946), 137–148.

SWANK, R. L. and DAVENPORT, H. A. "Marchi's staining method. Studies of some of underlying mechanisms involved." *Stain Technology, 9* (1934 A), 11–19.

—— and ——. "Marchi's staining method. II. Fixation." *Stain Technology, 9* (1934 B), 129–135.

—— and ——. "Marchi's staining method. III. Artifacts and effects of perfusion." *Stain Technology, 10* (1935 A), 45–52.

—— and ——. "Chlorate-osmic-formalin method for staining degenerating myelin." *Stain Technology, 10* (1935 B), 87–90.

SWIGART, RICHARD H., WAGNER, CHARLES E. and ATKINSON, WILLIAM B. "The preservation of glycogen in fixed tissues and tissue sections." *Journal Histochemistry and Cytochemistry, 8* (1960), 74–75.

SYMEONIDIS, A. "Neue Anwendungsmöglichkeiten der Gefrierschneidemethode mit Messertiefkühlung bei fixierten Gewebe." *Centralblatt für allgemeine Pathologie und Pathologische Anatomie, 63* (1935), 245–246.

TAFT, E. B. "The problem of standardized technique for the methyl-green-pyronin stain." *Stain Technology, 26* (1951), 205–212.

TAFT, P. D. and ARIZAGA-CRUZ, J. M. "A comparison of the cell block, Papanicolaou, and millipore filter technics for the cytological examination of serous fluids." *Technical Bulletin, Registry of Medical Technologists, 30* (1960), 189–192.

TANDLER, C. J. "The use of cobalt acetate in the histochemical technic for acid phosphatase." *Journal Histochemistry and Cytochemistry, 1* (1953), 151–153.

TARKHAM, A. A. "The effect of fixatives and other reagents on cell size and tissue bulk." *Journal Royal Microscopical Society, 51* (1931), 387–399.

TERNER, JACOB Y. and CLARK, GEORGE. "Gallocyanin-chrome alum: I. Technique and specificity." *Stain Technology, 35* (1960), 167–168.

THOMAS, JOHN T. "Phloxine-methylene blue staining of formalin fixed tissue." *Stain Technology, 28* (1953), 311–312.

THOMAS, LLOYD E. "An improved arginine histochemical method." *Stain Technology, 25* (1950), 143–148.

THOMPSON, E. C. "A tray for staining frozen sections in quantity." *Stain Technology, 32* (1957), 255–257.

TILDEN, I. L. and TANAKA, MASSO. "Fite's fuchsin-formaldehyde method for acid fast bacilli applied to frozen sections." *American Journal Clinical Pathology, 9* (1945), 95–97.

TJIO, J. H. and PUCK, T. T. "Genetics of somatic mammalian cells. II. Chromosomal constitution of cells in tissue culture." *Journal Experimental Medicine, 108* (1958), 259–269.

TOBIE, JOHN E. "Certain technical aspects of fluorescence microscopy and the Coons fluorescent antibody technique." *Journal Histochemistry and Cytochemistry, 6* (1958), 271–277.

TOMLINSON, W. J. and GROCOTT, R. G. "A

simple method of staining malaria protozoa and other parasites in paraffin sections." *American Journal Clinical Pathology*, 14 (1944), 316–326.

TONNA, EDGAR A. "Factors which influence the latent image in autoradiography." *Stain Technology*, 33 (1958), 255–260.

———. "Decalcification of bon? by means of an automatic continuous flow apparatus." *American Journal Clinical Pathology*, 31 (1959), 160–164.

TUAN, HSU-CHUAN. "Picric acid as a destaining agent for iron alum hematoxylin." *Stain Technology*, 5 (1930), 135–138.

UBER, FRED M. "Microtome knife sharpeners operating on the abrasive ground glass principle." *Stain Technology*, 11 (1936), 93–98.

UECKERT, EDWIN. "Polyester embedding for sectioning hard and soft tissues." *Stain Technology*, 35 (1960), 261–265.

UMIKER, WILLIAM and PICKLE, LARRY. "The cytologic diagnosis of lung cancer by fluorescence microscopy: Acridine orange fluorescence technic in routine screening and diagnosis." *Laboratory Investigation*, 9 (1960), 613–624.

UNGEWITTER, LUISE H. "A controllable silver stain for nerve fibers and nerve endings." *Stain Technology*, 18 (1943), 183–186.

———. "A urea silver nitrate method for nerve fibers and nerve endings." *Stain Technology*, 26 (1951), 73–76.

UZMAN, L. LAHUT. "Histochemical localization of copper with rubeanic acid." *Laboratory Investigation*, 5 (1956), 299–305.

VACEK, Z. and PLACKOVA, A. "Silver impregnation of nerve fibers in teeth after decalcification with ethylenediaminetetraacetic acid." *Stain Technology*, 34 (1959), 1–3.

VANCLEAVE, HARLEY J. and ROSS, JEAN A. "A method of reclaiming dried Zoological specimens." *Science*, 105 (1947), 318.

VASSAR, PHILIP S. and CULLING, CHARLES F. A. "Fluorescent stains with special reference to amyloid and connective tissue." *American Medical Association, Archives Pathology*, 68 (1959), 487–498.

VERNINO, DAVID M. and LASKIN, DAVID M. "Sex chromatin in mammalian bone." *Science*, 132 (1960), 675–676.

VICKERS, A. E. J. *Modern Methods of Microscopy*. N.Y., Interscience Publishers, Inc. (1956).

VINEGAR, RALPH. "Metachromatic differential fluorochroming of living and dead Ascites tumor cells with acridine orange." *Cancer Research*, 16 (1916), 900–906.

VLACHOS, JOHN. "Desaturation of staining solutions for lipids, a means of avoiding precipitation on stained sections." *Stain Technology*, 34 (1959), 292.

VON BERTALANFFY, LUDWIG and BICKIS, IVAR. "Identification of cytoplasmic basophilia (ribonucleic acid) by fluorescence microscopy." *Journal Histochemistry and Cytochemistry*, 4 (1956), 481–493.

———, MASIN, MARIANNA and MASIN, FRANCIS. "A new and rapid method for diagnosis of vaginal and cervical cancer by fluorescence microscopy." *Cancer*, 11 (1958), 873–887.

——— and VON BERTALANFFY, FELIX D. "A new method for cytological diagnosis of pulmonary cancer." *Annals of N.Y. Academy of Sciences*, 84 (1960), 225–238.

WACHSTEIN, M. and WOLF, GERTA. "The histochemical demonstration of esterase activity in human blood and bone marrow smears." *Journal Histochemistry and Cytochemistry*, 6 (1958), 457.

WADE, W. H. "Notes on the carbowax method of making tissue sections." *Stain Technology*, 27 (1952), 71–79.

———. "A modification of the Fite formaldehyde (Fite I) method for staining acid fast bacilli in paraffin sections." *Stain Technology*, 32 (1957), 287–292.

WAGNER, BERNARD M. and SHAPIRO, SYLVIA H. "Application of alcian blue as a histochemical method." *Laboratory Investigation*, 6 (1957), 472–477.

WALKER, P. M. B. "Ultraviolet microspectrophotometry." *General Cytochemical Methods*, ed., J. F. Danielli. N.Y., Academic Press (1958).

WALL, PATRICK. "Staining and recognition of fine degenerating nerve fibers." *Stain Technology*, 25 (1950), 125–126.

WALLS, G. L. "The hot celloidin technic for animal tissues." *Stain Technology*, 7 (1932), 135–145.

———. "A rapid celloidin method for the rotary microtome." *Stain Technology*, 11 (1936), 89–92.

———. "The microtechnique of the eye with suggestions as to material." *Stain Technology*, 13 (1938), 69–72.

WARMKE, HARRY E. "A permanent root tip smear method." *Stain Technology*, 10 (1935), 101–103.

———. "Precooling combined with chromosmo-acetic fixation in studies of somatic chromosomes in plants." *Stain Technology, 21* (1946), 87–90.

WARREN, O. "Some facts about nerve ending preparations." *Turtox News, 22* (1944), #11, General Biological Supply House, Chicago, Ill.

WATSON, BARBARA K. "Distribution of mumps virus in tissue cultures as determined by fluorescein-labeled antiserum." *Proceedings, Society Experimental Biology and Medicine, 79* (1952), 222–224.

WATSON, M. L. "Carbon films and specimen stability." *Journal Biophysical and Biochemical Cytology,* Supplement 2 (1956), 31–37.

WEAVER, HARRY LLOYD. "An improved gelatine adhesive for paraffin sections." *Stain Technology, 30* (1955), 63–64.

WEINER, S. "A simplified vacuum embedder." *Stain Technology, 32* (1957), 195–196.

WEISS, JULES. "The nature of the reaction between orcein and elastin." *Journal Histochemistry and Cytochemistry, 2* (1954), 21–28.

WERTH, VON G. "Fluoeszenz mikroskopische Beobachtungen an menschlichem Knochenmark." *Acta Haematologica, 10* (1953), 209–222.

WESTFALL, JANE A. "Obtaining flat serial sections for electron microscopy." *Stain Technology, 36* (1961), 36–38.

WETMORE, R. H. "The use of celloidin in Botanical technic." *Stain Technology, 7* (1932), 37–62.

WHEATLEY, WALTER B. "A rapid procedure for intestinal amoebae and flagellates." *American Journal Clinical Pathology, 21* (1951), 990–991.

WHITE, LOWELL, E., JR. "Enhanced reliability in silver impregnation of terminal axonal degeneration—original Nauta method." *Stain Technology, 35* (1960), 5–9.

WHITE, ROBERT G., COONS, ALBERT H. and CONNOLLY, JEANNE M. "Studies on antibody production. III. The alum granuloma. IV. The role of a wax fraction of mycobacterium tuberculosis in adjuvant emulsions on the production of antibody to egg albumin." *Journal Experimental Medicine, 102* (1955), 73–103.

WILCOX, AIMEE. "Manual for the Microscopical Diagnosis of Malaria in Man." *National Institute of Public Health, Bulletin 180,* U.S. Government Printing Office (1943), 39 pages.

WILDER, H. C. "An improved technique for silver impregnation of reticular fibers."

American Journal Pathology, 11 (1935) 817–819.

WILLIAMS, G. and JACKSON, D. S. "Two organic fixatives for acid mucopolysaccharides." *Stain Technology, 31* (1956), 189–191.

WILLIAMS, R. C. and BACKUS, R. C. "The electron micrographic structure of shadow-cast films." *Journal Applied Physics, 20* (1949), 98–106.

—— and KALLMAN, F. "Examination of tissue-cultured Hela cells by electron microscopy of serial sections." *Journal Applied Physics, 25* (1954), 1455.

—— and WYCKOFF, R. W. G. "Thickness of electron microscopic objects." *Journal Applied Physics, 15* (1944), 712–715.

WILLIAMS, T. D. "Mounting and preserving serial celloidin sections." *Stain Technology, 32* (1957), 97.

WINTERINGHAN, F. P. W., HARRISON, A. and HAMMOND, J. H. "Autoradiography of water-soluble tracers in histological sections." *Nature, 165* (1950), 149–152.

WITTEN, VICTOR H. and HOLMSTROM, VERA. "New histologic technics for autoradiography." *Laboratory Investigation, 2* (1953), 368–375.

WOLMAN, N. "Differential staining of acidic tissue components by the improved Bi-col method." *Stain Technology, 36* (1961), 21–25.

WOODRUFF, LOIS A. and NORRIS, WILLIAM P. "Sectioning of undecalcified bone; with special reference to radioautographic applications." *Stain Technology, 30* (1955), 179–188.

WOODS, PHILIP S. and POLLISTER, A. W. "An ice-solvent method of drying frozen tissue for plant cytology." *Stain Technology, 30* (1955), 123–131.

WRIGHT, J. H. "A rapid method for the differential staining of blood films and malarial parasites." *Journal of Medical Research, 7* (1902), 138–144.

YAEGER, JAMES A. "Methacrylate embedding and sectioning of calcified bone." *Stain Technology, 33* (1958), 229–239.

YETWIN, I. J. "A simple permanent mounting medium for *Necator americanus.*" *Journal of Parasitology, 30* (1944), 201.

ZBAR, MARCUS J. and WINTER, WILLIAM J. "A method of concentrating particles of bone marrow for paraffin sections." *Amer-*

ican Journal Clinical Pathology, 32 (1959), 41–44.

ZEIGER, K., HARDERS, H. and MÜLLER, W. "Der Strugger-effekt an der Nervenzelle." *Protoplasma, 40* (1951), 76–84.

ZIRKLE, CONWAY. "Aceto-carmine mounting media." *Science, 85* (1937), 528.

———. "Combined fixing, staining, and mounting media." *Stain Technology, 15* (1940), 139–153.

ZUCK, ROBERT K. "Simplified permanent aceto-carmine smears with a water-miscible mountant." *Stain Technology, 22* (1947), 109–110.

ZUGIBE, FREDERICK T., BROWN, KENNETH D. and LAST, JULES H. "A new technique for the simultaneous demonstration of lipid and acid mucopolysaccharides on the same tissue section." *Journal Histo-* *chemistry and Cytochemistry, 7* (1959), 101–106.

———, FINK, MARILYN L. and BROWN, KENNETH W. "Carbowax flotation method." *Journal Histochemistry and Cytochemistry, 6* (1958), 381.

———, ——— and ———. "Carbowax 400, a new solvent for oil red O and sudan IV for staining carbowax embedded and frozen sections." *Stain Technology, 34* (1959), 33–37.

———, KOPACZYK, KRYSTYNA C., CAPE, WILLIAM E. and LAST, JULES H. "A new carbowax method for routinely performing lipid, hematoxylin, and eosin and elastic staining techniques on adjacent freeze dried or formalin fixed tissues." *Journal Histochemistry and Cytochemistry, 6* (1958), 133–138.

Index

458